OFFICIAL TOURIST BOARD G

C000030458

CAMPING

TOURING & HOLIDAY PARKS

Quality-assessed parks in England, Scotland and Wales

2012

GUIDE

Thank you for thinking of Britain for your next holiday and welcome to this official guide to hundreds of our country's camping and caravan parks. We hope that 2012 will again benefit from the British passion for holidays at home as millions discover the many special places and surprising experiences that this country has to offer.

I am delighted that you have chosen to holiday in Britain at such an opportune moment. Over 2 billion people globally saw the Royal Wedding at Westminster Abbey and this summer the eyes of the worlds will be focused on the opening ceremony of the London 2012 Games.

This guide will give you all the practical advice you need in order to take advantage of the unique and wonderful things in Britain and appreciate the very best of England, Scotland and Wales. Exploring all that Britain has to offer has never been easier, thanks to this latest guide and never more affordable.

A holiday at home offers an unrivalled social season and a calendar of unbeatable events – from Royal Ascot to Cowes Week, Edinburgh Tattoo to the Chelsea Flower Show, the British Grand Prix to Nottinghill Carnival, Duxford Air Show to the Glyndebourne Festival. British destinations have inspired some of the world's greatest authors and poets, and produced number one musicians, leading fashion designers and award-winning actors, as well as sporting legends and iconic characters from Harry Potter to James Bond.

Or explore Britain by foot, by journeying through the relaxing 'Royal Footprints' in the South East of England. Or, if you want to really experience the delights of our historical towns or sample some fantastic local food, witnessing truly mind blowing scenery why not visit Scotland's Islands?

Take the time to discover the very best places to pitch your tent or park your caravan throughout England, Scotland and Wales and you'll find an enormous variety of experiences. You'll also realise just how easily every corner of Britain can be explored.

Enjoy your stay.

Christopher Rodrigues
Chairman, VisitBritain

Contents

How to use this guide

This official **VisitBritain** guide is packed with information from where to stay, to how to get there and what to see and do. In fact, everything you need to know to enjoy Britain.

Choose from a wide range of quality-assessed places to stay to suit all budgets and tastes. This guide contains a comprehensive listing of touring, camping and holiday parks, and holiday villages participating in the British-Graded Holiday Parks Scheme.

Each park is visited annually by a professional assessor who applies nationally agreed standards so that you can book with confidence knowing your accommodation has been checked and rated for quality.

Check out the places to visit in each region, from towns and cities to spectacular coast and countryside, plus historic homes,

castles and great family attractions! Maps show accommodation locations, selected destinations and some of the National Cycle Networks. For even more ideas go online at visitbritain.com

Regional tourism contacts and tourist information centres are listed – Contact them for further information. You'll also find events, travel information, maps and useful indexes.

Accommodation entries explained

Each accommodation entry contains detailed information to help you decide if it is right for you. This has been provided by proprietors and our aim is to ensure that it is as objective and factual as possible.

① ② ③ ④ ⑤ ⑥

NOTTINGHAM, Nottinghamshire Map ref 4C2   SAT NAV NG12 2LU

National Water Sports Centre Caravan & Camping Park
Adbolton Lane, Holme Pierrepont, Nottingham NG12 2LU
t 01159 824 721 : e nwsccampsite@nottscc.gov.uk
nwscnotts.com : ONLINE MAP GUEST REVIEWS LAST MINUTE OFFERS

🚐 (52)   £10.00–£13.00
🚍 (52)   £13.00–£15.00
▲ (360)   £7.00–£13.00
52 touring pitches

Special Promotions Available Upon Request. Electric hook-up available for £4.00.

Set in a 270 Acre country park the National Water Sports Centre is just 3 miles from Nottingham City Centre with local bus and train services. At the main centre activities available include, white water rafting, water skiing, windsurfing and canoeing along with great walks and good cycling too.

open All year
payment credit/debit cards, cash, cheques

directions 3 Miles From City Centre on A52. (Please See Website)

General   Leisure

⑦   ⑧ ⑨   ⑩   ⑪   ⑫

Sample Enhanced Entry

1   Listing under town or village with map reference

2   Rating (and/or) Award where applicable

3   Prices per pitch per night for touring pitches; per unit per week for static holiday units

4   Establishment name, address, telephone and email

5   Website information

6   Satellite navigation

7   Accessible rating where applicable

8   Walkers, cyclists, pets and families welcome where applicable

9   Payment accepted

10   At-a-glance facility symbols

11   Accommodation details

12   Travel directions

On a CD inside this guide you will find further listings of Parks in England assessed under the British Holiday Parks Scheme.

The information includes brief contact details for each place to stay, together with its star rating and classification. The listing also shows if an establishment has a National Accessible rating or participates in the Welcome schemes: Cyclists Welcome, Walkers Welcome, Welcome Pets! and Families Welcome (see page 7 for further information).

More detailed information on the places is provided in the main 'Where to Stay' sections (where parks have paid to have their details included). To find these entries please refer to the park index at the back of this guide.

Key to symbols

Information about many of the accommodation services and facilities is given in the form of symbols.

Pitches/Units

- ⊕ Caravans (number of pitches and rates)
- 🚐 Motor caravans (number of pitches and rates)
- ⅄ Tents (number of pitches and rates)
- ⊞ Caravan holiday homes (number of pitches and rates)
- ⬛ Log cabins/lodges (number of units and rates)
- ⬛ Chalets/villas (number of units and rates)

Leisure

- ⌇ Swimming pool – indoor
- ⌇ Swimming pool – outdoor
- ⥌ Clubhouse with bar
- ♫ Regular evening entertainment
- ♠ Games room
- ⛶ Outdoor play area
- ⚘ Tennis court(s)
- ↺ Riding/pony-trekking nearby
- ⤳ Fishing nearby
- ▸ Access to golf
- ☃ Cycle hire on site/nearby

General

- ⊡ Overnight holding area
- ⊞ Motor home pitches reserved for day trips off-site
- ⊕ Electrical hook-up points
- ⊙ Calor Gas/Camping Gaz purchase/exchange service
- ⬩ Chemical toilet disposal point
- ⊡ Motor home waste disposal point
- ⌂ Showers
- ▣ Public telephone
- ▣ Laundry facilities
- ⬛ Food shop on site
- ⛾ Restaurant on site
- ✚ Pets welcome by arrangement
- ☼ Prior booking recommended in summer
- ⊙ Wi-Fi
- ℛ Internet access

 Businesses displaying this logo have undergone a rigorous verification process to ensure that they are sustainable (green). See page 16 for further information.

National Accessible Scheme

The National Accessible Scheme includes standards for hearing and visual impairment as well as mobility impairment – see pages 8-9 for further information.

Welcome schemes

Walkers, cyclists, families and pet owners are warmly welcomed where you see these signs – see page 7 for further information.

Visitor Attraction Quality Assurance

Participating attractions are visited annually by a professional assessor. High standards in welcome, hospitality, services, presentation; standards of toilets, shop and café, where provided, must be achieved to receive these awards.

Motorway Service Area Assessment Scheme

The star ratings cover over 300 different aspects of each operation including cleanliness, the quality and range of catering and also the quality of the physical aspects as well as the service - see page 316 for further information.

Places of Interest Quality Assurance

The Places of Interest sign indicates that the site has a biennial visit from an independent assessor and meets the standard required to be awarded the Quality Rose Marque.

A special welcome

To help make your selection of accommodation easier VisitEngland has four special Welcome schemes which accommodation in England can be assessed to. Owners participating in these schemes go the extra mile to welcome walkers, cyclists, families or pet owners and provide additional facilities and services to make your stay even more comfortable.

Families Welcome

If you are searching for a great family break look out for the Families Welcome sign. The sign indicates that the proprietor offers additional facilities and services catering for a range of ages and family units. For families with young children, the accommodation will have special facilities such as cots and highchairs, storage for push-chairs and somewhere to heat baby food or milk. Where meals are provided, children's choices will be clearly indicated, with healthy options available. They'll also have information on local walks, attractions, activities or events suitable for children, as well as local child-friendly pubs and restaurants. Not all accommodation is able to cater for all ages or combinations of family units, so do check when you book.

Welcome Pets!

Want to travel with your faithful companion? Look out for accommodation displaying the Welcome Pets! sign. Participants in this scheme go out of their way to meet the needs of guests bringing dogs, cats and/or small birds. In addition to providing water and food bowls, torches or nightlights, spare leads and pet washing facilities, they'll buy in food on request, and offer toys, treats and bedding. They'll also have information on pet-friendly attractions, pubs, restaurants and recreation. Of course, not everyone is able to offer suitable facilities for every pet, so do check if there are any restrictions on the type, size and number of animals when you book.

Walkers Welcome

If walking is your passion seek out accommodation participating in the Walkers Welcome scheme. Facilities include a place for drying clothes and boots, maps and books for reference and a first-aid kit. Packed breakfasts and lunch are available on request in hotels and guesthouses, and you have the option to pre-order basic groceries in self-catering accommodation. A wide range of information is provided including public transport, weather, local restaurants and attractions, details of the nearest bank and all night chemists.

Cyclists Welcome

If you like to explore by bike, seek out accommodation displaying the Cyclists Welcome symbol. Facilities include a lockable undercover area and a place to dry outdoor clothing and footwear, an evening meal if there are no eating facilities available within one mile, and a packed breakfast or lunch on request. Information is also provided on cycle hire and cycle repair shops, maps and books for reference, weather and details of the nearest bank and all night chemists and more.

For further information go online at visitengland.org/busdev/accreditation

National Accessible Scheme

Finding suitable accommodation is not always easy, especially if you have to seek out rooms with level entry or large print menus. Use the National Accessible Scheme to help you make your choice.

Proprietors of accommodation taking part in the National Accessible Scheme have gone out of their way to ensure a comfortable stay for guests with special hearing, visual or mobility needs. These exceptional places are full of extra touches to make everyone's visit trouble-free, from handrails, ramps and step-free entrances (ideal for buggies too) to level-access showers and colour contrast in the bathrooms. Members of staff may have attended a disability awareness course and will know what assistance will really be appreciated.

Appropriate National Accessible Scheme symbols are included in the guide entries (shown opposite). If you have additional needs or special requirements we strongly recommend that you make sure these can

be met by your chosen establishment before you confirm your reservation. The index at the back of the guide gives a list of accommodation that have received a National Accessible rating.

For the widest possible selection of places to stay OpenBritain is 'the' guide to accessible accommodation in Britain. Packed with Hotels, B&B's, Self Catering and Caravan and Camping sites – OpenBritain is the perfect accessible travel planner. Available from all good bookstores or direct from Tourism for All priced £9.99 (plus £4.50 P&P)

The criteria VisitEngland and national/regional tourism organisations have adopted do not necessarily conform to British Standards or to Building Regulations. They reflect what the organisations understand to be acceptable to meet the practical needs of guests with mobility or sensory impairments and encourage the industry to increase access to all.

For tips and advice on holiday travel in England and to search for NAS accredited accommodation, go to:
www.enjoyengland.com/access

Additional help and guidance on accessible tourism can be obtained from the national charity Tourism for All:

Tourism for All

Tourism for All c/o Vitalise
Shap Road Industrial Estate
Kendal LA9 6NZ

Information helpline 0845 124 9971
Reservations 0845 124 9973
(lines open 9-5 Mon-Fri)
F 01539 735567
E info@tourismforall.org.uk
W http://www.tourismforall.org.uk

England
Mobility Impairment Symbols

Older and less mobile guests
Typically suitable for a person with sufficient mobility to climb a flight of steps but who would benefit from fixtures and fittings to aid balance.

Part-time wheelchair users
Typically suitable for a person with restricted walking ability and for those who may need to use a wheelchair some of the time and can negotiate a maximum of three steps.

Independent wheelchair users
Typically suitable for a person who depends on the use of a wheelchair and transfers unaided to and from the wheelchair in a seated position. This person may be an independent traveller.

Assisted wheelchair users
Typically suitable for a person who depends on the use of a wheelchair and needs assistance when transferring to and from the wheelchair in a seated position.

Access Exceptional is awarded to establishments that meet the requirements of independent wheelchair users or assisted wheelchair users shown above and also fulfil more demanding requirements with reference to the British Standards BS8300.

Visual Impairment Symbols

Typically provides key additional services and facilities to meet the needs of visually impaired guests.

Typically provides a higher level of additional services and facilities to meet the needs of visually impaired guests.

Hearing Impairment Symbols

Typically provides key additional services and facilities to meet the needs of guests with hearing impairment.

Typically provides a higher level of additional services and facilities to meet the needs of guests with hearing impairment.

OPEN BRITAIN

OpenBritain is a partnership between Tourism for All UK, with support from the National Federation of Shopmobility, and the backing of the national tourism agencies VisitEngland, VisitScotland and Visit Wales.

OpenBritain is the one-stop-shop to accessible Britain for those with access needs and their carers. You'll find just what you're looking for if you, or a member of your party, has an access need - whether impaired mobility, vision or hearing. If you need a ground floor room because you can't manage stairs, or you have a child in a buggy, or a wheelchair, or if you need staff trained to offer a welcome to all...

OpenBritain is the answer.

- Places to stay for holidays and short breaks

- Ideas for great days out

- Travel tips and resources

- Services and equipment

and much much more!

For further information on OpenBritain please visit www.openbritain.net or call 01603 216461

Magazine

The OpenBritain magazine is published each quarter, and distributed via Tourism for All, Shopmobility and Motability. It is filled with inspiring content: places to visit, human interest stories, and reviews, together with a wealth of practical information. The OpenBritain magazine is also available in digital format.

Website

www.openbritain.net is an unrivalled searchable website offering help, advice and inspiration, to make the most of all the UK has to offer. We are working with specialist partners to create a truly national and exciting website that meets the needs of all. Stay informed, inspired and active, and add your own feedback to help others with similar needs benefit from your experience.

App

The new OpenBritain GPS activated App will be available on both the Apple and Android platforms, allowing travellers to constantly search for access provision in real time.

VisitBritain

VisitBritain is Britain's national tourism agency, responsible for marketing Britain worldwide and for developing Britain's visitor economy. VisitBritain work in partnership with thousands of organisations in the UK and overseas.

Tourism for All UK is a national charity dedicated to standards of world class tourism which are welcoming to all. **Tourism for All UK** contains the knowledge gained over the past 30 years in providing information to the public, especially to disabled or older people, on where their access needs can be met so that they can fully participate in travel and leisure.

Peace of mind with Star Ratings

Most camping and caravan parks in Britain have a star rating from one of the four assessing bodies – VisitEngland, VisitScotland, Visit Wales or the AA. They all assess to the same national standards so you can expect comparable services, facilities and quality standards at each star rating.

All the parks in this guide are checked annually by national tourist board assessors. So when you see the star rating sign you can be confident that we've checked it out.

The national standards are based on our research of consumer expectations. The independent assessors decide the type (classification) of park – for example if it's a 'touring park', 'holiday park', 'holiday village', etc. – and award a star rating based on over fifty separate aspects, from landscaping and layout to maintenance, customer care and, most importantly, cleanliness.

The Quality marque helps you choose with confidence knowing that the park has been thoroughly checked out before you check in.

Accommodation Types

Always look at or ask for the type of accommodation as each offers a very distinct experience. The parks you'll find in this guide are:

Camping Park – these sites only have pitches available for tents.

Touring Park – sites for your own caravan, motor home or tent.

Holiday Park – sites where you can hire a caravan holiday home for a short break or longer holiday, or even buy your own holiday home. Sites range from small, rural sites to larger parks with added extras, such as a swimming pool.

Many of the above parks will offer a combination of these classifications.

Holiday Villages – usually comprise a variety of types of accommodation, with the majority in custom-built rooms, chalets, for example. The option to book on a bed and breakfast, or dinner, bed and breakfast basis is normally available. A range of facilities, entertainment and activities are also provided which may, or may not, be included in the tariff. Holiday Villages must meet minimum requirements for provision and quality of facilities and services, including fixtures, fittings, furnishings, décor and any other extra facilities.

Forest Holiday Village – a holiday village situated in a forest setting with conservation and

sustainable tourism being a key feature. Usually offer a variety of accommodation, often purpose built, and with a range of entertainment, activities and facilities on site free of charge or at extra cost.

Star ratings are based on a combination of range of facilities, level of service offered and quality - if a park offers facilities required to achieve a certain star rating but does not achieve the quality score required for that rating, a lower star rating is awarded.

A random check is made of a sample of accommodation provided for hire (caravans, chalets, etc) and the quality of the accommodation itself is included in the grading assessment.

Holiday Villages are assessed under a separate rating scheme (for details see qualityintourism. com).

Also included in this guide **Bunkhouses and Camping Barns** – safe, budget-priced, short-term accommodation for individuals and groups.

The more stars, the higher the quality and the greater the range of facilities and level of service:

★ One-Star
Park must be clean with good standards of maintenance and customer care.

★ ★ Two-Star
As above plus improved level of landscaping, lighting, maintenance and refuse disposal. May be less expensive than more highly rated parks.

★ ★ ★ Three-Star
This represents the industry standard as most parks fall within this category. The range of facilities may vary from park to park, but they will be of good standard and will be well maintained.

★ ★ ★ ★ Four-Star
These parks rank among the industry's best and provide careful attention to detail in the provision of all services and facilities.

★ ★ ★ ★ ★ Five-Star
The highest level of customer care provided. All facilities will be maintained in pristine condition in attractive surroundings.

Caravan Holiday Home Award Scheme

VisitEngland and VisitScotland run award schemes for individual holiday caravan homes on highly graded caravan parks. In addition to complying with standards for Holiday Parks, these exceptional caravans must have a shower or bath, toilet, mains electricity and water heating (at no extra charge) and a fridge (many also have a colour TV).

Award-winning parks listed in this guide show the relevant logo by their entry.

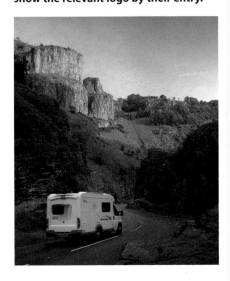

What to expect

Star ratings

Parks are required to meet progressively higher standards of quality as they move up the scale from one to five stars:

ONE-STAR   Acceptable   ★
To achieve this grade, the park must be clean with good standards of maintenance and customer care.

TWO-STAR   Good   ★★
All the above points plus an improved level of landscaping, lighting, refuse disposal and maintenance. May be less expensive than more highly rated parks.

THREE-STAR   Very Good   ★★★
Most parks fall within this category; three stars represent the industry standard. The range of facilities provided may vary from park to park, but they will be of a very good standard and will be well maintained.

FOUR-STAR   Excellent   ★★★★
You can expect careful attention to detail in the provision of all services and facilities. Four star parks rank among the industry's best.

FIVE-STAR   Exceptional   ★★★★★
The highest levels of customer care will be provided. All facilities will be maintained in pristine condition in attractive surroundings.

picnic **2 HOURS**

country walk **1 AFTERNOON**

riverside cottage **1 WEEK**

train ride **90 MINUTES**

pony trekking **3 HOURS**

fishing **1 MORNING**

There are 112 Saturdays, Sundays and Bank Holidays each year.
So why not make the most of them by getting out and about and enjoying England.
For hundreds of money saving offers and ideas visit **enjoyEngland.com**

ENJOY EVERY MINUTE, enjoy**England**.com

Enjoy England Awards for Excellence

Enjoy England awards for Excellence are all about recognizing the best places to stay and visit, whether it's for a day trip, a weekend break or a fortnight's holiday.

Now in their 23rd year, organised by VisitEngland, The Enjoy England Awards for Excellence are the annual accolades for English tourism. Celebrating the best of English tourism, they promote healthy industry competition and high standards, helping to ensure England's place as a world-class destination.

Competition is fierce and entries are submitted to regional tourism organizations across England before being short-listed for the national finals, culminating in an Awards ceremony in April each year.

The 17 award categories are fiercely contested and this year's winners include stylish and contemporary guest accommodation with stunning views of the Lake District, beautifully restored 18th century self catering barns in North Yorkshire, and a charming Cotswold hotel steeped in history and character.

Seek them out and experience them for yourself – you won't be disappointed.

The complete list of winners can be found online at **www.enjoyengland.com**

Set within the beautiful valley of the River Lune, between the Yorkshire Dales and the Lake District National Park, this years Caravan Holiday Park Gold winner, Woodclose Park, takes pride in offering customers a wonderfully relaxing holiday experience.

A beautifully quiet and serene place set in nine acres, Wood Close is a well located site providing a unique holiday base in an area of outstanding natural beauty. The outlying fields provide habitats for a rich variety of animals, birds, flora and fauna and a short walk away you will find yourself beside the River Lune and the three ribbed medieval arches of Devil's Bridge, linked to legend in local tales. Nearby, the picturesque market town of Kirkby Lonsdale has a fine selection of award winning tea-rooms, restaurants and pubs.

Quality of service and facilities are of the utmost priority at Wood Close and this well laid out park offers a varied choice of accommodation including a number of hard-standing and grass pitches for touring caravans, motor homes, a small grassed Camping Field, well sheltered with trees and hedges and home to 7 self catering wigwams and up to 4 tent pitches with electric hook up, as well as an exclusive holiday home and lodge development. Excellent communal facilities include two heated washrooms with individual large wet room style showers and a fully equipped laundry room.

Welcoming, friendly, excellent facilities and all in a beautiful location, what more is there to say!

Caravan Holiday Park of the Year 2011

GOLD WINNER

Woodclose Park, Cumbria ★ ★ ★ ★ ★

SILVER WINNERS

Poston Mill Park, Peterchurch, Herefordshire ★ ★ ★ ★ ★

Faweather Grange, Yorkshire ★ ★ ★ ★ ★

Sustainable Tourism in England

More and more operators of accommodation, attractions and events in England are becoming aware of sustainable or "green" issues and are acting more responsibly in their businesses. But how can you be sure that businesses that 'say' they're green, really are?

Who certifies green businesses?

There are a number of green certification schemes that assess businesses for their green credentials. VisitEngland only promotes those that have been checked out to ensure they reach the high standards expected. The members of those schemes we have validated are truly sustainable (green) businesses and appear amongst the pages of this guide with our heart-flower logo on their entry.

 Businesses displaying this logo have undergone a rigorous verification process to ensure that they are sustainable (green) and that a qualified assessor has visited the premises.

The number of participating green certification scheme organisations applying to be recognised by us is growing all the time. At the moment we promote the largest green scheme in the world - Green Tourism Business Scheme (GTBS).

Green Tourism Business Scheme

 GTBS recognises places to stay and attractions that are taking action to support the local area and the wider environment. With over 2000 members in the UK it's the largest sustainable (green) scheme

to operate globally and assesses hundreds of fantastic places to stay and visit in Britain. From small bed and breakfasts to large visitor attractions and activity holiday providers.

Businesses that meet the standard for a GTBS award receive a Bronze, Silver, or Gold award based on their level of achievement. Businesses are assessed in areas that include Management and Marketing, Social Involvement and Communication, Energy, Water, Purchasing, Waste, Transport, Natural and Cultural Heritage and Innovation.

How are these businesses being green?

Any business that has been certified 'green' will have implemented initiatives that contribute to reducing their negative environmental and social impacts whilst trying to enhance the economic and community benefits to their local area.

Many of these things may be behind the scenes such as energy efficient boilers, insulated lofts or grey water recycling, but there are many fun activities that you can expect to find too. For example, your green business should be able to advise you about traditional activities nearby, the best places to sample local food and buy craft products, or even help you to enjoy a 'car-free' day out.

Walkers and cyclists welcome

Look out for quality-assessed accommodation displaying the Walkers Welcome and Cyclists Welcome signs.

Participants in these schemes actively encourage and support walking and cycling. In addition to special meal arrangements and helpful information, they'll provide a water supply to wash off the mud, an area for drying wet clothing and footwear, maps and books to look up cycling and walking routes and even an emergency puncture-repair kit! Bikes can also be locked up securely undercover.

The standards for these schemes have been developed in partnership with the tourist boards in Northern Ireland, Scotland and Wales, so wherever you're travelling in the UK you'll receive the same welcome.

Award winning sites

Family togetherness

Life balance

Community spirit

Freedom

Five ways to get rich on a Camping and Caravanning Club Site

Camping is the perfect way to enjoy life's simple pleasures in the great outdoors and share those wonderful moments with family and friends. There is always something new to discover, so why not choose one of the Club Sites as your base.

The **Camping** and **Caravanning Club**

The Friendly Club

GET RICH QUICK

For more information visit **thefriendlyclub.co.uk** or call us on **0845 130 7633 / 024 7647 5426 quoting code 3385**.

Mon-Fri 8.00am-8.00pm (10am-7pm Wed) Sat 9am-1pm (Jan-Aug)

David Bellamy Conservation Award

'These well-deserved awards are a signpost to parks which are making real achievements in protecting our environment. Go there and experience wrap-around nature ... you could be amazed at what you find!' says Professor David Bellamy.

More than 600 gold, silver and bronze parks were named this year in the David Bellamy Conservation Awards, organised in conjunction with the British Holiday and Home Parks Association.

These parks are recognised for their commitment to conservation and the environment through their management of landscaping, recycling policies, waste management, the cultivation of flora and fauna and the creation of habitats designed to encourage a variety of wildlife onto the park. Links with the local community and the use of local materials are also important considerations.

Parks wishing to enter for a David Bellamy Conservation Award must complete a detailed questionnaire covering different aspects of their environmental policies, and describe what positive conservation steps they have taken. The park must also undergo an independent audit from a local wildlife or conservation body which is familiar with the area. Final assessments and the appropriate level of any award are then made personally by Professor Bellamy.

An index of award-winning parks featured in the regional pages of this guide can be found on page 334.

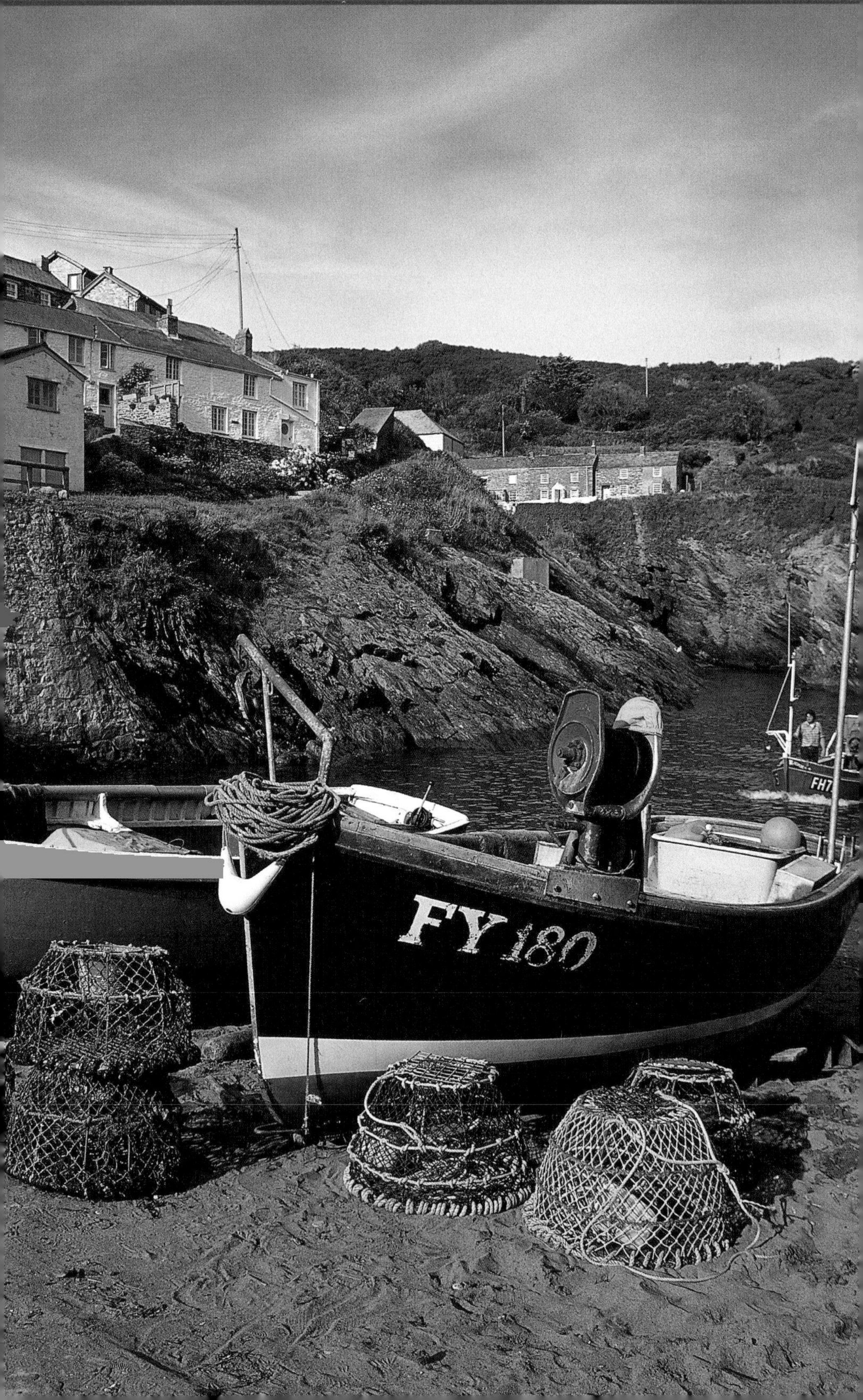
FY 180

South West

Cornwall & Isles of Scilly, Devon, Dorset,
Gloucestershire, Somerset, Wiltshire

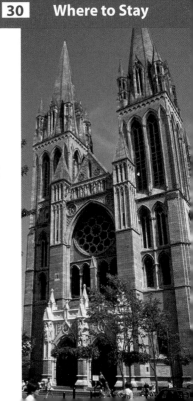

If you love the great outdoors then take your pick from Wiltshire's ancient countryside where Stonehenge reigns supreme, Devon's rolling hills, the magical Forest of Dean, the idyllic Cotswold villages, the dramatic Dorset coast, the surf beaches of Cornwall and the beautiful Isles of Scilly. But urbanites fear not - Bristol delivers cutting-edge culture and Bath awe-inspiring heritage.

Basically, you want it, come get it in the wild and wonderful South West.

History and Heritage

Attempt to solve the mystery of Stonehenge which was erected between 3,000 BC and 1,600 BC or soak up maritime history at Bristol where you'll find the SS GreatBritain. Take a subterranean history lesson at Exeter's medieval passageways or explore Cornwall's mining past along 50 miles of heritage coastline.

The Jurassic Coast (Studland Bay, Dorset to Orcombe Rocks, Devon) has 95 miles of beautiful coastline with 185 million years of Earth history to explore. With the Roman Baths and Royal Crescent, the UNESCO World Heritage City of Bath is simply unmissable.

Arts and Culture

From Banksy's satirical styling on the streets of Bristol to Frome's Black Swan and Rook Lane galleries, art is alive and kicking in the South West. Exeter's Phoenix Centre celebrates cutting-edge visual arts and performances whereas St Ives with its harbourside galleries, artists' workshops and excellent Tate is Cornwall's cultural epicentre. For theatre, there are few places more dramatic than the cliff-side Minack Theatre and Bristol's Old Vic has over 200 years experience in hosting exhilarating productions.

Literati will love the Bath Literature Festival in February and camping out for the festival of words and music at Port Eliot, Cornwall.

Food and Drink

The West Country is packed full of flavourful treats – Cornish pasties, Devonshire fudge, Wiltshire Ham, Cheddar cheese, Somerset cider and that's just for starters. When it comes to fine-dining you're spoilt for choice – there's Michelin-starred finery at The Dining Room in Malmesbury and Michael Caines' Gidleigh Park in Devon. For prime Cornish seafood, visit Padstow, affectionately renamed Padstein thanks to the TV chef's four restaurants.

Sports

Cornwall is home to Britain's best surf beaches so be sure to catch a wave at Newquay's Fistral Beach or at stunning Sennen Cove. Enjoy the thwack of leather on willow in Taunton, catch rugby at the Rec in Bath; or watch Bristol City and Rovers play the beautiful game. Scuba divers have plenty to explore with the HMS Scylla off Plymouth and numerous wrecks off the Falmouth coast.

Music and Nightlife

Having spawned Massive Attack and Portishead, Bristol remains a Mecca for music-lovers - check the latest acts at the Thekla. Catch bands before they blow up at Exeter's The Cavern or for hands-in-the-air clubbing action look no further than Slinky at the Opera House in Bournemouth. And with over 2,000 acts rocking out in the spiritual Somerset countryside each June, there's simply no better festival than Glastonbury.

Shopping

Soak up the atmosphere at one of the South West's historic markets or for designers and high street fashion hit Bristol's Cabots Circus. When it comes to antiques, the delightful Cotswolds have it in the bag; Tetbury and Stow-on the-Wold are overflowing with collectable goodies. To get your hands on local art and crafts, vintage clothing and records explore the cobbled streets of Frome.

Family Fun

Encounter over 450 species of animals at Bristol Zoo or drive amongst them on safari at Longleat, just watch out for those cheeky monkeys. With plenty of hands-on exhibits @Bristol really does make science fun, but thrill-seekers may want to head to The Adrenalin Quarry near Liskeard to experience the UK's Longest Zip Wire.

Handy Hints

Breathtaking - the train journey from Exeter to Newton Abbott is one of the most spectacular in the country with breathtaking views as you travel along the coast atop the seawall.

Well Preserved - go fossil-hunting on the beaches between Lyme Regis and Charmouth.

Fine Food - for stunning views of Dartmoor dine-out at Michel Caines' Gidleigh Park in Devon, recently voted the 'Number 1 Restaurant' in Sunday Times Top 100 British Restaurants.

Fancy a Tipple? - make your own gin at Plymouth Gin Distillery.

OUT & ABOUT IN THE SOUTH WEST

Day 5 - Cornish Quality

- Visit St Ives Tate gallery for cutting edge contemporary art
- Cycle the Mineral Tramways and experience Cornwall's rich mining heritage
- Stroll around Padstow harbour before eating out at Rick Stein's Seafood Restaurant

Day 1 - Say cheese

- Visit the Roman Baths and the Royal Crescent in Bath Spa
- Go shopping and gallery shopping in Frome
- Explore Cheddar's spectacular show caves and sample the cheese

Day 6 - Devonshire Delights

- Walk or cycle the beautiful Dartmoor National Park
- Explore Exeter's medieval underground passageways
- Visit the picturesque Lynton and Lynmouth - Devon's Little Switzerland

Day 2 - Inspiring

- Admire the country's tallest spire and the world's oldest copy of Magna Carta at Salisbury Cathedral
- Visit the magnificent and mysterious Stonehenge
- Drive the animal safari at Longleat

Day 3 - Bristol or Bust

- Walk the streets of Bristol to experience graffiti art including works by Banksy
- Take a ferry from the waterfront to SS Great Britain
- Cross Brunel's Clifton Suspension Bridge for stunning views of the Avon Gorge

Day 7 - Beachcomber

- Sunbathe on Bournemouth's seven miles of Blue Flag Beach
- Explore Dorset's Jurassic Coast by foot or by boat from Poole Quay
- Visit Brownsea Island for wildlife and scouting history and perhaps a red squirrel

Day 4 - Avalon

- Visit King Arthur's grave at Glastonbury Abbey
- Climb Glastonbury Tor for an impressive panorama and a legendary atmosphere
- Enjoy contemporary cuisine at The Old Spot in Wells

Where to Go

 Attractions with this sign participate in the **Places of Interest Quality Assurance Scheme**.

 Attractions with this sign participate in the **Visitor Attraction Quality Assurance Scheme**.

Both schemes recognise high standards in all aspects of the visitor experience (see page 6)

ENTERTAINMENT & CULTURE

Castle Combe Museum
Castle Combe, Wiltshire SN14 7HU
(01249) 782250
www.castle-combe.com
Displays of life in Castle Combe over the years.

City Sightseeing - The Bristol Tour
Central Bristol, BS1 4AH
(03333) 210101
www.citysightseeingbristol.co.uk
Open-top bus tours, with guides and headphones, around the city of Bristol, a service that runs daily throughout the summer months.

Corinium Museum
Cirencester, Gloucestershire GL7 2BX
(01285) 655611
www.cotswold.gov.uk/go/museum
Discover the treasures of the Cotswolds as you explore its history at this award winning museum.

Dean Heritage Centre
Cinderford, Gloucestershire GL14 2UB
(01594) 822170
www.deanheritagemuseum.com
The Centre is open again after the fire. On display is an exhibition showing the damage caused by the fire so that visitors can come along and see what plans the Museum has in place to clean and refurbish

Gloucester Waterways Museum
Gloucester GL1 2EH
(01452) 318200
www.nwm.org.uk
Three floors of a Victorian warehouse house, interactive displays and galleries, which chart the story of Britain's waterways.

Haynes International Motor Museum
Yeovil, Somerset BA22 7LH
(01963) 440804
www.haynesmotormuseum.co.uk
An excellent day out for everyone. With more than 400 vehicles displayed in stunning style, dating from 1886 to the present day, it is the largest international motor museum in Britain.

National Maritime Museum Cornwall
Falmouth, Cornwall TR11 3QY
(01326) 313388
www.nmmc.co.uk
Voted SW Attraction of the Year, this Museum delivers something for everyone.

Plymouth City Museum and Art Gallery
Devon PL4 8AJ
(01752) 304774
www.plymouth.gov.uk/museumpcmag.htm
The museum presents a diverse range of contemporary exhibitions, from photography to textiles, modern art to natural history.

Roman Baths
Bath, Somerset BA1 1LZ
(01225) 477785
www.romanbaths.co.uk
The Romans built a magnificent temple and bathing complex that still flows with natural hot water.

Tate St Ives
St. Ives, Cornwall TR26 1TG
(01736) 796226
www.tate.org.uk/stives
Tate St Ives offers an introduction to international Modern and contemporary art, including works from the Tate Collection.

The Jane Austen Centre
Bath, Somerset BA1 2NT
(01225) 443000
www.janeausten.co.uk
Celebrating Bath's most famous resident.

FAMILY FUN

At-Bristol
Bristol BS1 5DB
0845 345 1235
www.at-bristol.org.uk
21st-century science and technology centre, with hands-on activities, interactive exhibits.

Corfe Castle Model Village and Gardens
Corfe Castle, Dorset BH20 5EZ
(01929) 481234
www.corfecastlemodelvillage.co.uk
Detailed 1/20th scale model of Corfe Castle and village before its destruction by Cromwell.

Cornwall's Crealy Great Adventure Park
Wadebridge, Cornwall PL27 7RA
(01841) 540276
www.crealy.co.uk/cornwall/index.aspx.
Enter the magical land of Cornwall's Crealy and hold on tight for Morgawr, the exciting NEW roller coaster.

Flambards
Helston, Cornwall TR13 0QA
(01326) 573404
www.flambards.co.uk
Do not forget to visit the award-winning and unique exhibitions including the Victorian Village and the Britain in the Blitz."

FOOD & DRINK

Wadworth Visitor Centre
Devizes, Wiltshire SN10 1JW
(01380) 732277
www.wadworthvisitorcentre.co.uk
Sample the delights and discover the history & heritage of Wadworth brewing. Featuring an exhibition of Wadworth brewing memorabilia, and products created by our Master Cooper.

HERITAGE

Avon Valley Railway
Bristol, Gloucestershire BS30 6HD
(0117) 932 5538
www.avonvalleyrailway.org
Railway that's much more than your average steam train ride, offering a whole new experience for some or a nostalgic memory for others.

Brunel's ss Great Britain
Bristol BS1 6TY
(0117) 926 0680
www.ssgreatbritain.org
Award-winning attraction showing the world's first great ocean liner and National Brunel Archive.

Dartmouth Castle
Dartmouth, Devon TQ6 0JN
(01803) 833588
www.english-heritage.org.uk/dartmouthcastle
For over six hundred years Dartmouth Castle has guarded the narrow entrance to the Dart Estuary and the busy, vibrant port of Dartmouth.

Forde Abbey & Gardens
Chard, Dorset TA20 4LU
(01460) 221290
www.fordeabbey.co.uk
Founded 850-years-ago, Forde Abbey was converted into a private house in c1649.

Glastonbury Abbey
Somerset BA6 9EL
(01458) 832267
www.glastonburyabbey.com
Glastonbury Abbey – Somewhere for all seasons ! From snowdrops and daffodils in the Spring, to family trails and quizzes during the school holidays and Autumn colour on our hundreds of trees.

Gloucester Cathedral
Gloucestershire GL1 2LR
(01452) 528095
www.gloucestercathedral.org.uk
A place of worship and an architectural gem with crypt, cloisters, Chapter House set in its precincts.

Lulworth Castle & Park
Wareham, Dorset BH20 5QS
0845 450 1054
www.lulworth.com
Walk in the footsteps of Kings & Queens as you enjoy wide open spaces, historic buildings & stunning landscapes. Enjoy the tranquillity of the nearby 18C Chapel, wander through the park & woodland & bring a picnic..

Number One Royal Crescent
Bath, Somerset BA1 2LR
(01225) 428126
www.bath-preservation-trust.org.uk
The magnificently restored and authentically furnished town house creates a wonderful picture of fashionable life in 18th century Bath.

Old Sarum
Salisbury, Wiltshire SP1 3SD
(01722) 335398
www.english-heritage.org.uk/oldsarum
Discover the story of the original Salisbury and take the family for a day out to Old Sarum, 2 miles north of where the city stands now. The mighty Iron Age hill fort was where the first cathedral once stood and the Romans, Normans and Saxons have all left their mark..

Quay House Visitor Centre
Exeter, Devon EX2 4AN
(01392) 271611
www.exeter.gov.uk/quayhouse
Discover the history of Exeter in 15 minutes at the Quay House Visitor Centre on Exeter's Historic Quayside.

Portland Castle
Portland, Dorset DT5 1AZ
(01305) 820539
www.english-heritage.org.uk/portland
A well preserved coastal fort built by Henry VIII to defend Weymouth harbour against possible French and Spanish attack.

Salisbury Cathedral
Salisbury, Wiltshire SP1 2EJ
(01722) 555120
www.salisburycathedral.org.uk
Britain's finest 13th century cathedral with the tallest spire in Britain. Discover nearly 800 years of history, the world's best preserved Magna Carta (AD 1215) and Europe's oldest working clock (AD 1386).

Stonehenge
Amesbury, Wiltshire SP4 7DE
0870 333 1181
www.english-heritage.org.uk/stonehenge
Stonehenge stands impressively as a prehistoric monument of unique importance, a World Heritage Site, surrounded by remains of ceremonial and domestic structures - some older than the monument itself.

Sudeley Castle Gardens and Exhibition
Winchcombe, Gloucestershire GL54 5JD
(01242) 602308
www.sudeleycastle.co.uk
Award-winning gardens surrounding Castle and medieval ruins.

Swanage Railway
Swanage, Dorset BH19 1HB
(01929) 425800
www.swanagerailway.co.uk
Enjoy a nostalgic steam-train ride on the Purbeck line.

West Somerset Railway
Minehead, Somerset TA24 5BG
(01643) 704996
www.west-somerset-railway.co.uk
Longest independent steam railway in Britain, (20 miles).

NATURE & WILDLIFE

Blue Reef Aquarium
Newquay, Cornwall TR7 1DU
(01637) 878134
www.bluereefaquarium.co.uk
A dazzling undersea safari through the oceans of the world.

Bristol Zoo Gardens
Bristol BS8 3HA
(0117) 974 7300
www.bristolzoo.org.uk
A visit to this city zoo is your passport for a day trip into an amazing world of animals, exhibits and other attractions.

Eden Project
St. Austell, Cornwall PL24 2SG
(01726) 811911
www.edenproject.com
With a worldwide reputation this epic destination definitely deserves a day of your undivided attention.

Escot Gardens, Maze & Forest Adventure
Ottery St. Mary, Devon EX11 1LU
(01404) 822188
www.escot-devon.co.uk
Historical gardens and fantasy woodland surrounding the ancestral home of the Kennaway family.

Fistral Beach
Newquay, Cornwall TR7 1HY
(01637) 850584
www.fistralbeach.co.uk
Excellent surfing conditions, a large beach, west facing with fine golden sand. International surfing events regularly take place here.

Hidcote Manor Garden
Chipping Campden, Gloucestershire GL55 6LR
(01386) 438333
www.nationaltrust.org.uk/hidcote
Famous for its rare trees and shrubs, outstanding herbaceous borders and unusual plants from all over the world.

HorseWorld
Bristol, Somerset BS14 0QJ
(01275) 540173
www.horseworld.org.uk
Meet and help feed the rescued horses, ponies, donkeys in order to support this charity's animal welfare work.

Ilfracombe Aquarium
Ilfracombe, Devon EX34 9EQ
(01271) 864533
www.ilfracombeaquarium.co.uk
A fascinating journey of discovery into the aquatic life of North Devon.

Longleat
Warminster, Wiltshire BA12 7NW
(01985) 844400
www.longleat.co.uk
Widely regarded as one of the best loved tourist destinations in the UK, Longleat has a wealth of exciting attractions and events to tantalise your palate.

Lost Gardens of Heligan
St. Austell, Cornwall PL26 6EN
(01726) 845100
www.heligan.com
An exploration through Victorian Productive Gardens & Pleasure Grounds, a sub-tropical Jungle, pioneering Wildlife Project and beyond.

National Seal Sanctuary
Helston, Cornwall TR12 6UG
(01326) 221361
www.sealsanctuary.co.uk
The National Seal Sanctuary rescues, rehabilitates and releases over 40 seal pups a year, providing a home for those that can't be released back to the wild.

Newquay Zoo
Newquay, Cornwall TR7 2LZ
01637) 873342
www.newquayzoo.org.uk
Multi-award winning Newquay Zoo set in sub-tropical lakeside gardens and home to over 130 species of animals.

Painswick Rococo Garden
Painswick, Gloucestershire GL6 6TH
(01452) 813204
www.rococogarden.org.uk
A unique Garden restoration, situated in a hidden valley.

Stourhead House and Garden
Warminster, Wiltshire BA12 6QD
(01747) 841152
www.nationaltrust.org.uk/stourhead
A breathtaking 18th century landscape garden with lakeside walks, grottoes and classical temples is only the beginning.

Westonbirt, The National Arboretum
Tetbury, Gloucestershire GL8 8QS
(01666) 880220
www.forestry.gov.uk/westonbirt
600 acres with one of the finest collections of trees in the world.

Events 2012

Bath Fringe Festival
Bath
www.bathfringe.co.uk
May - June

Chippenham Folk Festival
Chippenham
www.chippfolk.co.uk
May

Chipping Campden Music Festival
Chipping Campden
www.campdenmusicfestival.co.uk
May

Devizes Festival
Devizes
www.devizesfestival.co.uk
June

Festival of Nature
Bristol
www.festivalofnature.org
June

Glastonbury Festival
Shepton Mallet
www.glastonburyfestivals.co.uk
June

North Devon Festival
Barnstaple
www.northdevonfestival.org
June

Wiltshire Jazz Festival
Salisbury
www.wiltshirejazzfestival.co.uk
June

Bristol Harbour Festival
Bristol
www.bristolharbourfestival.co.uk
July

Dorset Seafood Festival
Weymouth
www.dorsetseafood.co.uk
July

Frome Festival
Frome
www.fromefestival.co.uk
July

St Paul's Carnival
Bristol
www.stpaulscarnival.co.uk
July

The Royal International Air Tattoo
Fairford
www.airtattoo.com
July

Dartmoor Folk Festival
South Zeal
www.dartmoorfolkfestival.co.uk
August

Taunton Flower Show
Taunton
www.tauntonflowershow.co.uk
August

The Great Dorset Steam Fair
Blandford Forum
www.gdsf.co.uk
August - September

The Jane Austen Festival
Bath
www.janeausten.co.uk/festival
September

Dartmouth Food Festival
Dartmouth
www.dartmouthfoodfestival.com
October

Tourist Information Centres

When you arrive at your destination, visit an Official Partner Tourist Information Centre for quality assured help with accommodation and information about local attractions and events, or email your request before you go. To find a Tourist Information Centre by region look at http://www.enjoyengland.com under Destination Finder.

AVEBURY	Avebury Chapel Centre	01672 539179	all.tics@wiltshire.gov.uk
BATH	Abbey Chambers	0906 711 2000	tourism@bathtourism.co.uk
BODMIN	Shire Hall	01208 76616	bodmintic@visit.org.uk
BOURTON-ON-THE-WATER	Victoria Street	01451 820211	bourtonvic@btconnect.com
BRIDPORT	47 South Street	01308 424901	bridport.tic@westdorset-dc.gov.uk
BRISTOL : HARBOURSIDE	E Shed 1	0333 321 0101	ticharbourside@destinationbristol.co.uk
BRIXHAM	The Old Market House	01803 211 211	holiday@torbay.gov.uk
BUDE	Bude Visitor Centre	01288 354240	budetic@visitbude.info
BURNHAM-ON-SEA	South Esplanade	01278 787852	burnham.tic@sedgemoor.gov.uk
CAMELFORD	North Cornwall Museum	01840 212954	manager@camelfordtic.eclipse.co.uk
CARTGATE	South Somerset TIC	01935 829333	cartgate.tic@southsomerset.gov.uk
CHARD	The Guildhall	01460 260051	chard.tic@chard.gov.uk
CHELTENHAM	Municipal Offices	01242 522878	info@cheltenham.gov.uk
CHIPPENHAM	Yelde Hall	01249 665970	tourism@chippenham.gov.uk
CHIPPING CAMPDEN	The Old Police Station	01386 841206	information@visitchippingcampden.com
CHRISTCHURCH	49 High Street	01202 471780	enquiries@christchurchtourism.info
CIRENCESTER	Corinium Museum	01285 654180	cirencestervic@cotswold.gov.uk
CORSHAM	Arnold House	01249 714660	enquiries@corshamheritage.org.uk
DEVIZES	Cromwell House	01380 734669	all.tics@wiltshire.gov.uk
DORCHESTER	11 Antelope Walk	01305 267992	dorchester.tic@westdorset-dc.gov.uk
FALMOUTH	11 Market Strand	01326 312300	info@falmouthtic.co.uk
FOWEY	5 South Street	01726 833616	info@fowey.co.uk
FROME	The Library	01373 465757	touristinfo@frome-tc.gov.uk
GLASTONBURY	The Tribunal	01458 832954	glastonbury.tic@ukonline.co.uk
GLOUCESTER	28 Southgate Street	01452 396572	tourism@gloucester.gov.uk

LOOE	The Guildhall	01503 262072	looetic@btconnect.com
LYME REGIS	Guildhall Cottage	01297 442138	lymeregis.tic@westdorset-dc.gov.uk
MALMESBURY	Town Hall	01666 823748	tic@malmesbury.gov.uk
MORETON-IN-MARCH	High Street	01608 650881	moreton@cotswold.gov.uk
PADSTOW & WADEBRIDGE	Red Brick Building	01841 533449	padstowtic@btconnect.com
PAIGNTON	The Esplanade	01803 211 211	holiday@torbay.gov.uk
PENZANCE	Station Road	01736 362207	pztic@penwith.gov.uk
PLYMOUTH	Plymouth Mayflower Centre	01752 306330	barbicantic@plymouth.gov.uk
SALISBURY	Fish Row	01722 334956	visitorinfo@salisbury.gov.uk
SHEPTON MALLET	70 High Street	01749 345258	sheptonmallet.tic@ukonline.co.uk
SHERBORNE	3 Tilton Court	01935 815341	sherborne.tic@westdorset-dc.gov.uk
SOMERSET VISITOR CENTRE	Sedgemoor Services	01934 750833	somersetvisitorcentre@somerset.gov.uk
ST AUSTELL	Southbourne Road	01726 879 500	tic@cornish-riviera.co.uk
ST IVES	The Guildhall	01736 796297	ivtic@penwith.gov.uk
STREET	Clarks Village	01458 447384	street.tic@ukonline.co.uk
STROUD	Subscription Rooms	01453 760960	tic@stroud.gov.uk
SWANAGE	The White House	01929 422885	mail@swanage.gov.uk
SWINDON	37 Regent Street	01793 530328	infocentre@swindon.gov.uk
TAUNTON	The Library	01823 336344	tauntontic@tauntondeane.gov.uk
TETBURY	33 Church Street	01666 503552	tourism@tetbury.org
TEWKESBURY	100 Church Street	01684 855043	tewkesburytic@tewkesburybc.gov.uk
TORQUAY	The Tourist Centre	01803 211 211	holiday@torbay.gov.uk
TRURO	Municipal Building	01872 274555	tic@truro.gov.uk
WAREHAM	Holy Trinity Church	01929 552740	tic@purbeck-dc.gov.uk
WARMINSTER	Central Car Park	01985 218548	visitwarminster@btconnect.com
WELLS	Wells Museum	01749 671770	visitwellsinfo@gmail.com
WESTON-SUPER-MARE	Beach Lawns	01934 888800	westontouristinfo@n-somerset.gov.uk
WEYMOUTH	The Pavilion	01305 785747	tic@weymouth.gov.uk
WINCHCOMBE	Town Hall	01242 602925	winchcombetic@tewkesbury.gov.uk
YEOVIL	Hendford	01935 845946/7	yeoviltic@southsomerset.gov.uk

Regional Contacts and Information

For more information on accommodation, attractions, activities, events and holidays in South West England, contact one of the following regional or local tourism organisations. Their websites have a wealth of information and many produce free publications to help you get the most out of your visit.

Visit the following websites for further information on South West England:

- visitsouthwest.co.uk
- swcp.org.uk
- accessiblesouthwest.co.uk

Publications available from South West Tourism:
- The Trencherman's Guide to Top Restaurants in South West England
- Adventure South West
  Your ultimate activity and adventure guide.
- World Heritage Map
  Discover our World Heritage.

Where to Stay

Entries appear alphabetically by town name in each county. A key to symbols appears on page 6. Maps start on page 298. Further listings of VisitEngland assessed accommodation appear on the CD at the back of this guide.

BLACKWATER, Cornwall Map ref 1B3

SAT NAV TR4 8HR

Trevarth Holiday Park
Blackwater, Truro TR4 8HR
t (01872) 560266 **e** trevarth@btconnect.com
w **trevarth.co.uk** ONLINE MAP LAST MINUTE OFFERS

(30)	£11.00–£18.00
(30)	£11.00–£18.00
(30)	£11.00–£18.00
(20)	£160.00–£620.00

30 touring pitches

Luxury caravan holiday homes, touring and camping. A small, quiet park conveniently situated for north and south-coast resorts. Level touring and tent pitches with electric hook-up.

open April to October
payment credit/debit cards, cash, cheques

directions Leave A30 at Chiverton roundabout (signed St Agnes). At the next roundabout take the road to Blackwater. Park on right after 200m.

General 🖥 📶 📺 📡 ☀ 🍳 🚿 💬 📤 📞 Leisure ∪ ⚓ 🔍 ⛰

Looking for something else?

You can also buy a copy of our popular 'B&B' guide including guest accommodation, B&B's, guest houses, farmhouses, inns, and campus and hostel accommodation in England 2012.

Now available in good bookshops and online at **visitbritainshop.com**   **£8.99**

BUDE, Cornwall Map ref 1C2 — SAT NAV EX23 0NA

Budemeadows Touring Park
Widemouth Bay, Bude, Cornwall EX23 0NA
t (01288) 361646 f 0870 7064825 e holiday@budemeadows.com
w **budemeadows.com** ONLINE MAP GUEST REVIEWS LAST MINUTE OFFERS

🚐 (145)	£14.00–£26.50
🚛 (145)	£14.00–£26.50
⛺ (145)	£14.00–£26.50
145 touring pitches	

SPECIAL PROMOTIONS
Over 60's winter rates £12/
night (2 adults, 2 dogs,
hook-up. Prices are 2011
rates for 2 adults + electric.

Great family run site providing a superb base for surfing, scenery and sightseeing. All usual facilities, heated pool, licensed bar, shop, launderette, large childrens playground, games room with TV and pool table. Well maintained grounds. 4 miles from Bude and a mile from the surf and sand at Widemouth Bay.

open All year
payment credit/debit cards, cash, cheques

directions Signposted from A39, 3 miles south of Bude. Look for signs after signpost to Widemouth Bay. Full directions available on our website.

General 🔥🗂♿🐕🛋🏠🛖☀🚿🅿🔌🚽♿ Leisure ▶∪🎣🌿🍽🔍🎱

BUDE, Cornwall Map ref 1C2 — SAT NAV EX23 0LF

Hentervene Park
Hentervene Park, Crackington Haven, Bude EX23 0LF
t (01840) 230365 e contact@hentervene.co.uk
w **hentervene.co.uk** ONLINE MAP GUEST REVIEWS LAST MINUTE OFFERS

🚐 (20)	£14.00–£20.00
🚛 (8)	£14.00–£20.00
🏠 (2)	£290–£850
🚐 (8)	£190.00–£650.00
25 touring pitches	

A peaceful holiday retreat in the stunningly beautiful countryside of North Cornwall, 2 miles from the glorious sandy beach at Crackington Haven. An ideal base for exploring Cornwall and Devon. **directions** Simple to find, a couple of miles off the A39. Best route, take the B3263 towards Boscastle. Signposted from there. Website has best printable directions. **open** All year **payment** credit/debit cards, cash, cheques

General 🔥🗂♿🐕🛋🏠☀🚿🅿🔌🚽 Leisure ▶∪🎣🔍🎱

BUDE, Cornwall Map ref 1C2 — SAT NAV EX23 9HW

Sandymouth Holiday Park
Sandymouth Holiday Park, Stibb, Bude, Cornwall EX23 9HW
t 0844 272 9530 f (01288) 354822 e enquiries@sandymouthbay.co.uk
w **sandymouthbay.co.uk** ONLINE MAP ONLINE BOOKING LAST MINUTE OFFERS

22 touring pitches

Enjoy the best of beach and rural life at this five-star park, with superb on-park facilities including clubhouse with live entertainment every night, restaurant, bar and a superb childrens playground. **directions** On M5 from north, exit jct 27. Travel on A361/A39 towards Bude. Just past the village of Kilkhampton, take right-hand turning signposted Sandymouth. **open** March to November **payment** credit/debit cards, cash, cheques

General 🔥🗂♿🐕🛋🏠☀🖵🅿🔌🚽♿✕ Leisure ∪♿🎣🌿🍽🎵🔍🎱

BUDE, Cornwall Map ref 1C2

SAT NAV EX23 9HJ

Wooda Farm Holiday Park
Poughill, Bude, Cornwall EX23 9HJ
t (01288) 352069 **f** (01288) 355258 **e** enquiries@wooda.co.uk
w wooda.co.uk ONLINE MAP GUEST REVIEWS ONLINE BOOKING LAST MINUTE OFFERS

(80)	£15.00–£29.00
(60)	£15.00–£29.00
(60)	£12.00–£25.00
(55)	£210.00–£819.00

200 touring pitches

SPECIAL PROMOTIONS
See our website for special offers.

Stunning views over Bude Bay and countryside; 1.5 miles from safe, sandy beaches. Family-owned and run with excellent facilities for touring and camping and luxury holiday homes for hire. Activities include fishing, sports barn, tennis court, woodland walks, golf. An ideal base for touring the delights of Devon and Cornwall.

open April to October
payment credit/debit cards, cash, cheques

directions 1.5 miles from Bude, just outside the village of Poughill.

General ⚡ ⬛ ⌘ ✝ ⤵ ⬛ ⟡ ☼ ⬛ ⬛ ⬛ ⬛ ⬛ ⬛ ✕   Leisure ▶ ∪ ⚲ ⚴ ✦ ⬛

Looking for something else?

You can also buy a copy of our popular guide 'Hotels' including country house and town house hotels, metro and budget hotels, serviced apartments and restaurants with rooms in England 2012.

Now available in good bookshops and online at
visitbritainshop.com

£7.99

CAMELFORD, Cornwall Map ref 1B2 SAT NAV PL32 9RF

enjoyEngland.com ★★★★ HOLIDAY, TOURING & CAMPING PARK

£19.00–£24.00
£19.00–£24.00
£108.00–£610.00
39 touring pitches

SPECIAL PROMOTIONS
Seasonal tourers are welcome for further information contact Kim on 01840 213302.

Juliots Well Holiday Park

Juliots well, Camelford, Cornwall PL32 9RF
t (01840) 213302 **f** (01840) 212700 **e** holidays@juliotswell.com
w **juliotswell.com**

Juliots well is a family run park which is open all year and set in 33 acres of woodlands with extensive views across some of the finest Cornish Countryside. An ideal touring base for all of Cornwall.

There are excellent facilities for guest including Coach House Bar and Restaurant serving breakfast and daily meals.

Outdoor heated swimming pool is open mid May to Mid September. For fishermen we have a trout fishing lake set in the most tranquil part of the park. There is a games room, play area, and a small shop and Launderette. Wi-Fi is available in the Coach House.

open All year
payment credit/debit cards, cash, cheques

directions Follow A30 from Exeter. By-passing Launceston, turn right onto A395 Turn left onto the A39 to Camelford. Beyond the town (just after the sign for Valley Truckle) turn right onto BS266 and then left on sharp bend sign posted Juliots Well, we are 300 yard on the right.

General **Leisure**

For **key to symbols** see page 6

FALMOUTH, Cornwall Map ref 1B3   SAT NAV TR11 5BJ

RATING APPLIED FOR

 (65)   £260.00–£1050.00

Pendra Loweth Cottages

Pendra Loweth Cottages, Maen Valley, Falmouth TR11 5BJ
t (01326) 312190   **f** (01326) 211120   **e** contact@pendra.co.uk
w pendraloweth.co.uk ONLINE MAP GUEST REVIEWS ONLINE BOOKING LAST MINUTE OFFERS

A village of four-star holiday cottages within landscaped gardens set in a secluded Cornish valley. Self-catering facilities include a bar, restaurant, Wi-Fi facilities, splash pool, spa and all-weather tennis court. **directions** Set in peaceful Maen Valley, less than a mile from Swanpool Beach, near Falmouth. Postcode TR11 5BJ. **open** All year **payment** credit/debit cards, cash, cheques

General ⏣ ⌂ ✕   Leisure ► ⚲

FOWEY, Cornwall Map ref 1B3   SAT NAV PL23 1JU

HOLIDAY, TOURING & CAMPING PARK

⌗ (35)   £50.00
⌗ (16)   £8.00–£18.00
⚑ (56)   £8.00–£18.00
⌗ (10)   £195.00–£535.00
56 touring pitches

Penhale Caravan & Camping Park

Penhale Caravan & Camping Park, Penhale Farm, Fowey, Cornwall PL23 1JU
t (01726) 833425   **f** (01726) 833425   **e** info@penhale-fowey.co.uk
w penhale-fowey.co.uk ONLINE MAP LAST MINUTE OFFERS

Friendly, uncrowded family run park overlooks un-spoilt farmland and lovely views of the sea. In Area of Outstanding Natural Beauty close to sandy beaches, many scenic walks and the Eden Project. David Bellamy Award. Choice of caravans. Touring pitches, electric hook-ups, free showers.

payment credit/debit cards, cash, cheques

directions From A30 west from Lostwithiel, on A390 turn left after 1 mile onto B3269, after 3 miles turn right onto A3082.

General ⟨icons⟩   Leisure ► ∪ ⚲ ✎

HAYLE, Cornwall Map ref 1B3   SAT NAV TR27 5AW

HOLIDAY, TOURING & CAMPING PARK

⌗ (80)   £9.00–£32.00
⌗ (80)   £9.00–£32.00
⚑ (80)   £9.00–£32.00
⌗ (117)   £210–£895
80 touring pitches

Beachside Holiday Park

Phillack, Hayle TR27 5AW
t (01736) 753080   **f** (01736) 757252   **e** reception@beachside.co.uk
w beachside.co.uk ONLINE MAP ONLINE BOOKING LAST MINUTE OFFERS

Beachside is a family holiday park amidst sand dunes beside the sea in the famous St Ives Bay. Our location is ideal for the beach and for touring West Cornwall. **directions** Travel west on A30 and turn off into Hayle. Turn right, following the sign to Phillack & Beachside. Our entrance is approximately 400m on right. **open** Easter to End October **payment** credit/debit cards, cash, cheques

General ⟨icons⟩   Leisure ∪ ⚲ ⟨icons⟩

HAYLE, Cornwall Map ref 1B3 — SAT NAV TR27 5BH

St Ives Bay Holiday Park

73 Loggans Road, Upton Towans, Hayle TR27 5BH
t (01736) 752274 **f** (01736) 754523 **e** stivesbay@btconnect.com
w stivesbay.co.uk ONLINE MAP GUEST REVIEWS ONLINE BOOKING

(250)	£10.00–£32.00
(250)	£10.00–£32.00
(250)	£10.00–£32.00
(4)	£136–£1512
(150)	£136–£1512
(250)	£142.00–£997.00

250 touring pitches

Magnificent location in dunes overlooking huge sandy beach. Caravans, chalets and camping. Many units and pitches with sea views. **directions** Take first Hayle exit from A30 going West. Turn immediately right at Lidl. Park entrance 500 metres on left. **open** Easter to October **payment** credit/debit cards, cash, cheques

General Leisure

HAYLE (2MILES), Cornwall Map ref 1B3 — SAT NAV TR27 5BL

Atlantic Coast Holiday Park

53 Upton Towans, Hayle, Cornwall TR27 5BL
t (01736) 752071 **e** enquiries@atlanticcoastpark.co.uk
w atlanticcoastpark.co.uk ONLINE MAP GUEST REVIEWS ONLINE BOOKING LAST MINUTE OFFERS

(15)	£17.50–£21.50
(15)	£17.50–£21.50
(15)	£17.50–£21.50
(19)	£276.00–£748.00

15 touring pitches

The park is situated alongside the sand dunes of St Ives bay, bordering Gwithian beach, a fantastic quiet beach ideal for families and surfers. The park is also pet friendly. **directions** Leave the A30 at the Hayle exit, turn right onto the B3301, approx 1 mile on left is where we are situated. **open** 1st March - January **payment** credit/debit cards, cash, cheques

General Leisure

HELSTON, Cornwall Map ref 1B3 — SAT NAV TR13 9NN

Poldown Camping & Caravan Park

Carleen, Breage, Helston TR13 9NN
t (01326) 574560 **e** stay@poldown.co.uk
w poldown.co.uk ONLINE MAP ONLINE BOOKING LAST MINUTE OFFERS

(13)	£10.50–£16.25
(13)	£10.50–£16.25
(13)	£10.50–£16.25
(7)	£195.00–£545.00

13 touring pitches

Small and pretty countryside site. Peace and quiet guaranteed. Within easy reach of West Cornwall's beaches, walks and attractions. Very good touring facilities. Modern holiday caravans. **directions** From Helston Penzance for 0.5mile, right direction Camborne 2nd left direction Carleen. From A30 take Camborne exit, follow Helston, 2miles before Helston right direction Carleen. **open** April to October **payment** credit/debit cards, cash, cheques, euros

General Leisure

HELSTON, Cornwall Map ref 1B3 — SAT NAV TR12 7LZ

Silver Sands Holiday Park

Gwendreath, Kennack Sands, Helston TR12 7LZ
t (01326) 290631 **f** (01326) 290631 **e** info@silversandsholidaypark.co.uk
w silversandsholidaypark.co.uk ONLINE MAP GUEST REVIEWS LAST MINUTE OFFERS

(16)	£14.50–£20.50
(16)	£14.50–£20.50
(20)	£12.50–£20.50
(17)	£159.00–£559.00

16 touring pitches

Quiet family-run holiday park in 9 acres of landscaped grounds with large pitches separated by hedges & within a walking distance of sandy beaches. Dogs welcome. No clubhouse. Nearby bar/shop. **directions** A3083 from Helston past RNAS Culdrose, left onto B3293 (St Keverne). Right turn after passing Goonhilly satellite station. Left after 1.5 miles to Gwendreath. **open** March to November **payment** credit/debit cards, cash, cheques

General Leisure

For **key to symbols** see page 6

LANDRAKE, Cornwall Map ref 1C2　　　SAT NAV PL12 5AF

🚐 (60)	£17.50–£23.00
🚐 (60)	£17.50–£23.00
⛺ (20)	£6.00–£23.00
60 touring pitches	

Dolbeare Caravan & Camping Park
Landrake, Saltash PL12 5AF
t (01752) 851332　**f** (01752) 547871　**e** reception@dolbeare.co.uk
w dolbeare.co.uk ONLINE MAP GUEST REVIEWS ONLINE BOOKING LAST MINUTE OFFERS

2011 Top 100 Awards Regional Winner. Countryside location. Large hardstanding and grass pitches. Centrally located for exploring Devon and Cornwall, just four miles into Cornwall. Easy access. Warm welcome awaits. **directions** From M5 follow A38 and over Tamar Bridge. At Landrake, turn right just under footbridge and follow signs. One mile from A38. **open** All year **payment** credit/debit cards, cash

General 🔥🗗🍴🐕🏊▨🅿☼🚬🔌🚼🚻🔲　Leisure ▶ ∪ ⟋ ⚂

LANIVET, Cornwall Map ref 1B2　　　SAT NAV PL30 5HD

🚐 (6)	£150.00–£490.00

SPECIAL PROMOTIONS
Weekend and mini-breaks subject to availability. The garden adjacent to caravan park is available to visitors.

Kernow Caravan Park
Clann Farm, Clann Lane, Lanivet, Bodmin PL30 5HD
t (01208) 831343

Kernow Caravan Park is quiet and peaceful, in a tranquil setting run by a Cornish family. An ideal touring location to visit Eden Project, Heligan Lost Gardens, Lanhydrock, Camel Trail, Saints Way or Wenford Steam Railway. A few minutes' walk from Lanivet village shop, pub, fish and chip restaurant.

open March to October
payment cash, cheques

directions Leave A30 Innis Downs roundabout. Follow sign to Lanivet 0.75 miles. Left in village centre, opposite shop. Along Clann Lane 300m left into concrete drive.

General 🅿☼　Leisure ⟋

LOOE, Cornwall Map ref 1C2　　　SAT NAV PL13 2JR

🚐 (100)	£11.00–£20.50
🚐 (40)	£11.00–£20.50
⛺ (100)	£11.00–£20.50
🚐 (100)	£125.00–£530.00
240 touring pitches	

Tencreek Holiday Park
Polperro Road, Looe PL13 2JR
t (01503) 262447　**f** (01503) 262760　**e** reception@tencreek.co.uk
w dolphinholidays.co.uk ONLINE MAP ONLINE BOOKING LAST MINUTE OFFERS

The nearest holiday park to Looe-panoramic countryside and coastal views. Selection of fully equipped modern caravans. Marked grass and hardstanding pitches. Newly built Heated Toilet and Shower facilities. **directions** A38 from Tamar bridge. Left at roundabout. Follow Looe signs. Right onto A387, becomes B3253. Through Looe towards Polperro. Tencreek 1.25 miles from Looe bridge. **open** All year **payment** credit/debit cards, cash, cheques

General 🗗🍴🐕🏊▨🅿☼🚬🔲🚬🔌🚼🚻✕　Leisure ▶ ∪ 🎣 ⟋ ⚄ 🎱 ♪ 🔍 ⚂

LOOE, Cornwall Map ref 1C2

SAT NAV PL13 1PB

Tregoad Park Quality Family Touring Site
St Martins, Looe PL13 1PB
t (01503) 262718 **f** (01503) 264777 **e** info@tregoadpark.co.uk
w **tregoadpark.co.uk** GUEST REVIEWS ONLINE BOOKING LAST MINUTE OFFERS

🚐 (150)	£19.00–£35.00
🚌 (40)	£19.00–£35.00
▲ (50)	£7.00–£32.00
🏠 (11)	£240–£885
🏕 (8)	£135.00–£649.00

190 touring pitches

SPECIAL PROMOTIONS
Short breaks in low/mid season for cottages, static holiday homes & touring pitches. Call 01503 262718 for details.

Set in 55 acres of rolling countryside with sea views, Safely away from roads, 190 electric pitches, indoor heated swimming pool and jacuzzi spa. Close to Looe, Polperro & Beaches. Clean, modern facilities, bar, restaurant and take-away in mid/high season. Great low season offers. See our website for more.

open All year
payment credit/debit cards, cash, cheques, euros

directions 1.5 miles from Looe on the B3254. A38 to Trerulefoot, turn left then take A387 Looe (6 miles), road becomes B3253. Tregoad Park on left.

General 🔗📷♿🐕🎣🛒🚿♨🛁🅿🛗🏪💳✕ Leisure ▶🏊🎣🍽🎵🎱⛰

LUXULYAN, Cornwall Map ref 1B2

SAT NAV PL30 5EQ

Croft Farm Holiday Park
Luxulyan, Bodmin, Cornwall PL30 5EQ
t (01726) 850228 **f** (01726) 850498 **e** enquiries@croftfarm.co.uk
w **croftfarm.co.uk** LAST MINUTE OFFERS

🚐 (9)	£12.50–£17.50
🚌 (9)	£12.50–£17.50
▲ (4)	£11.50–£16.50
🏠 (2)	£240–£598
🏕 (3)	£200.00–£520.00

52 touring pitches

A beautifully secluded holiday park, situated just 1 mile from Eden Project. A peaceful, friendly base from which to explore Cornwall. Statics & cottages for rent. **directions** A30, follow Eden Project. Eden left, Luxulyan. 1 mile left. A380 right after level crossing St Blazey. T-junction right, Luxulyan. T-junction right, 500 yds left. **open** 21st March to 21st January **payment** credit/debit cards, cash, cheques

General 🔗📷♿🐕🎣🛒🚿♨🛁🅿🛗🏪 Leisure 🏊🎣⛰

MAWGAN PORTH, Cornwall Map ref 1B2

SAT NAV TR8 4BB

Cosy Corner Holiday Park
Mawgan Porth, Newquay TR8 4BB
t (01637) 860611 **f** (01637) 860611 **e** info@cosycorner.co.uk
w **cosycorner.co.uk** ONLINE MAP GUEST REVIEWS LAST MINUTE OFFERS

🏕 (6)	£265.00–£560.00

Small caravan Park, beautiful gardens, 200yards on level road to unspoilt sandy bay, between Newquay and Padstow. Ideal location to visit all areas of Cornwall. Open Easter-October. **directions** From A30 turn off at Roche/Victoria exit, following Airport signs. After airport follow Mawgan Porth signs. Turn right along Valley Road 200yards. **open** Easter to October **payment** cash, cheques

General 🔗♿☀ Leisure ▶⛳🎣

MEVAGISSEY, Cornwall Map ref 1B3

SAT NAV PL26 6LL

🚐 (189)	£7.00–£30.00
🚙 (189)	£7.00–£30.00
⛺ (189)	£7.00–£30.00
🏠 (38)	£149.00–£999.00

189 touring pitches

SPECIAL PROMOTIONS
Please visit the website for special offers.

Seaview International Holiday Park

Boswinger, Gorran, St. Austell PL26 6LL
t (01726) 843425 **f** (01726) 843358 **e** holidays@seaviewinternational.com
w seaviewinternational.com
ONLINE BOOKING LAST MINUTE OFFERS

At Seaview International we are dedicated to making your holiday a truly enjoyable and memorable experience. Perhaps it's because we are a 5 star park with everything from level camping pitches to exclusive holiday lodges with incredible sea views, but we like to think that it's our attention to detail that keeps our guests coming back time and time again.

Set in over 30 acres of beautifully maintained grounds with far reaching views of the south coast and countryside. We have an out door heated pool, large childrens play area with Free Tennis, Badminton & Volley Ball, the convenience of the Seaview Shop, Sea Breeze Cafe and Wi-Fi throughout the park.

There truly is no better place to spend your holiday. Come and experience for yourself why so many families return time and time again.

open Mid-March to October
payment credit/debit cards, cash, cheques

directions From St Austell roundabout take B3273 to Mevagissy, at brow of hill before village turn right follow signs for Gorran and then brown Seaview signs.

General 🗑 ℗ 🐾 ⛽ 🛉 🚻 ☼ 📠 🚮 🚐 🕐 🚽 📶   Leisure ▶ ∪ ℺ 🚴 ⚓ 🎣 🏔

NEWQUAY, Cornwall Map ref 1B2
SAT NAV TR8 4NY

Hendra Holiday Park
Hendra Holiday Park, Lane, Newquay TR8 4NY
t (01637) 875778 **f** (01637) 879017 **e** enquiries@hendra-holidays.com
w hendra-holidays.com ONLINE MAP GUEST REVIEWS LAST MINUTE OFFERS

ᐱ (725)	£17.20–£27.10
ᐱ (725)	£17.20–£27.10
Å (725)	£11.55–£27.10
⊡ (300)	£195.00–£1069.00
725 touring pitches	

SPECIAL PROMOTIONS
See website for offers, 3/4-night short breaks, caravans for all budgets and our range of touring/camping options.

Award-winning Hendra is ideal for families and couples offering superb-quality holiday homes and touring/camping pitches. With entertainment, indoor and outdoor play areas, amusements, childrens club, cafes and restaurant, and Oasis Fun Pool complex. An ideal location for exploring Cornwall - you will have your best holiday ever!

open Easter to October
payment credit/debit cards, cash, cheques, euros

directions Take the M5 south to Exeter, then A30 westbound. Stay on A30 until you see Newquay signposted. We are on the A392 into Newquay.

General 🔥🖥️♿🐕🛴📞🏠☀️🍳🚿⊡🛒🚽♿️⊡✕ **Leisure** ▶♿⚲🚵⚓🎣🏆♪🔍⚂

NEWQUAY, Cornwall Map ref 1B2
SAT NAV TR7 3NH

Porth Beach Tourist Park
Porth, Newquay TR7 3NH
t (01637) 876531 **e** info@porthbeach.co.uk
w porthbeach.co.uk ONLINE MAP ONLINE BOOKING LAST MINUTE OFFERS

ᐱ	£14.00–£40.00
ᐱ	£14.00–£40.00
Å	£11.00–£35.00
⊡ (18)	£300.00–£740.00
200 touring pitches	

Situated only 100m from beautiful Porth Beach the park has superb pitches, excellent award-winning facilities and luxury caravans set in a quiet valley location. Families and couples only. **directions** A30 then A392 Newquay Road. At Quintrell Downs roundabout follow signs for Porth. Turn right at Porth Four Turnings, park is 0.5 miles on right. **open** March to November **payment** credit/debit cards, cash, cheques

General 🖥️♿🐕🏠☀️🍳🚿📞🚿🛒🚽♿⊡ **Leisure** ♿🚵⚓⚂

NEWQUAY, Cornwall Map ref 1B2
SAT NAV TR8 4PE

Riverside Holiday Park
Lane, Newquay TR8 4PE
t (01637) 873617 **f** (01637) 877051 **e** info@riversideholidaypark.co.uk
w riversideholidaypark.co.uk

ᐱ	£13.00–£17.00
⊡ (19)	£200.00–£700.00
60 touring pitches	

Peaceful riverside family park. 2 miles to Newquay. Sheltered, level touring pitches, luxury lodges and caravans. Covered, heated pool and bar. **directions** Follow A392 for Newquay, at Quintrell Downs go straight over at roundabout, we are first left after Hendra Holiday Park. **open** Easter to end of October **payment** credit/debit cards, cash, cheques

General 🖥️🐕🛴📞🏠☀️🚿🚽♿✕ **Leisure** ▶♿🚵⚓🏆🔍⚂

NEWQUAY, Cornwall Map ref 1B2 SAT NAV TR8 4JN

enjoyEngland.com
★★★★
TOURING &
CAMPING PARK

🚐 (200) £10.00–£16.50
🚐 (200) £10.00–£16.50
⛺ (200) £10.00–£16.50
200 touring pitches

SPECIAL PROMOTIONS
Free-night offers early and
late season. Conditions
apply.

Treloy Touring Park

Newquay TR8 4JN
t (01637) 872063 f (01637) 876279 e treloy.tp@btconnect.com
w **treloy.co.uk** ONLINE MAP

A family-run park catering exclusively for touring caravans, tents and motor homes. We aim to offer fun and enjoyable holidays for families and couples, in a pleasant, relaxed setting with clean, modern facilities. Nearby is Treloy Golf Club and driving range. Coarse fishing available at Porth Reservoir, 1 mile away.

open April to end of September
payment credit/debit cards, cash

directions Leave A30 at Highgate Hill, take 3rd exit (Newquay). At Halloon roundabout take A39 Wadebridge (3rd exit). Then Trekenning roundabout 1st left, Treloy 4 miles.

General 🖥️ 📶 🐕 🧺 📷 ☀️ 🔥 🍳 🚼 💶 ✕ Leisure ► ∪ ✈ ⅋ 🍷 🎵 🔍 ⚲

NEWQUAY, Cornwall Map ref 1B2 SAT NAV TR7 2JY

enjoyEngland.com
★★★★
HOLIDAY, TOURING
& CAMPING PARK

🚐 (50) £7.50–£9.50
🚐 (50) £7.50–£9.50
⛺ (50) £7.50–£9.50
🚍 (21) £245–£605
🏠 (134) £180.00–£565.00
50 touring pitches

Trenance Holiday Park

Edgcumbe Avenue, Newquay TR7 2JY
t (01637) 873447 f (01637) 852677 e enquiries@trenanceholidaypark.co.uk
w **trenanceholidaypark.co.uk** ONLINE MAP GUEST REVIEWS

The nearest holiday park to Newquay Town Centre about 10 minutes walk from the park to beaches and all the entertainment in Newquay. Our unrivalled location combined with a well run clean park makes Trenance the ideal holiday location.

directions On main B3075 Newquay Truro Road about 1 Mile from Newquay Town Centre.

General 🚐 🖥️ 🧺 📷 ☀️ 🍳 🚼 💶 ✕ Leisure ► ∪ ♒ ✈ 🔍 ⚲

PADSTOW, Cornwall Map ref 1B2 SAT NAV PL28 8SL

Mother Ivey's Bay Holiday Park (Camping)
Mother Ivey's Bay Holiday Park, Trevose Head, Padstow, Cornwall PL28 8SL
t (01841) 520990 f (01841) 520550 e info@motheriveysbay.com
w **motheriveysbay.com** ONLINE MAP

🚐	£12.00–£52.00
🚙	£12.00–£52.00
⛺	£12.00–£52.00
🏠	£210.00–£1295.00

126 touring pitches

5 Star holiday park situated on the coast with spectacular sea views and our own private sandy beach, perfect for traditional family holidays, with luxurious holiday caravans and touring area.
directions 4 miles west of Padstow, signed from St Merryn on the B3276 Padstow to Newquay coast road. On Trevose Head. **open** April to October **payment** credit/debit cards, cash, cheques

General 🖥 🕎 🐕 🎣 🚻 ☼ 🎱 🍽 💧 WP   Leisure ⚑ ∪ ⚡ 🎣 ⛰

PADSTOW, Cornwall Map ref 1B2 SAT NAV PL28 8LE

Padstow Touring Park
Padstow, Cornwall PL28 8LE
t (01841) 532061 e mail@padstowtouringpark.co.uk
w **padstowtouringpark.co.uk** ONLINE MAP GUEST REVIEWS ONLINE BOOKING

🚐 (180)	£14.00–£22.00
🚙 (180)	£14.00–£22.00
⛺ (180)	£10.00–£18.00
🏠	£220–£610
🏠	£175.00–£610.00

180 touring pitches

Located 1mile from Padstow with footpath access. Quiet family park with panoramic views. Sandy beaches 2 miles. Three modern amenity blocks, one underfloor heated. Some en suite pitches. Easy access. **directions** Situated off the main road (B3274/A389) in to Padstow, approx 1 mile before Padstow. **open** All year **payment** credit/debit cards, cash, cheques

General ♿ 🖥 🕎 🐕 🎣 🚻 ☼ 🎱 🚗 🍽 💧 WP   Leisure ∪ ⚡ 🎣 ⛰

PENZANCE, Cornwall Map ref 1A3 SAT NAV TR19 6BZ

Tower Park Caravans & Camping
Tower Park Caravans & Camping, St Buryan, Penzance, Cornwall TR19 6BZ
t (01736) 810286 e enquiries@towerparkcamping.co.uk
w **towerparkcamping.co.uk** ONLINE MAP LAST MINUTE OFFERS

🚐	£10.00–£18.50
🚙	£10.00–£18.50
⛺	£10.00–£14.50
🏠 (5)	£190.00–£480.00

102 touring pitches

Famiy-run campsite ideally situated for beaches, coast path and Minack Theatre. Level pitches for tents and tourers, yurts and static caravans for hire. Adjacent to village with pub and shop. **directions** From the A30 Lands End road, fork left onto the B3283 signposted St Buryan. On entering village, turn right. Site is 300 yds from village. **open** March to October **payment** credit/debit cards, cash, cheques

General 🖥 🕎 🐕 🚻 ☼ 🚗 🍽 💧 WP   Leisure ⚑ ∪ ⚡ 🎣 🔍 ⛰

PORTHTOWAN, Cornwall Map ref 1B3 SAT NAV TR4 8TY

Porthtowan Tourist Park
Mile Hill, Porthtowan, Truro, Cornwall TR4 8TY
t (01209) 890256 e admin@porthtowantouristpark.co.uk
w **porthtowantouristpark.co.uk** ONLINE MAP LAST MINUTE OFFERS

🚐 (35)	£9.25–£17.00
🚙 (10)	£9.25–£17.00
⛺ (35)	£9.25–£17.00

80 touring pitches

This quiet, family run park offers plenty of space and level pitches. Superb new toilet/laundry facilities with family rooms. Close to blue flag beach, coastal path and cycle trail. **directions** From A30, take 3rd exit off the roundabout signed Redruth/Porthtowan. Follow this road for 2mls. Turn right at T-junction. Site on left after 0.5mls. **open** April to September **payment** credit/debit cards, cash, cheques

General 🖥 🐕 🎣 🚻 ☼ 🚗 🍽 💧   Leisure ∪ ⚡ 🎣 🔍 ⛰

PORTREATH, Cornwall Map ref 1B3   SAT NAV TR16 4HT

Cambrose Touring Park
Portreath Road, Portreath, Redruth TR16 4HT
t (01209) 890747 **e** cambrosetouringpark@supanet.com
w **cambrosetouringpark.co.uk** GUEST REVIEWS

🚐 (60)   £10.00–£17.00
🚏 (60)   £10.00–£17.00
🅰 (60)   £10.00–£17.00
60 touring pitches

Six acres of well-sheltered land in a valley. Excellent suntrap. Most roads are tarmac finished. Facilities for the disabled. **directions** From Redruth take B3300 to Portreath passing treasure park on left 0.25 mile take road on the right (Porthtowan) Cambrose 150 yds on left. **open** April to October **payment** credit/debit cards, cash, cheques

General 🗓 🖤 🐕 🔌 🏪 🌡 ☼ ♿ 🔄 🚻 🚮   Leisure ∪ 🚴 ✈ ⟿ 🎣 ⛰

PORTREATH, Cornwall Map ref 1B3   SAT NAV TR16 4JQ

Tehidy Holiday Park
Harris Mill, Near Portreath, Cornwall TR16 4JQ
t (01209) 216489 **f** (01209) 213555 **e** holiday@tehidy.co.uk
w **tehidy.co.uk** ONLINE MAP GUEST REVIEWS ONLINE BOOKING LAST MINUTE OFFERS

🚐 (10)   £12.00–£19.00
🚏 (8)   £12.00–£19.00
🅰 (30)   £12.00–£19.00
🚍 (4)   £350–£690
🏕 (20)   £210.00–£630.00
30 touring pitches

SPECIAL PROMOTIONS
Short breaks welcome, from £42 per night, 3 nights minimum stay. Special offers on our website.

Cottages, holiday caravans and camping on our multi award winning holiday park, including Holiday Caravan Park and Holiday Village of the Year 2010 Visit Cornwall bronze, David Bellamy Gold Award 2010. Voted 6th in Top 100 Sites in UK 2011. Woodland walks, play area, excellent facilities, beaches, gardens.

open March to November
payment credit/debit cards, cash, cheques

directions Exit A30 to Redruth/ Porthtowan. Right to Porthtowan. 300m left at crossroads. Straight on over B3300 (Portreath) crossroads. Past Cornish Arms. Site 500m on left.

General ♿ 🗓 🖤 🔌 🏪 🌡 ☼ ♿ 🔄 🚻 🚮   Leisure ▶ ∪ 🚴 ✈ 🎣 ⛰

Looking for something else?

You can also buy a copy of our popular guide 'Self Catering' including self-catering holiday homes, approved caravan holiday homes, boat accommodation and holiday cottage agencies in England 2012.

Now available in good bookshops and online at
visitbritainshop.com   £8.99

QUINTRELL DOWNS, Cornwall Map ref 1B2

SAT NAV TR8 4QR

Trethiggey Touring Park
Quintrell Downs, Newquay TR8 4QR
t (01637) 877672 **f** (01637) 879706 **e** enquiries@trethiggey.co.uk
w **trethiggey.co.uk** ONLINE MAP ONLINE BOOKING LAST MINUTE OFFERS

🚐 (77)	£14.00–£21.00
🚐 (30)	£14.00–£21.00
⛺ (40)	£9.00–£21.00
🏠 (10)	£200.00–£785.00
157 touring pitches	

Two miles from Newquay and surf beaches and 15 miles from Eden Project, a sheltered well landscaped park with beautiful panoramic views, shop, off-license, bar, restaurant, children's play areas and games room. Two modern shower blocks and 8 acre recreation field.

open March 2nd to January 2nd
payment credit/debit cards, cash, cheques, euros

directions Please contact us for directions

General 🔊 🗘 👤 🛏 🔌 🥾 ☀ 🖾 🚗 🔋 🔆 🍽 ✕ **Leisure** 🏌 ∪ 🚲 ⚓ ♨ 🔍 ⛰

ST AGNES, Cornwall Map ref 1B3

SAT NAV TR5 0NU

Beacon Cottage Farm Touring Park
Beacon Drive, Saint Agnes TR5 0NU
t (01872) 552347 **e** beaconcottagefarm@lineone.net
w **beaconcottagefarmholidays.co.uk** ONLINE MAP GUEST REVIEWS LAST MINUTE OFFERS

🚐 (69)	£15.00–£21.00
🚐 (69)	£15.00–£21.00
⛺ (69)	£15.00–£21.00
🏠	£285–£750
69 touring pitches	

Peaceful, secluded park on a working family farm in an Area of Outstanding Natural Beauty and Heritage Coast. Pitches in six small, landscaped paddocks. Beautiful sea views, lovely walks, 10 minutes' walk to sandy beach. Ideal location for touring Cornwall. **directions** From A30 take B3277 to St Agnes at mini roundabout turn left and follow signs to park. **open** April to October **payment** credit/debit cards, cash, cheques

General 🗘 🛏 🔌 🥾 ☀ 🖾 🚗 🔋 🔆 🍽 **Leisure** ∪ 🚲 ⚓ ⛰

ST AUSTELL, Cornwall Map ref 1B3

SAT NAV PL26 7AP

River Valley Holiday Park
Pentewan Road, London Apprentice, St Austell PL26 7AP
t (01726) 73533 **e** mail@cornwall-holidays.co.uk
w **rivervalleyholidaypark.co.uk** ONLINE MAP GUEST REVIEWS ONLINE BOOKING LAST MINUTE OFFERS

🚐 (45)	£12.00–£28.00
🚐 (45)	£12.00–£28.00
⛺ (45)	£12.00–£28.00
🏠 (40)	£180.00–£710.00
45 touring pitches	

Two miles from the beach, near Mevagissey. A small, family run hoiday park. We welcome visitors to immaculate, modern caravans and spacious pitches for tents and touring vans. **directions** Take B3273 from St Austell to Mevagissey. When entering London Apprentice, park is on left-hand side. **open** April to October **payment** credit/debit cards, cash, cheques

General 🔊 🗘 👤 🛏 🔌 🥾 ☀ 🚗 🔋 🔆 **Leisure** 🏌 ∪ 🚲 ⚓ 🐟 🔍 ⛰

ST BURYAN, Cornwall Map ref 1A3

SAT NAV TR19 6HX

Cardinney Caravan & Camping Park

Main A30, Nr Crows-an-Wra, St Buryan, Penzance TR19 6HX
t (01736) 810880 **e** cardinney@btinternet.com
w **cardinney-camping-park.co.uk**

🚐	£13.50–£17.50
🚗	£13.50–£17.50
⛺	£10.00–£14.00
90 touring pitches	

A small family run site, situated in quiet countryside, and conveniently placed for visiting local beaches and attractions. All pitches are individually marked with mature hedging for privacy and shelter. **directions** Stay on the main A30 trunk road, heading in the direction of Lands End. We are situated five miles west of Penzance. **open** All year **payment** credit/debit cards, cash, cheques

General 🌀 🗄 ✇ ⊨ ⊾ ⌕ ☼ 💬 🕒 🐾 ✕ Leisure ∪ 🏊 ♟

ST ISSEY, Cornwall Map ref 1B2

SAT NAV PL27 7RL

Trewince Farm Holiday Park

Trewince Farm, St Issey PL27 7RL
t (01208) 812830 **e** enquiries@trewincefarm-holidaypark.co.uk
w **trewincefarm-holidaypark.co.uk** GUEST REVIEWS

🚐	£12.25–£17.25
⛺ (30)	£10.75–£16.00
🚐 (19)	£220.00–£670.00
120 touring pitches	

SPECIAL PROMOTIONS
Between 3rd April – 17th July, book any 2 weeks and the cheaper week half price. Extra large super pitches available.

Trewince is a quiet family holiday park, camping, touring and static holidays, set in own working farm. Outdoor heated swimming pool, childrens play area, croquet lawn, table tennis, badminton grass and shop. Fully equipped amenity blocks. Fishing lake with woodland walk, dogs welcome. Ideal place to relax and enjoy.

open Easter to end of October
payment credit/debit cards, cash, cheques

directions From Wadebridge take the A389 signposted Padstow. Turn first left when you see our sign. We are a short distance on the right.

General 🌀 🗄 ✇ ⊨ ⊾ ⌕ ☼ 💬 🕒 🐾 Leisure ► ∪ 🚲 🏊 ⟲ 🎣 ⛰

ST IVES, Cornwall Map ref 1B3

SAT NAV TR26 1EJ

Ayr Holiday Park

Higher Ayr, St Ives TR26 1EJ
t (01736) 795855 **f** (01736) 798797 **e** recept@ayrholidaypark.co.uk
w **ayrholidaypark.co.uk** ONLINE MAP GUEST REVIEWS

🚐 (14)	£15.50–£30.00
🚗 (14)	£15.50–£30.00
⛺ (52)	£11.00–£30.00
🏠 (2)	£320–£745
🚐 (50)	£300.00–£1100.00
80 touring pitches	

The only park in St Ives itself, ten minutes walk to town, harbour or beach. Beautiful views and direct access to the coastal footpath. Latest holiday caravans and touring pitches. **directions** From A.30, follow signs for Tate Gallery via B3311 and B3306. 1/2 mile before centre turn left at mini roundabout for Porthmeor Beach and Ayr. **open** All year **payment** credit/debit cards, cash, cheques

General 🗄 ✇ ⊨ ⌕ ☼ ♿ 💬 🕒 🐾 🚐 Leisure ∪ 🏊 🎣 ⛰

ST IVES, Cornwall Map ref 1B3

SAT NAV TR26 3BJ

Trevalgan Touring Park

Trevalgan, St Ives TR26 3BJ
t (01736) 792048 f (01736) 798797 e recept@trevalgantouringpark.co.uk
w **trevalgantouringpark.co.uk** ONLINE MAP GUEST REVIEWS

(60)	£13.50–£24.00
(40)	£13.50–£24.00
(32)	£9.50–£24.00
132 touring pitches	

Two miles from St Ives in beautiful countryside but close to the coastal footpath. A friendly, family park with good views and excellent facilities. **directions** From A.30 follow signs for Tate Gallery St Ives. When joining B3306 turn left as signposted for Trevalgan. After 1/2 mile turn right, signposted. **open** May till end September **payment** credit/debit cards, cash, cheques

General Leisure

ST JUST IN ROSELAND, Cornwall Map ref 1B3

SAT NAV TR2 5JF

Trethem Mill Touring Park

St Just in Roseland, Nr St Mawes, Truro, Cornwall TR2 5JF
t (01872) 580504 f (01872) 580968 e reception@trethem.com
w **trethem.com** ONLINE MAP

(84)	£17.00–£25.00
(55)	£17.00–£25.00
(30)	£17.00–£25.00
84 touring pitches	

Offering peace and tranquillity with an exceptional standard of facilities. Caravan Park of the Year EnjoyEngland Excellence Awards 2010 'Consistent winners offering consistent quality.' Say hello to a new experience. **directions** A3078 towards Tregony/St Mawes, over Tregony bridge. After 5 miles follow brown caravan and camping signs from Trewithian. Site 2 miles beyond on right-hand side. **open** April to mid-October **payment** credit/debit cards, cash

General Leisure

ST MERRYN, Cornwall Map ref 1B2

SAT NAV PL28 8PR

Trevean Farm Caravan & Camping Park

St Merryn, Padstow PL28 8PR
t (01841) 520772 f (01841) 520772 e trevean.info@virgin.net
w **treveancaravanandcamping.net**

	£8.00–£12.00
	£8.00–£12.00
	£8.00–£12.00
(3)	£200.00–£475.00
70 touring pitches	

Small, pleasant farm site, 1 mile from the sea. Ideally situated for beaches, walking and many visitor attractions. **directions** From St Merryn crossroads take B3276 towards Newquay. Take first left after approx ¾ mile. We are along this road on right. **open** 1st April to end of October **payment** credit/debit cards, cash, cheques

General Leisure

TINTAGEL, Cornwall Map ref 1B2

SAT NAV PL34 0BQ

Trewethett Farm Caravan Club Site

Trethevy, Tintagel PL34 0BQ
t (01840) 770222 e enquiries@caravanclub.co.uk
w **caravanclub.co.uk**

THE
CARAVAN
CLUB

(142)	£15.30–£35.51
(142)	£15.30–£35.51
142 touring pitches	

Breathtaking views from cliff top setting. Safe and sandy beach. Tintagel is a popular coastal resort with shops, bars and restaurants aplenty. **directions** A30 onto A395 (Camelford). Right A39 (Bude). Left before transmitter. Right B3266 (Boscastle). Left B3263. Site entrance on right 2 miles. **open** March to November **payment** credit/debit cards, cash, cheques

General Leisure

WATERGATE BAY NEWQUAY, Cornwall Map ref 1B2   SAT NAV TR8 4AD

Watergate Bay Touring Park
Tregurrian, Newquay, Cornwall TR8 4AD
t (01637) 860387 **f** 0871 661 7549 **e** email@watergatebaytouringpark.co.uk
w watergatebaytouringpark.co.uk ONLINE MAP GUEST REVIEWS

⊕ (171)	£11.00–£20.00
⊟ (171)	£11.00–£20.00
▲ (171)	£11.00–£20.00
⊡ (2)	£200.00–£595.00

171 touring pitches

SPECIAL PROMOTIONS
Outside of the dates 22nd
July - 29th August book 7
nights or more and receive
a 10% discount.

Half mile from Watergate Bays sand, surf and cliff walks. Rural Location in an Area of Outstanding Natural Beauty. Personally run & supervised by resident owners. Heated indoor/outdoor pool, tennis courts, skate park, games room, shop/cafe, licensed clubroom, free entertainment including kids club, kids play area.

open March to end of October
payment credit/debit cards, cash

directions From A30 follow signs for Newquay then airport. After passing the airport, turn left onto the B3276. Park 0.5 mile on right.

General ⚓ 🖥 🛈 🛏 🚲 🎱 🝙 ☼ 🖾 🛋 📺 🐕 🚿 ⊞ ✕   Leisure ∪ ⚲ 🏊 🎿 ⚓ 🛝 ♪ 🐟 ⁄

BRAUNTON (1 MILE), Devon Map ref 1C1   SAT NAV EX33 1HG

Lobb Fields Caravan and Camping Park
Saunton Road, Braunton EX33 1HG
t (01271) 812090 **f** (01271) 812090 **e** info@lobbfields.com
w lobbfields.com

⊕ (100)	£9.50–£28.50
⊟ (40)	£9.50–£28.50
▲ (40)	£8.50–£28.50

180 touring pitches

South facing grass park with panoramic views across Taw Estuary. On edge of good shopping village, within easy reach of wonderful beaches, ideal for surfing and children. Surf board hire. **directions** From Barnstaple to Braunton on A361. Then follow B3231 for 1 mile towards Saunton. Lobb Fields is marked on the right of the road. **open** 23rd March to 28th October **payment** credit/debit cards, cash, cheques

General ⚓ 🖥 🛏 🝙 ☼ 🖾 🛋 🐕 🚿 ⊞   Leisure ⊢ ∪ 🚵 🏊 ⁄

BRIXHAM, Devon Map ref 1D2   SAT NAV TQ5 0EP

Galmpton Touring Park
Greenway Road, Galmpton, Brixham TQ5 0EP
t (01803) 842066 **f** (01803) 842519 **e** enquiries@galmptontouringpark.co.uk
w galmptontouringpark.co.uk ONLINE MAP

⊕ (60)	£13.00–£25.50
⊟ (10)	£13.00–£25.50
▲ (50)	£13.00–£20.50
⊞ (2)	£220.00–£410.00

120 touring pitches

Family managed park in stunning location with superb views. Quiet base for couples and families to explore South Devon. Beaches, boat trips, steam railway, gardens, village pub and beautiful walks. **directions** South on Ring Road (A380) then straight onto A3022 towards Churston. At lights turn right, then 2nd right, through village 600yds past school. **open** April to September **payment** credit/debit cards, cash, cheques

General 🖥 🛏 🚲 🝙 ☼ 🖾 🛋 🐕 🚿   Leisure ⊢ 🏊 ⁄

BRIXHAM, Devon Map ref 1D2

Hillhead Caravan Club Site
Hillhead, Brixham TQ5 0HH
t (01803) 853204 **e** enquiries@caravanclub.co.uk
w **caravanclub.co.uk**

THE CARAVAN CLUB

🚐 (239)   £16.00–£48.75
🚏 (239)   £16.00–£48.75
239 touring pitches

Set in 22 acres of Devon countryside with many pitches affording stunning views. Outdoor heated swimming pool, skateboard ramp, games room, shop, restaurant and bar. Evening entertainment. **directions** Right off A380. 3 miles onto ring road (Brixham). 7 miles right, A3022. 0.75 miles, right, A379. 2 miles keep left B3025. Site on left. **open** March 2011 to January 2012 **payment** credit/debit cards, cash, cheques

General 🔲 📶 🐕 🎱 🛢 🎣 ☼ 🔄 📞 🛒 🚮 💻 ✕   Leisure ▶ 🏌 ⚓ 🎣 ♪ 🎣 ⚙

CROCKERNWELL, Devon Map ref 1C2

Dartmoor Barley Meadow Camping & Caravanning Club Site Crockernwell, Exeter, Devon EX6 6NR
t (01647) 281629 **e** dartmoor.site@thefriendlyclub.co.uk
w **campingandcaravanningclub.co.uk/dartmoor** ONLINE MAP GUEST REVIEWS

The Camping and Caravanning Club The Friendly Club

🚐   £23.00–£26.00
🚏   £23.00–£26.00
▲   £23.00–£26.00
63 touring pitches

East of the Dartmoor National Park in the heart of Devon. The moorland landscape, wooded valleys and wind-swept tors are complimented by many local attractions for all the family. **directions** OS Map Reference: 191 -SX744923 Latitude: 50.71747 Longitude: -3.78287 Railway: Exeter 13 Miles. **open** 10th March - 7th November

General 🔲 📶 🐕 🎱 🛢 🎣 ☼ 📞 🛒 🚮   Leisure ⚙

DARTMOUTH, Devon Map ref 1D3

Woodlands Grove Caravan & Camping Park
Blackawton, Dartmouth, Devon TQ9 7DQ
t (01803) 712598 **f** (01803) 712680 **e** holiday@woodlandsgrove.com
w **woodlands-caravanpark.com** ONLINE MAP LAST MINUTE OFFERS

🚐 (200)   £13.50–£23.00
🚏 (50)   £13.50–£23.00
▲ (100)   £13.50–£23.00
350 touring pitches

SPECIAL PROMOTIONS
Adults Midweek Special 5 nights £45 (tariff A Sun–Thurs). Families staying 2 nights or more: free entry to Woodlands Themepark.

Spacious pitches and tranquil surroundings 5 miles from Dartmouth and stunning South Devon coast. Beautifully equipped family bathrooms, laundries & showers. Ideal for a relaxed adult break during term time. Families have the option of Free entry into 90 acre Themepark for the perfect family holiday.

open Easter to end October
payment credit/debit cards, cash, cheques

directions 5 miles from Dartmouth on A3122. From A38 Devon Expressway, southbound take Totnes/Dartmouth turnoff and follow brown tourist board signs.

General 🔧 🔲 📶 🐕 🎱 🛢 🎣 ☼ 🔄 🚿 📞 🛒 🚮 💻 ✕   Leisure ▶ ∪ 🏌 ⚓ ⚙

DAWLISH, Devon Map ref 1D2

Cofton Country Holidays
Starcross, Nr Dawlish, Devon EX6 8RP
t (01626) 890111 **f** (01626) 890160 **e** info@coftonholidays.co.uk
w **coftonholidays.co.uk** ONLINE MAP ONLINE BOOKING LAST MINUTE OFFERS

🚐 (450) £14.50–£29.00
🚎 (450) £14.50–£29.00
⛺ (450) £14.50–£29.00
🏠 (18) £295.00–£930.00
🚙 (66) £200.00–£780.00
450 touring pitches

SPECIAL PROMOTIONS
Save 25% on touring/
camping in low, mid and
high season for advance
bookings of 5 or more
nights.

A stunning setting surrounded by rolling meadows, mature woods, fishing lakes and just minutes from Dawlish Warren's Blue Flag beach. Superb countryside views. Limited hardstanding and super pitches available. Fantastic facilities in clean, tidy surroundings with swimming pool, play areas, Swan pub, park shop, take-away, games room and Wi-Fi.

open All year
payment credit/debit cards, cash, cheques

directions Leave M5 at junction 30, take A379 towards Dawlish. After passing through harbour village of Cockwood, park is on the left after half a mile.

General 🔲 ♿ 🐕 🛒 📶 🔥 ☼ 🍴 🍽 ✕ Leisure ∪ 🚴 ♪ 🎾 🏆 🔍 ⚲

DAWLISH WARREN, Devon Map ref 1D2

Welcome Family Holiday Park
Welcome Family Holiday Park, Dawlish Warren, Dawlish EX7 0PH
t 08451 65 62 65 **f** (01626) 868988 **e** fun@welcomefamily.co.uk
w **welcomefamily.co.uk** ONLINE MAP GUEST REVIEWS LAST MINUTE OFFERS

🏠 (50) £250.00–£995.00
🏠 (56) £185.00–£805.00
🚙 (134) £120.00–£695.00

SPECIAL PROMOTIONS
Please see our website:
www.welcomefamily.co.uk
for last minute offers!

Four indoor heated fun pools, entertainment 7 days and nights, Spanish-style lodges, bungalows and all-electric caravans set in award-winning gardens, a short level walk to the beach and Nature reserve. Fantastic local attractions. Over 2 out of 3 come back to Welcome Family: Where the fun always shines!

open Easter to Autumn Half-term
payment credit/debit cards, cash, cheques

directions By train to Dawlish or Dawlish Warren. By Car to M5 to Exeter, exit Junction 30. Take A379 to Dawlish, turn off to Dawlish Warren.

General 🔲 🐕 🛒 📶 ☼ ✕ Leisure ▶ ♪ 🎾 🏆 🎵 🔍 ⚲

HAWKCHURCH, Devon Map ref 1D2

SAT NAV EX13 5UL

299 touring pitches

Hawkchurch Country Park

Hawkchurch, Axminster, Devon EX13 5UL
t 0844 272 9502 **f** (01297) 678720 **e** enquiries@hawkchurchpark.co.uk
w **hawkchurchpark.co.uk** ONLINE MAP ONLINE BOOKING LAST MINUTE OFFERS

Located in the Axe Valley offering first-class facilities in tranquil settings, including modern shower and laundry facilities, play area, shop, bar and restaurant, perfect for a caravan or camping retreat.
directions Leave the A35 at the B3165 between Axminster and Charmouth, turn left onto Wareham Road, the park is situated on the left. **payment** credit/debit cards, cash, cheques

General 🔌🖥️👍🐕🏧📷⌂☼💬🏠🔒✕ Leisure ▶️♻️🚵🏊♫🎹🔍🎢

HOLSWORTHY, Devon Map ref 1C2

SAT NAV EX22 7JB

🔌 (5)	£4.00–£7.00
🚐 (5)	£4.00–£7.00
⛺ (15)	£4.00–£7.00
🏠 (1)	£150.00–£400.00

Noteworthy Caravan and Campsite

Bude Road, Holsworthy EX22 7JB
t (01409) 253731 **f** (01409) 253731 **e** enquiries@noteworthy-devon.co.uk
w **noteworthy-devon.co.uk**

6 berth self catering static park home, and touring caravan and camping site. On the Devon/Cornwall borders, 4 miles Holsworthy, 6 miles Bude. Based on a working Angora goat farm. Lovely country views. Good road access.

open All year
payment cash, cheques

directions We are on the A3072 Holsworthy to Bude road. We are approx 1 mile from Holsworthy Golf Course.

General 🐕🏧📷☼💬🏠 Leisure ▶️♻️🚵🎢

ILFRACOMBE, Devon Map ref 1C1

SAT NAV EX34 9QZ

Beachside Holiday Park

Beachside Holiday Park, Hele Bay, Ilfracombe, Devon EX34 9QZ
t 0844 272 9500 **f** (01271) 867296 **e** enquiries@beachsidepark.co.uk
w **beachsidepark.co.uk** ONLINE MAP ONLINE BOOKING LAST MINUTE OFFERS

Amazing sea views with an emphasis on relaxation and tranquillity. Take time to unwind and explore the beautiful surroundings and take in the sublime views from our beautifully appointed caravans.
directions Continue on A399 towards Combe Martin. 1 mile after Ilfracombe, Hele Bay Hotel is on left: Beachside is a further 75 yards on the left. **payment** credit/debit cards, cash, cheques

General 🖥️🐕🏧☼ Leisure ▶️♻️🚵

IPPLEPEN, Devon Map ref 1D2

SAT NAV TQ12 5TT

TOURING & CAMPING PARK

Ross Park

Park Hill Farm, Moor Road, Ipplepen, Newton Abbot, Devon TQ12 5TT
t (01803) 812983 **f** (01803) 812983 **e** enquiries@rossparkcaravanpark.co.uk
w **rossparkcaravanpark.co.uk** GUEST REVIEWS LAST MINUTE OFFERS

(110)   £13.00–£27.20
   £13.00–£27.20
   £13.00–£27.20
110 touring pitches

SPECIAL PROMOTIONS
Weekly rates available
except Easter, Whitsun and
July, August.

Ross Park is an award winning family-run park which provides an excellent range of facilities in beautiful rural surroundings with magnificent floral displays, high standards in all aspects of the Park whilst retaining a friendly and tranquil atmosphere and service with a personal touch to help you enjoy you stay.

open March - 2nd January   **directions** Please contact us for directions
payment credit/debit cards, cash, cheques

General ▯ ⓦ ⫟ ⛟ ▥ ⋔ ☼ ⇄ ⊕ ⋒ ☎ ⌨ ✕ **Leisure** ▶ ∪ ⤵ ⚑ ◆ ⟋

KENNFORD, Devon Map ref 1D2

SAT NAV EX6 7XS

TOURING & CAMPING PARK

Exeter Racecourse Caravan Club Site

Kennford, Exeter, Devon EX6 7XS
t (01392) 832107 **e** enquiries@caravanclub.co.uk
w **caravanclub.co.uk**

CARAVAN CLUB

(100)   £10.70–£28.00
(100)   £10.70–£28.00
100 touring pitches

Superb views of rolling countryside. Site set on top of Haldon Hill. Scenic walks along River Exe. City centre nearby. **directions** At end of M5 continue onto A38, turn left at top of hill and then immediately right. **open** March to October **payment** credit/debit cards, cash, cheques

General ▯ ⫟ ⛟ ⋒ ☎ ⇄ **Leisure** ⤵

KENTISBEARE, Devon Map ref 1D2

SAT NAV EX15 2DT

ROSE AWARD CARAVAN HOLIDAY PARK

HOLIDAY & TOURING PARK

Forest Glade Holiday Park

Forest Glade, Near Kentisbeare, Cullompton EX15 2DT
t (01404) 841381 **f** (01404) 841593 **e** enquiries@forest-glade.co.uk
w **forest-glade.co.uk** ONLINE MAP LAST MINUTE OFFERS

   £14.50–£20.50
   £14.50–£20.50
   £12.50–£16.50
(25)   £255.00–£505.00
80 touring pitches

Free indoor heated pool on family-owned park surrounded by forest with deer. Large, flat, sheltered touring pitches. Modern six berth holiday homes for hire. **directions** From M5, A373, 2.5 miles at Keepers Cottage inn then 2.5 miles on Sheldon road. Touring caravans take Dunkeswell road from Honiton, follow brown signs. **open** Mid-March to end of October **payment** credit/debit cards, cash, cheques

General ▯ ⓦ ⫟ ⛟ ⋒ ⋒ ☼ ⊡ ⇄ ⊕ ☎ ⌨ **Leisure** ∪ ⚲ ⚘ ⤵ ⚑ ◆ ⟋

MODBURY, Devon Map ref 1C3

SAT NAV PL21 0SH

Broad Park Caravan Club Site

Higher East Leigh, Modbury, Devon PL21 0SH
t (01548) 830714 e enquiries@caravanclub.co.uk
w **caravanclub.co.uk**

THE **CARAVAN CLUB**

🚐 (113) £13.50–£32.79
🚏 (113) £13.50–£32.79
113 touring pitches

This site makes a splendid base from which to explore South Devon. Head for Dartmoor, or seek out the small villages of the South Hams. **directions** From B3027 (signposted Modbury), site on left after 1 mile. **open** March to November **payment** credit/debit cards, cash, cheques

General 🔲 📠 ⬛ 🔌 🔋 🗑 🆗

MORTEHOE, Devon Map ref 1C1

SAT NAV EX34 7EG

North Morte Farm Caravan & Camping Park

North Morte Road, Mortehoe, Woolacombe EX34 7EG
t (01271) 870381 f (01271) 870115 e info@northmortefarm.co.uk
w **northmortefarm.co.uk** ONLINE MAP

🚐 (25) £15.75–£20.50
🚏   £12.00–£20.50
⛺ (150) £12.00–£18.50
🏠 (24) £250.00–£605.00

Set in beautiful countryside overlooking Rockham Bay, close to village of Mortehoe, and Woolacombe. **directions** Take A361 from Barnstaple, turn left at Mullacott roundabout signed Mortehoe and Woolacombe, head for Mortehoe, turn right at Post Office, park 500m on left. **open** April to October **payment** credit/debit cards, cash

General 🔲 📶 🐕 🐾 📠 ☀ 🔌 🗑 🚻 🆗 Leisure ∪ 🏊 ⛰

NEWTON ABBOT, Devon Map ref 1D2

SAT NAV TQ12 6DD

Dornafield Touring Park

Two Mile Oak, Newton Abbot TQ12 6DD
t (01803) 812732 f (01803) 812032 e enquiries@dornafield.com
w **dornafield.com** ONLINE MAP GUEST REVIEWS ONLINE BOOKING

🚐 (119) £13.50–£25.00
🚏 (119) £13.50–£25.00
⛺ (16) £13.50–£24.00
135 touring pitches

SPECIAL PROMOTIONS
Early and late-season bookings. Book for 7 days and pay only for 5. Details on request.

Beautiful location in 30 acres of glorious South Devon countryside. So quiet and peaceful, yet so convenient for Torbay and Dartmoor. Superb facilities to suit the discerning caravanner, including all hardstanding serviced pitches. Shop, games room, adventure play area and tennis court. Our brochure is only a phone call away.

payment credit/debit cards, cash, cheques

directions Take A381 Newton Abbot to Totnes. In 2.5 miles at Two Mile Oak turn right. In 0.5 miles 1st turn left, 200 yards on right.

General ♿ 🔲 📶 🐕 🐾 📠 ☀ 🚿 🔌 🗑 🚻 🆗 Leisure ▶ 🎾 🎣 ⛰

NORTH MOLTON, Devon Map ref 1C1

SAT NAV EX36 3HQ

Riverside Caravan and Camping Park

Marsh Lane, North Molton Road, South Molton EX36 3HQ
t (01769) 579269 **f** (01769) 574853 **e** relax@exmoorriverside.co.uk
w **exmoorriverside.co.uk** ONLINE MAP GUEST REVIEWS LAST MINUTE OFFERS

(42)	£15.00–£22.00	
(42)	£15.00–£22.00	
(40)	£10.00–£20.00	
(1)	£210.00–£400.00	

42 touring pitches

40 acres of parkland with lakes and rivers for fishing woods and meadowland for walking we are a 4 star park with 5 star facilities. **directions** M5 turn off on junction 27 onto the A361 turn right when you see north molton and riverside sign. **open** All year **payment** credit/debit cards, cash, cheques

General ▢ ⚓ ⚒ ▦ ⌂ ☼ ▣ ⚐ ⊕ ⊕ ⚑ ♿ ✕   Leisure ∪ ♪ ♟ ♫

Bonus CD inside

enjoyEngland.com

BED & BREAKFAST 2012
England's quality-assessed guest accommodation

OFFICIAL TOURIST BOARD GUIDE

Looking for something else?

You can also buy a copy of our popular 'B&B' guide including guest accommodation, B&B's, guest houses, farmhouses, inns, and campus and hostel accommodation in England 2012.

Now available in good bookshops and online at
visitbritainshop.com   **£8.99**

OTTERTON, Devon Map ref 1D2   SAT NAV EX9 7BX

Ladram Bay Holiday Park

Otterton, Budleigh Salterton, Devon EX9 7BX
t (01395) 568398 **f** (01395) 568338 **e** welcome@ladrambay.co.uk
w ladrambay.co.uk
ONLINE MAP GUEST REVIEWS ONLINE BOOKING LAST MINUTE OFFERS

🚐 (100)	£15.00–£32.00
🚎 (100)	£15.00–£32.00
⛺ (105)	£15.00–£32.00
🏠 (500)	£170.00–£1250.00

305 touring pitches

SPECIAL PROMOTIONS
Short Breaks Available. Over
55s / Under 5s Discounts up
to £20 Off. Early Booking
Discounts. Special Offers.

Nestled in the rolling Devon Hills overlooking the unspoilt Jurassic Coast, Ladram Bay is the
Holiday Park in Devon that has something to offer everyone. Voted as one of the to 50 holiday
parks in the UK in 2010 and also as a finalist in the South West 2009 tourism awards, you can be
assured that your holiday be better than ever before!

Whether you choose to stay in one of our luxury holiday homes or your own touring caravan or
tent our extensive range of facilities and breathtaking location will ensure your well earned
holiday is both fun and memorable. We have all the amenities on site that you'll ever need.

With our own private sheltered beach just a short stroll away from anywhere on the park, you'll
find Ladram Bay the perfect location for that unforgettable family holiday in Devon.

open Mid March - End of October
payment credit/debit cards, cash, cheques

directions M5 Junct 30, follow A376 to Clyst St
Mary then A3052 to Newton Poppleford, then
B3178 and follow signposts to Ladram Bay

General 🔑 📷 🛁 🐕 🍴 🏪 ☀ 🎮 🚻 🏧 💳 ✕ **Leisure** ⤷ ∪ ♦ ⚲ 🍹 🎵 🎵 ⚓ ⛰

PAIGNTON, Devon Map ref 1D2
SAT NAV TQ4 7JE

Beverley Holidays
Goodrington Road, Paignton, The English Riviera, South Devon TQ4 7JE
t (01803) 661971 **f** (01803) 845427 **e** info@beverley-holidays.co.uk
w beverley-holidays.co.uk ONLINE MAP ONLINE BOOKING LAST MINUTE OFFERS

🚐	£15.50–£38.50
🚐	£15.50–£38.50
🛖	£13.00–£32.50
🏠	£295.00–£1540.00
🚌 (189)	£120.00–£1050.00

175 touring pitches

SPECIAL PROMOTIONS
Special discounts for over-
50s and under-5s in holiday
caravans, plus lots more.
Specific dates apply.

Superb luxury holiday park overlooking English Riviera with fabulous sea views. Indoor/outdoor pools, spa, tennis, gym, crazy golf, playground, children's room, restaurant, bar, shop, plus golf, watersports, and unlimited coastal walks nearby. Less than 1 mile to the beach. South West Tourism 'Caravan Park of the Year' 2007/2008.

open All year
payment credit/debit cards, cash

directions Follow the A380/A3022 from the English Riviera roundabout towards Brixham for 5.6 miles. Turn left into Goodrington Road at the traffic lights at the garage.

General 🔌📷♿⚡🏪♨️🍴 Leisure ▶🎣⚓🎿🏊🍷🎵🎯⛰️

PAIGNTON, Devon Map ref 1D2
SAT NAV TQ9 6RN

Higher Well Farm Holiday Park
Waddeton Road, Stoke Gabriel, Totnes TQ9 6RN
t (01803) 782289 **e** higherwell@talk21.com
w higherwellfarmholidaypark.co.uk ONLINE MAP

🚐 (80)	£11.00–£18.00
🚐 (80)	£11.00–£18.00
🛖 (80)	£11.00–£18.00
🚌 (18)	£180.00–£550.00

80 touring pitches

Secluded farm park with static caravans and separate area welcoming touring caravans, tents and motor homes. Within 1 mile of Stoke Gabriel and the River Dart. 4 miles to Paignton. **directions** From Exeter and Newton Abbot take Torbay A380. Turn right onto A385 Totnes, turn left for Stoke Gabriel and follow brown signs. **payment** credit/debit cards, cash

General 🔌🐕♿📷♨️🚿⚡🏪 Leisure ▶

Looking for something else?

You can also buy a copy of our popular guide 'Hotels' including country house and town house hotels, metro and budget hotels, serviced apartments and restaurants with rooms in England 2012.

Now available in good bookshops and online at
visitbritainshop.com

£7.99

PAIGNTON, Devon Map ref 1D2

🚐 £15.50–£29.50
🚐 £15.50–£29.50
🏕 £13.80–£28.50
🚐 (60) £190.00–£660.00
260 touring pitches

SPECIAL PROMOTIONS
Over 50s holiday caravan
discount - specific dates
apply. Plus last minute
offers.

Whitehill Country Park

Stoke Road, Paignton, South Devon TQ4 7PF
t (01803) 782338 **f** (01803) 782722 **e** info@whitehill-park.co.uk
w **whitehill-park.co.uk** ONLINE MAP ONLINE BOOKING LAST MINUTE OFFERS

Beautifully situated in rolling South Devon countryside yet within easy reach of many picturesque beaches, the English Riviera and Dartmoor. Outdoor swimming pool, play area, craft room, table tennis, cycle and walking trails, bar and restaurant. An ideal location to explore the local area. Dogs accepted certain dates.

open Easter to September
payment credit/debit cards, cash

directions From the A358 Totnes Road, turn left at the Parker's Arms pub. We are 1 mile along towards Stoke Gabriel.

General 🎣 🗗 ⓦ 🐕 🛒 📦 🏠 ☼ 🔌 🗗 🔒 ✗ **Leisure** 🎿 🍷 🎣 ⚲

PLYMOUTH, Devon Map ref 1C2

🚐 (57) £10.30–£25.20
🚐 (57) £10.30–£25.20
57 touring pitches

Plymouth Sound Caravan Club Site

Bovisand Lane, Down Thomas, Plymouth, Devon PL9 0AE
t (01752) 862325 **e** enquiries@caravanclub.co.uk
w **caravanclub.co.uk**

THE CARAVAN CLUB

Set on a headland outside Plymouth with superb views over the Sound and close to the South West Coastal Footpath, the Plym Valley Cycleway and lovely beaches. **directions** Turn right at village signposted Down Thomas into Bovisand Lane. Site on right. **open** March to October **payment** credit/debit cards, cash, cheques

General 🐕 🔌 🗗 ⓦ **Leisure** ►

ROUSDON, Devon Map ref 1D2

ROSE AWARD CARAVAN HOLIDAY PARK

🏠 (22) £177–£1649

Pinewood Holiday Homes

Sidmouth Road, Rousdon, Lyme Regis DT7 3RD
t (01297) 22055 **e** info@pinewood.uk.net
w **pinewood.uk.net** ONLINE BOOKING LAST MINUTE OFFERS

Quiet, secluded lodge park with glorious indoor & outdoor swimming pools on Devon/Dorset border. **directions** Pinewood is situated 3 miles from Lyme Regis on the A3052, ideal base to explore all that Devon & Dorset have to offer. **open** All year **payment** credit/debit cards, cash, cheques

General 🎣 🗗 ⓦ 📦 ☼ **Leisure** ► 🎿 🎣

SALCOMBE, Devon Map ref 1C3

Bolberry House Farm Caravan & Camping
Bolberry, Malborough, Kingsbridge TQ7 3DY
t (01548) 561251 **e** enquiries@bolberryparks.co.uk
w **bolberryparks.co.uk** ONLINE MAP GUEST REVIEWS LAST MINUTE OFFERS

🚐 (20)	£12.00–£21.00
🚏 (20)	£12.00–£21.00
▲ (50)	£8.00–£23.00
🏚	£180.00–£600.00
70 touring pitches	

Friendly family-run park between sailing paradise of Salcombe and Hope Cove (old fishing village). Peaceful, mostly level, good facilities. Children's play area. Good access to coastal footpaths. Sandy beaches nearby. **directions** A381 from Totnes, ringroad Kingsbridge to Salcombe. At Malborough sharp right through village, signs to Bolberry approx. 1m. DO NOT FOLLOW SATNAV FROM TOTNES. **open** Easter to October **payment** cash, cheques

General 🖥 🐾 ⚡ 🏕 🅿 ☼ 🖭 ♨ 🐕 🔔 Leisure ⮕ ∪ ⚓ ⚖

SIDBURY, Devon Map ref 1D2   SAT NAV EX10 0QQ

Putts Corner Caravan Club Site
Putts Corner, Sidbury, Sidmouth EX10 0QQ
t (01404) 42875 **e** enquiries@caravanclub.co.uk
w **caravanclub.co.uk**

THE
CARAVAN
CLUB

🚐 (118)	£13.50–£32.79
🚏 (118)	£13.50–£32.79
118 touring pitches	

A quiet site in pretty surroundings, with a private path to the local pub. Bluebells create a sea of blue in spring, followed by foxgloves. **directions** From M5 jct 25, A375 signposted Sidmouth. Turn right at Hare and Hounds onto B3174. 0.25 miles turn right into site entrance. **open** March to November **payment** credit/debit cards, cash, cheques

General 🖥 🐾 🏕 🅿 🖭 ♨ 🐕 🔔 🚾

TAVISTOCK, Devon Map ref 1C2   SAT NAV PL19 9LS

Harford Bridge Holiday Park
Harford Bridge Holiday Park, Peter Tavy, Tavistock, Devon PL19 9LS
t (01822) 810349 **f** (01822) 810028 **e** enquiry@harfordbridge.co.uk
w **harfordbridge.co.uk** ONLINE BOOKING LAST MINUTE OFFERS

🚐 (40)	£13.75–£22.80
🚏 (40)	£13.75–£22.80
▲ (40)	£13.75–£20.75
🏠 (1)	£345.00–£570.00
🏚 (13)	£280.00–£510.00
120 touring pitches	

WALKERS CYCLISTS
WALKERS CYCLISTS

Beautiful park set in Dartmoor beside the River Tavy offering riverside and other spacious pitches. Free showers. Luxury, self-catering caravan holiday homes and lodges, heat light and bedding included. **directions** M5 onto A30 to Sourton Cross; take A386 Tavistock Road. 2 miles north of Tavistock take Peter Tavy turn off, entrance 200 yrds on left. **open** All year **payment** credit/debit cards, cash, cheques

General 🖥 🐾 🏕 🅿 ☼ ♨ 🐕 🔔 🚾 Leisure ⮕ ∪ ⚑ ⚖ ⚓ ⚔ ⟁

Looking for something else?

You can also buy a copy of our popular guide 'Self Catering' including self-catering holiday homes, approved caravan holiday homes, boat accommodation and holiday cottage agencies in England 2012.

Now available in good bookshops and online at
visitbritainshop.com   **£8.99**

TAVISTOCK, Devon Map ref 1C2

Langstone Manor Holiday Park

Moortown, Tavistock, Devon PL19 9JZ
t (01822) 613371 f (01822) 613371 e jane@langstonemanor.co.uk
w **langstonemanor.co.uk** ONLINE MAP

⊕ (15)	£14.00–£18.00	
⊕ (15)	£14.00–£18.00	
▲ (15)	£14.00–£18.00	
⊕ (12)	£195.00–£511.00	

45 touring pitches

SPECIAL PROMOTIONS
Off peak weekly rate for
over 55's camping and self-
catering. A small party
discount on weekly bookings
(off-peak).

Fantastic location with direct access onto moor offering great walks straight from the park. Peaceful site with beautiful views of the surrounding moorland. Level pitches, some hardstanding with four star facilities. Camping pods also available. The Langstone Bar provides evening meals. A warm welcome awaits!

open March 15th to Oct 31st for camping and 15th Nov for self-catering
payment credit/debit cards, cash, cheques

directions Take the B3357 Princetown road from Tavistock. After approx 1.5 miles, turn right at x-roads, go over cattle grid, up hill, left following signs.

General ▣ ☂ ⬛ ⬛ ☀ ⊕ ⊕ ⊕ ⊕ ✕   Leisure ▶ ∪ ♿ ♪ ☂ ♦ ⬛

TEIGNGRACE, Devon Map ref 1D2

Twelve Oaks Farm Caravan Park

Teigngrace, Newton Abbot TQ12 6QT
t (01626) 335015 e info@twelveoaksfarm.co.uk
w **twelveoaksfarm.co.uk** ONLINE MAP ONLINE BOOKING

⊕ (50)	£9.00–£15.50	
⊕ (50)	£9.00–£15.50	
▲ (30)	£9.00–£15.50	
⊕ (6)	£300.00–£1350.00	

50 touring pitches

A working farm specializing in Charolais beef cattle. Friendly, personal service. Luxury showers and toilets, heated outdoor swimming pool. Coarse fishing. Good dog walks nearby. **directions** Please come via the A38 south bound exit for Teigngrace straight through the village for two miles Twelve oaks Farm on left. **open** All year **payment** credit/debit cards, cash, cheques

General ▣ ☂ ⬛ ⬛ ⬛ ☀ ⬛ ⊕ ⊕ ⊕ ⊕   Leisure ∪ ♿ ♪ ⟡

TOTNES, Devon Map ref 1D2

Broadleigh Farm Park

Coombe House Lane, Stoke Gabriel, Totnes TQ9 6PU
t (01803) 782309 e enquiries@broadleighfarm.co.uk
w **broadleighfarm.co.uk** ONLINE MAP LAST MINUTE OFFERS

⊕	£11.50–£20.50	
⊕	£11.50–£20.50	
▲	£11.50–£20.50	

85 touring pitches

Situated in beautiful South Hams village of Stoke Gabriel close to River Dart and Torbay's wonderful beaches. Local walks. Bus stop at end of lane. Dartmoor within easy reach. **directions** please visit our website for directions, www.broadleighfarm.co.uk. **open** All year **payment** cash, cheques

General ▣ ☂ ⬛ ☀ ⬛ ⬛ ⊕ ⊕ ⊕   Leisure ▶ ∪ ♪

TOTNES, Devon Map ref 1D2

SAT NAV TQ9 5AL

Steamer Quay Caravan Club Site

Steamer Quay Road, Totnes, Devon TQ9 5AL
t (01803) 862738 **e** enquiries@caravanclub.co.uk
w caravanclub.co.uk

🚐 (40)   £10.70–£28.00
🚃 (40)   £10.70–£28.00
40 touring pitches

A quiet, green and pleasantly open site with pastoral views. Within a short walk of the centre of Totnes with its pubs and restaurants. **directions** From Totnes cross railway bridge and turn right at roundabout. In 300 yards turn left over bridge and right into Seymour Road. Turn right. **open** March to October **payment** credit/debit cards, cash, cheques

General 🖥 🐕 📷 🕭

WEST DOWN, Devon Map ref 1C1

SAT NAV EX34 8NE

Brook Lea

Brook Lea Caravan Club Site, West Down, Ilfracombe, Devon EX34 8NE
t (01271) 862848 **e** enquiries@caravanclub.co.uk
w caravanclub.co.uk

🚐 (103)   £10.00–£18.00
🚃 (103)   £10.00–£18.00
103 touring pitches

This site has superb views to west and north coasts and inland to Dartmoor. Ideal base for beach lovers and walkers. Woolacombe beach and the footpaths of Exmoor close by. **directions** A361 at Mullacott roundabout turn right onto A3123, 0.75 miles right at caravan sign (signposted West Down). Site on left in 1 mile. **open** March to October **payment** credit/debit cards, cash

General 🐕 📷 🕭 📶   Leisure ▶ ⚓

WOODBURY, Devon Map ref 1D2

SAT NAV EX5 1HA

Castle Brake Holiday Park

Castle Lane, Woodbury, Exeter EX5 1HA
t (01395) 232431 **e** reception@castlebrake.co.uk
w castlebrake.co.uk LAST MINUTE OFFERS

🚐   £10.00–£25.00
🚃   £10.00–£25.00
⛺   £10.00–£25.00
🏠 (15)   £250.00–£700.00
28 touring pitches

Castle Brake is situated 1.5miles from the village of Woodbury in the idyllic setting of Woodbury Common. It is a short drive to the Jurassic Coast beaches at Exmouth, Budleigh Salterton & Sidmouth or the city of Exeter.

open 1st March - 30th November
payment credit/debit cards, cash, cheques

directions From M5Jct30 Follow A3052 to Halfway Inn. Turn right onto B3180. Turn right for Woodbury at the sign for Caravan Sites 500yds to Castle Brake.

General 🖥 ♿ 🐕 🦮 🚿 📷 ☼ 🛎 🎮 🕭 🍴 ✕   Leisure ▶ ∪ ⚓ ♟ ⛰

ALDERHOLT, Dorset Map ref 2B3

Hill Cottage Farm Camping and Caravan Park

Sandleheath Road, Alderholt, Fordingbridge SP6 3EG
t (01425) 650513 f (01425) 652339 e hillcottagefarmcaravansite@supanet.com
w **hillcottagefarmcampingandcaravanpark.co.uk** ONLINE MAP

(35)	£19.00–£25.00
(35)	£19.00–£25.00
(50)	£13.00–£29.00
35 touring pitches	

Listed in Top 100 Parks (Practical Caravan). Fully serviced pitches. Edge of New Forest, Dorset/Hants border. Large camping field. Rallies welcome with access to function room. 5 star AA pennant. **directions** From Fordingbridge take B3078 to Alderholt for 2 miles. On sharp left hand bend take a right, we are 0.5 mile on left. **open** March to November **payment** credit/debit cards, cash, cheques

General Leisure

BERE REGIS, Dorset Map ref 2B3

Rowlands Wait Touring Park

Rye Hill, Bere Regis, Wareham BH20 7LP
t (01929) 472727 f (01929) 472275 e enquiries@rowlandswait.co.uk
w **rowlandswait.co.uk** ONLINE MAP

(71)	£16.00–£21.00
(71)	£16.00–£21.00
(71)	£14.00–£18.00
71 touring pitches	

Set in an Area of Outstanding Beauty. Modern amenity block with family/disabled facilities. Central for many attractions and places of interest. Access to heathland, ideal for walkers and nature lovers. **directions** At Bere Regis follow signs to Wool/Bovington. Rowlands Wait is 0.75 miles (1.2 km) from the village, top of the hill on the right. **open** March to October **payment** credit/debit cards, cash

General Leisure

BLANDFORD FORUM, Dorset Map ref 2B3

Inside Park

Fairmile Road, Blandford Forum DT11 0HG
t (01258) 453719 e mail@theinsidepark.co.uk
w **theinsidepark.co.uk** ONLINE MAP

	£14.00–£22.00
	£14.00–£22.00
	£14.00–£22.00
125 touring pitches	

Secluded park and woodland with facilities built into 18th century stable and coach house. Ideal location for touring the county. 1.5 miles south west of Blandford on road to Winterborne Stickland. Country walks, cycling, wildlife, large play area, family-friendly camping.

open April to October
payment credit/debit cards, cash, cheques

directions Take Blandford St Mary exit at junction of A350/A354, proceed 1.5 miles SW of Blandford Forum on Fairmile Road. OS Ref: ST 864 052.

General Leisure

BOURNEMOUTH, Dorset Map ref 2B3

SAT NAV BH23 2PQ

Meadowbank Holidays

Stour Way, Christchurch BH23 2PQ
t (01202) 483597 **f** (01202) 483878 **e** enquiries@meadowbank-holidays.co.uk
w meadowbank-holidays.co.uk
ONLINE MAP LAST MINUTE OFFERS

(41)	£10.00–£31.00
(41)	£10.00–£31.00
(75)	£175.00–£975.00
41 touring pitches	

Meadowbank Holidays operate Bournemouth's closest holiday caravan and touring park. We are superbly located on the beautiful River Stour and provide a wonderful relaxing environment for a peaceful, carefree holiday or break visiting the superb local beaches, New Forest, the famous Jurassic Coast, the Isle of Wight and the lovely town of Christchurch.

We are a friendly family owned and run company operating Bournemouth's closest caravan holiday home, luxury holiday lodge and touring parks situated in superb riverside locations.

Grove Farm Meadow is a five star park offering luxury Rose award holiday caravans, touring pitches and holiday home sales. The park is beautifully landscaped and planted with an abundance of flowers, providing a peaceful and relaxing environment to compliment its stunning riverside location.

Beaulieu Gardens Retreat is a stunning new park development of luxury holiday lodges for private second home ownership. Please see the web link for more information on this exciting new project.

open March to October
payment credit/debit cards, cash, cheques

directions Please see www.meadowbank-holidays.co.uk, email us or tel 01202 483597 for directions.

General 🚗 🗂 ⓦ 🔋 ⑲ 🌣 🍴 🔌 🔯 🎱 📶 **Leisure** ► ∪ 🚴 🎣 🎯 ⚠

BRIDPORT, Dorset Map ref 2A3 — SAT NAV DT6 6JX

ROSE AWARD CARAVAN HOLIDAY PARK

		£13.25–£28.00
		£13.25–£28.00
	(159)	£13.25–£22.00
	(28)	£215.00–£600.00

108 touring pitches

Golden Cap Holiday Park

Seatown, Chideock, Bridport, Dorset DT6 6JX
t (01308) 422139 **f** (01308) 425672 **e** holidays@wdlh.co.uk
w **wdlh.co.uk** ONLINE MAP GUEST REVIEWS LAST MINUTE OFFERS

One hundred metres from beach overlooked by Dorset's highest cliff top - Golden Cap - surrounded by countryside on this World Heritage Coast. **directions** Follow A35 to Chideock, in village turn off opposite the church into Duck Street signposted for Seatown. Follow narrow road towards sea, park on left. **open** March to November **payment** credit/debit cards, cash, cheques

General **Leisure**

Looking for something else?

You can also buy a copy of our popular 'B&B' guide including guest accommodation, B&B's, guest houses, farmhouses, inns, and campus and hostel accommodation in England 2012.

Now available in good bookshops and online at **visitbritainshop.com** **£8.99**

BRIDPORT, Dorset Map ref 2A3

SAT NAV DT6 6AR

Highlands End Holiday Park

Eype, Bridport, Dorset DT6 6AR
t (01308) 422139 **f** (01308) 425672 **e** holidays@wdlh.co.uk
w wdlh.co.uk
ONLINE MAP GUEST REVIEWS LAST MINUTE OFFERS

🚐	£13.70–£24.50
🚃	£13.70–£24.50
▲ (80)	£10.50–£22.50
🏠 (21)	£274.00–£588.00
120 touring pitches	

SPECIAL PROMOTIONS
Please see our website for a
range of special offers.

It has been a favourite holiday destination since the family opened the Holiday Park in 1971. Being just 500 metres from the lovely unspoiled Eype Beach; Highlands End is at cliff top height with outstanding panoramic views over Lyme Bay - Portland Bill and Weymouth Harbour to the East and Lyme Regis, Beer and Torbay to the West. To the North, far reaching views of rural Dorset, with its picturesque villages, and home to the historic Thomas Hardy country.

Highlands End is a perfect setting for your family self-catering holiday whether you choose to take in the view while camping or touring in your own caravan or Motorhome or stay in one of our luxury Caravan Holiday Homes, Apartments or Bungalows.

The Holiday Park is ideal for trips out for all the family, this includes dogs who are welcome at all West Dorset Leisure Holidays' parks.

open March to November
payment credit/debit cards, cash, cheques

directions On approaching Bridport follow the A35 and take the turning signposted Eype. You will pass a service/picnic area on your right, take the fourth turning on your right which is indicated with a brick built welcome sign, this road leads up to the park entrance.

General 🖥 ⚲ ⟟ 🛒 🏧 📷 ☼ 🍴 🖨 🚿 🚐 ✕ Leisure ⚑ ⚲ ⤵ ⚲ 🍽 ⚓ ⛰

CHARMOUTH, Dorset Map ref 1D2 — SAT NAV DT6 6QL

enjoyEngland.com ★★★ HOLIDAY, TOURING & CAMPING PARK

(300)	£13.00–£26.00
(300)	£13.00–£26.00
(300)	£13.00–£26.00
(10)	£230.00–£690.00
(6)	£220.00–£660.00

300 touring pitches

Manor Farm Holiday Centre

The Street, Charmouth, Bridport DT6 6QL
t (01297) 560226 **f** (01297) 560429 **e** enq@manorfarmholidaycentre.co.uk
w manorfarmholidaycentre.co.uk

Large, open site in Area of Outstanding Natural Beauty. In Charmouth, only 10 min level walk to beach. Swimming pool and Bar. Seasonal pitches. Open all year. **directions** On A35 travelling west enter Charmouth Manor Farm Holiday Centre 3/4 mile on right. **open** All year **payment** credit/debit cards, cash, cheques

General **Leisure**

CHARMOUTH, Dorset Map ref 1D2 — SAT NAV DT6 6QS

enjoyEngland.com ★★★★★ HOLIDAY, TOURING & CAMPING PARK

(40)	£14.00–£18.50
(10)	£14.00–£18.50
(10)	£14.00–£18.50
	£420.00–£905.00
(68)	£195.00–£640.00

60 touring pitches

Seadown Holiday Park

Bridge Road, Charmouth, Bridport DT6 6QS
t (01297) 560154 **f** (01297) 561130 **e** bookings@seadownholidaypark.co.uk
w seadowncaravanpark.co.uk LAST MINUTE OFFERS

Quiet, family-run park which runs alongside the River Char. It has its own direct access to Charmouth's famous fossil beach, which is situated on the World Heritage Coastline. **directions** Please contact us for directions **open** Mid-March to end of October **payment** credit/debit cards, cash, cheques

General **Leisure**

CHRISTCHURCH, Dorset Map ref 2B3 — SAT NAV BH23 8JE

enjoyEngland.com ★★★ TOURING & CAMPING PARK

(60)	£15.75–£30.25
(60)	£15.75–£30.25
(14)	£15.75–£22.50

60 touring pitches

Harrow Wood Farm Caravan Park

Poplar Lane, Bransgore, Christchurch BH23 8JE
t (01425) 672487 **f** (01425) 672487 **e** harrowwood@caravan-sites.co.uk
w caravan-sites.co.uk/pages/harrowwood.htm

Quiet site bordered by woods and meadows. Take A35 from Lyndhurst, turn right at Cat and Fiddle pub, site approximately 1.5 miles into Bransgore, first right after school. **directions** OS: N=97758 E= 19237 GPS: 50.7719 North 1.72872 West **open** 1 March to 6 January **payment** credit/debit cards, cash, cheques

General **Leisure**

Looking for something else?

You can also buy a copy of our popular guide 'Hotels' including country house and town house hotels, metro and budget hotels, serviced apartments and restaurants with rooms in England 2012.

Now available in good bookshops and online at **visitbritainshop.com** **£7.99**

CORFE CASTLE, Dorset Map ref 2B3

SAT NAV BH20 5DS

TOURING &
CAMPING PARK

Norden Farm Campsite

Norden Farm, Corfe Castle BH20 5DS
t (01929) 480098 **f** (01929) 480098 **e** nordenfarm@fsmail.net
w nordenfarm.com

⊟	£19.00–£24.00
⊟	£19.00–£24.00
Å (120)	£16.00–£24.00

100 touring pitches

SPECIAL PROMOTIONS
5% discount for 7 nights or
more

Level fields on working farm site in the beautiful Purbeck Valley. Excellent toilet/shower facilities. Good family location. Set away from main road but with easy access. Family-run business with adjoining Farm Shop. Also B&B and Restaurant on site.

open March to October
payment credit/debit cards, cash, cheques

directions A351 Wareham to Corfe Castle, follow signs for Norden Park'n'Ride and look for us on right-hand side as castle comes into view.

General ⊟ 🏕 🛴 🏠 🔆 ⊡ ⏲ 🚻 ✕ Leisure ▶ ∪ 🚲 🎣 ⚘

DORCHESTER, Dorset Map ref 2B3

SAT NAV DT2 7TR

TOURING &
CAMPING PARK

Giants Head Caravan & Camping Park

Old Sherborne Road, Cerne Abbas, Dorchester, Dorset DT2 7TR
t (01300) 341242 **e** holidays@giantshead.co.uk
w giantshead.co.uk

⊟ (50)	£8.00–£16.00
⊟ (50)	£8.00–£16.00
Å (50)	£8.00–£16.00
⬛ (3)	£165.00–£275.00

50 touring pitches

A quiet site with wonderful views of Dorset Downs and the Blackmoor Vale. 2 miles north-east of Cerne Abbas, 3 miles south of Middlemarsh, 8 miles from Dorchester. **directions** On the Old Sherborne Road between Dorchester and Sherborne, 2 miles north of Cerne Abbas. **payment** cash, cheques

General ⊟ 🏕 🏠 🔆 ⊡ 🚐 ⊡ ⏲ 🚻 Leisure ▶ ∪ 🚲 🎣

DORCHESTER, Dorset Map ref 2B3

SAT NAV DT2 8HZ

HOLIDAY, TOURING
& CAMPING PARK

Sandyholme Holiday Park

Moreton Road, Owermoigne, Dorchester, Dorset DT2 8HZ
t (01308) 422139 **f** (01308) 425672 **e** holidays@wdlh.co.uk
w wdlh.co.uk

⊟ (50)	£13.50–£19.00
⊟ (52)	£14.60–£21.90
Å (70)	£12.00–£17.50
⊟ (26)	£235.00–£448.00

50 touring pitches

Sandyholme is pleasantly secluded and surrounded by trees. The Holiday Park is fully equipped, offering family holiday homes for hire and sale, with facilities for tourers, tents and motorhomes. **directions** Follow A35 to Dorchester turn onto A352. At roundabout take the second exit, continue through the village and take left turn onto Moreton Road. **open** March to November **payment** credit/debit cards, cash, cheques

General ⊟ 🍴 🏕 🛴 🏠 🔆 ⊡ ⏲ 🚻 ✕ Leisure ▶ 🎣 ⚓ ⚘

EYPE, Dorset Map ref 2A3   SAT NAV DT6 6AL

Eype House Caravan Park Ltd
Eype, Bridport, Dorset DT6 6AL
t (01308) 424903 **f** (01308) 424903 **e** enquiries@eypehouse.co.uk
w **eypehouse.co.uk** ONLINE MAP

🚐 (20)	£13.00–£20.00	
⛺ (20)	£13.00–£20.00	
🏠 (35)	£230.00–£515.00	

20 touring pitches

Small quiet site 200 yds from the beach on the Jurassic Coast in area of outstanding natural beauty. **directions** from A35 turn to Eype. Take 3rd turn, sign Lower Eype and to the beach, follow lane past pub and Hotel Caravan Park on right. **open** Easter to October **payment** cash, cheques

General 🔲 🐾 ⬛ 🏠 ☀ 🔵 🍴 ✕ Leisure 🎣

LYME REGIS, Dorset Map ref 1D2   SAT NAV DT7 3XW

Shrubbery Touring Park
Rousdon, Lyme Regis DT7 3XW
t (01297) 442227 **f** (01297) 446086 **e** info@shrubberypark.co.uk
w **shrubberypark.co.uk** GUEST REVIEWS

🚐	£11.25–£16.25
🚐	£11.25–£16.25
⛺	£11.25–£16.25

120 touring pitches

Ten acre level site, on the Devon & Dorset border. Pitches for tents, motor vans & caravans. Electric Hook-ups. Spacious modern shower blocks. Large children's play area. Crazy golf. Dog Walking Area. Rallies welcome. Off peak special offers.

open 1st April to 31st October
payment credit/debit cards, cash, cheques

directions 3 miles west of Lyme Regis on the A3052 Coast Road.

General 🔲 🐾 ⬛ 🏠 ☀ 🔵 🍴 ⬛ Leisure 🎢

POOLE, Dorset Map ref 2B3   SAT NAV BH16 6LA

Pear Tree Holiday Park
Organford Road, Holton Heath, Poole, Dorset BH16 6LA
t 0844 272 9504 **e** enquiries@peartreepark.co.uk
w **peartreepark.co.uk** ONLINE MAP ONLINE BOOKING LAST MINUTE OFFERS

155 touring pitches

Peacefully located in the heart of Dorset, an ideal holiday destination with a wealth of attractions including Poole just a short drive away for all looking for a relaxing getaway. **directions** From A35 take A351 to Wareham. After approximately 2 miles, at traffic lights, turn right. The park is a further 0.5 mile on the left. **payment** credit/debit cards, cash, cheques

General 🔲 🐾 🏠 ☀ 🍴 🔵 Leisure 🎢

POOLE, Dorset Map ref 2B3　　　　　　　　SAT NAV BH16 6JB

South Lytchett Manor Caravan & Camping Park
Dorchester Road, Poole, Dorset BH16 6JB
t (01202) 622577 **e** info@southlytchettmanor.co.uk
w southlytchettmanor.co.uk ONLINE MAP GUEST REVIEWS LAST MINUTE OFFERS

⚐ (120)　£15.00–£25.00
⚐ (120)　£15.00–£25.00
▲ (30)　£15.00–£25.00
150 touring pitches

SPECIAL PROMOTIONS
Saver season special rates.
Voucher for a free botttle
wine with 2 main courses
at the local village pub.

Situated in 20 acres of stunning parkland. Just 3 miles from Poole. Within walking distance of 2 village pubs with restaurants. Bus service at gates to Poole and Heritage Coastline.

open 1st March to 2nd January
payment credit/debit cards, cash, cheques, euros

directions Follow signs towards Poole from the A31. Continue on A35 signposted Dorchester. Right at the Bakers Arms roundabout Lytchett Minster, on left 300 outside village.

General ⚲ 🗗 ⚇ 🐕 🎇 📠 🅁 ☼ ⚐ 🗗 ⚑ 🖳 Leisure ▶ ∪ ⚵ ✦ 🔍 ⚓ 🏔

STEEPLE, Dorset Map ref 2B3

Corfe Castle Camping and Caravanning Club Site
Bucknowle, Wareham, Dorset BH20 5PA
t (01929) 480280 **e** CorfeCastle.Site@thefriendlyclub.co.uk
w campingandcaravanningclub.co.uk/corfecastle ONLINE MAP GUEST REVIEWS

The Camping and Caravanning Club
The Friendly Club

⚐　£23.00–£30.00
⚐　£23.00–£30.00
▲　£23.00–£30.00
80 touring pitches

The site lies at the foot of the Purbeck Hills in an Area of Outstanding Natural Beauty, the gateway to many wonderful walks. Near beautiful beaches. **directions** Use map and not satnav via A351. Turn right at foot of the castle, after 3/4 mile turn right at first brown camping sign. **open** 1st March- 31st October **payment** credit/debit cards, cash, cheques

General 🗗 ⚇ 🐕 🎇 📠 🅁 ☼ ⚐ 🗗 ⚑ 🖳 Leisure 🏔

SWANAGE, Dorset Map ref 2B3　　　　　　　SAT NAV BH19 2QS

Swanage Bay View Holiday Park
Panorama Road, Swanage BH19 2QS
t (01929) 422130 **f** (01929) 427952 **e** enquiries@swanagebayviewholidaypark.co.uk
w swanagebayviewholidaypark.co.uk ONLINE MAP ONLINE BOOKING LAST MINUTE OFFERS

🏕 (5)　£200.00–£900.00

Boasting an outstanding setting in the Isle of Purbeck, enjoy dazzling views and all the benefits of the park's outstanding facilities including indoor pool, superb restaurant and entertainment venue. **directions** Herston Cross, right at lights, High Street. Second right. Left at top, left again, Priest Road, next right, Panorama Road, park is at the end. **payment** credit/debit cards, cash, cheques

General ⚲ 🗗 ⚇ 🐕 🎇 📠 🅁 ☼ ✕ Leisure ≋ 🍽 🎵 🔍

WAREHAM, Dorset Map ref 2B3 — SAT NAV BH20 5PU

Durdle Door Holiday Park

West Lulworth, Wareham BH20 5PU
t (01929) 400200 f (01929) 400260 e durdle.door@lulworth.com
w **lulworth.com** LAST MINUTE OFFERS

(39)	£15.00–£50.00
(18)	£15.00–£50.00
(50)	£10.00–£40.00
(60)	£260.00–£800.00

107 touring pitches

Situated between Weymouth & Swanage, the park has direct access to 2 beaches and is surrounded by stunning countryside. Open & woodland camping areas; electric & fully serviced pitches; seafront pitches available for tourers & motorhomes. Holiday homes available. Close to the picturesque Lulworth Cove & many other family attractions.

open 1st March to 31st October
payment credit/debit cards, cash, cheques

directions See www.lulworth.com for details.

General ⚹ ▣ ⍾ ↟ ⚞ ⁌ ⋔ ☼ ⚟ ☝ ☎ ⓦ ✕ Leisure ∪ ⚲ ⫐ ⵟ ⛰

WAREHAM, Dorset Map ref 2B3 — SAT NAV BH20 5AZ

The Lookout Holiday Park

Corfe Road, Stoborough, Wareham BH20 5AZ
t (01929) 552546 f (01929) 556662 e enquiries@caravan-sites.co.uk
w **caravan-sites.co.uk**

(126)	£16.00–£29.50
(22)	£15.00–£29.50
(24)	£11.00–£25.00
(37)	£199.00–£657.00

150 touring pitches

This small holiday park is situated 1 mile south of Wareham in the village of Stoborough on A351, just 3 miles from Corfe Castle.

open All year
payment credit/debit cards, cash, cheques

directions Take the A351 from Poole to Wareham go through Wareham town crossing the river Frome, pass through Stoborough village and we are on the left.

General ▣ ⍾ ⚞ ⁌ ⋔ ☼ ⚟ ☝ ☎ Leisure ∪ ⚲ ⫐ ✎ ⛰

WEYMOUTH, Dorset Map ref 2B3

SAT NAV DT3 4EA

Bagwell Farm Touring Park

Knights In The Bottom, Chickerell, Weymouth DT3 4EA
t (01305) 782575 **f** (01305) 780554 **e** vb@bagwellfarm.co.uk
w bagwellfarm.co.uk ONLINE MAP GUEST REVIEWS

 (160) £15.50–£29.00
(80) £15.50–£29.00
Å (80) £12.00–£25.50
320 touring pitches

Find a friendly welcome all year round at Bagwell Farm: tranquil rural site just 5 miles from Weymouth's sandy beach. Ideal base for exploring Dorset and its stunning Jurassic coastline. **directions** On the B3157, 3 miles west of Weymouth, between Chickerell & Portesham. From A354 follow signs for Town Centre then B3157/Abbotsbury. On X53 Bus Route. **open** All year **payment** credit/debit cards, cash

General  Leisure

---

WEYMOUTH, Dorset Map ref 2B3

SAT NAV DT2 8BE

Crossways Caravan Club Site

Crossways, Weymouth, Dorchester DT2 8BE
t (01305) 852032 **e** enquiries@caravanclub.co.uk
w caravanclub.co.uk

THE
CARAVAN
CLUB

(112) £11.80–£30.80
(112) £11.80–£30.80
112 touring pitches

Nearby to Dorchester and Weymouth's award winning, sandy beach. Visit Lawrence of Arabia's house at Cloud's Hill. Railway station is just 5 minutes walk. **directions** North from A35 or south from A352, join B3390. Site on right within 1 mile. Entrance to site by forecourt of filling station. **open** April to October **payment** credit/debit cards, cash, cheques

General

WIMBORNE MINSTER, Dorset Map ref 2B3

SAT NAV BH21 4HW

Wilksworth Farm Caravan Park

Cranborne Road, Furzehill, Wimborne BH21 4HW
t (01202) 885467 **e** rayandwendy@wilksworthfarmcaravanpark.co.uk
w wilksworthfarmcaravanpark.co.uk ONLINE MAP

(60) £16.00–£30.00
(60) £16.00–£30.00
Å (25) £16.00–£30.00
60 touring pitches

SPECIAL PROMOTIONS
7-night booking outside peak times - 1 night free. Monday-Thursday outside of peak times - £15 pitch fee per night.

Wilksworth Farm Caravan Park is a five star, premier park surrounding a grade 2 star listed farmhouse once belonging to Henry VIII and listed in the Doomsday Book. Newly refurbished swimming pool and children's pool, a large children's adventure play area, Tea Room and modern, fully refurbished toilet block.

open April to October
payment credit/debit cards, cash, cheques

directions 1 mile north of Wimborne on B3078 (Cranborne Road).

General Leisure

WOOL, Dorset Map ref 2B3

SAT NAV BH20 6HG

Whitemead Caravan Park

East Burton Road, Wool, Wareham BH20 6HG
t (01929) 462241 **f** (01929) 462241 **e** whitemeadcp@aol.com
w whitemeadcaravanpark.co.uk

(95)	£13.50–£21.00	
(95)	£13.50–£21.00	
(95)	£11.50–£18.50	
95 touring pitches		

Within easy reach of beaches and beautiful countryside, this friendly site is maintained to a high standard of cleanliness. Turn west off the A352 near Wool level crossing. **directions** Turn west off A352, Wareham–Dorchester Road, along East Burton Road, by Wool level crossing. We are along this road on the right. **open** 15 March to 31 October **payment** credit/debit cards, cash, cheques

General 🔲 💧 🐕 💺 ⛱ ☼ 📅 📢 🚪 🚻 **Leisure** 🚣 🎣 ⛰

BOURTON-ON-THE-WATER, Gloucestershire Map ref 2B1

SAT NAV GL54 3BU

Notgrove Caravan Club Site

Cheltenham Road, Bourton-on-The-Water, Gloucestershire GL54 3BU
t (01451) 850249 **e** enquiries@caravanclub.co.uk
w caravanclub.co.uk

THE
CARAVAN
CLUB

(70)	£10.70–£25.20	
(70)	£10.70–£25.20	
70 touring pitches		

Beautiful site high up in the Cotswolds, surrounded by open countryside. Nearby perfumery, miniture village and motor museum. **directions** M5 jct11a A417 (Cirencester). Roundabout follow A436. Left at roundabout A435. 2nd roundabout right onto A436. Left onto A40. Right onto A436. Site on right. **open** March to October **payment** credit/debit cards, cash, cheques

General 📢 🚪 🚻 🅿 **Leisure** ▶

BRISTOL, Gloucestershire Map ref 2A2

SAT NAV BS1 6XG

Baltic Wharf Caravan Club Site

Cumberland Road, Southville, Bristol BS1 6XG
t (0117) 926 8030 **f** (0117) 926 8030 **e** enquiries@caravanclub.co.uk
w caravanclub.co.uk

THE
CARAVAN
CLUB

(55)	£16.60–£38.90	
(55)	£16.60–£38.90	
55 touring pitches		

Set in the heart of Bristol's beautiful dockland, linked to the city centre by river ferry. Zoo nearby and Downs Park; an ideal picnic spot. Good access to cycle paths. **directions** M5 jct18, A4. Left lane, follow Historic Harbour, into Hotwells Road. Right lane at lights, left lane after pedestrian crossing. Over bridge, site on left. **open** All year **payment** credit/debit cards, cash, cheques

General 🔲 💧 📱 ⛱ ☼ 🚿 📢 🚪 🚻 🅿 **Leisure** ▶

CHRISTCHURCH, Gloucestershire Map ref 2A1

SAT NAV GL16 7NN

Bracelands Campsite Caravan and Camping Site

Bracelands Drive, Christchurch, Coleford GL16 7NN
t (01594) 837258 **e** forestofdean.site@forestholidays.co.uk
w campingintheforest.co.uk ONLINE MAP ONLINE BOOKING

	£12.00–£21.50	
	£12.00–£21.50	
	£12.00–£21.50	
520 touring pitches		

An open site on the edge of the Forest of Dean and close to the Welsh border, Bracelands boasts fantastic views across the River Wye. **directions** Please be aware not to use a Sat Nav as you get closer to the site. **open** 4th April - 31st October **payment** credit/debit cards, cash, cheques

General 🔲 📱 ⛱ 📢 🚪 🚻 🅿

CHRISTCHURCH, Gloucestershire Map ref 2A1   SAT NAV GL16 7NN

Christchurch Campsite
Bracelands Drive, Christchurch, Coleford GL16 7NN
t (01594) 837165
w forestholidays.co.uk ONLINE MAP GUEST REVIEWS

⚬	£12.00–£27.00
⚬	£12.00–£27.00
⚬	£12.00–£27.00
280 touring pitches	

Perfect for a family holiday. Symonds Yat offers great views and walks down to the river. several activity centres in the area that car offer canoeing on the river itself. **directions** Grid Ref: OS16575129 M5 at Junction 8 take the M50 which leads onto the A40. Monmouth -A4136. Turn left at the crossroads into Bracelands Drive. **open** All year **payment** credit/debit cards, cash

General ▯ ⌕ ⚏ ⬚ ⌁ ◷ ◷ ☎ Leisure ⟋⟍

MORETON-IN-MARSH, Gloucestershire Map ref 2B1   SAT NAV GL56 0BT

THE
CARAVAN
CLUB

Moreton-in-Marsh Caravan Club Site
Bourton Road, Moreton-in-Marsh, Gloucestershire GL56 0BT
t (01608) 650519 **e** enquiries@caravanclub.co.uk
w caravanclub.co.uk

⚬ (183)	£16.00–£38.90
⚏ (183)	£16.00–£38.90
183 touring pitches	

An attractive, well-wooded site within easy walking distance of the market town of Moreton-in-Marsh. On-site crazy golf, volleyball and boules. **directions** From Moreton-in-Marsh on A44 the site entrance is on the right 250 yds past the end of the speed limit sign. **open** All year **payment** credit/debit cards, cash, cheques

General ▯ ⚘ ⌕ ⬚ ⌁ ☼ ▦ ◷ ◷ ☎ ⬚ Leisure ⟍ ⟋⟍

PRESTBURY, Gloucestershire Map ref 2B1   SAT NAV GL50 4SH

THE
CARAVAN
CLUB

Cheltenham Racecourse Caravan Club Site
Prestbury Park, Cheltenham, Gloucestershire GL50 4SH
t (01242) 523102 **e** enquiries@caravanclub.co.uk
w caravanclub.co.uk

⚬ (80)	£12.50–£30.80
⚏ (80)	£12.50–£30.80
80 touring pitches	

On the edge of spa town, this site is a good base from which to explore the area. Shops, cafes and restaurants nearby. **directions** M25 onto A40, turn left onto A4013, turn right and cross level crossing. After 1 mile turn left into racecourse. Follow Club signs. **open** April to October **payment** credit/debit cards, cash, cheques

General ▯ ⬚ ◷ ◷ ⬚

TEWKESBURY, Gloucestershire Map ref 2B1   SAT NAV GL20 5PG

THE
CARAVAN
CLUB

Tewkesbury Abbey Caravan Club Site
Gander Lane, Tewkesbury GL20 5PG
t (01684) 294035 **e** enquiries@caravanclub.co.uk
w caravanclub.co.uk

⚬ (157)	£13.10–£25.40
⚏ (157)	£13.10–£25.40
157 touring pitches	

Located a short walk away from the old town, with superb mature trees screening it. Historic buildings, interesting walks and excellent museums. **directions** M5 j9 onto A438. 3 miles at cross-junction turn right. 200 yds left into Gander Lane. M50 leave by j1 onto A38. **open** April to October **payment** credit/debit cards, cash, cheques

General ▯ ⌕ ⬚ ⌁ ☼ ▦ ◷ ◷ ☎ ⬚ Leisure ⤸ ⟍

BEETHAM, Somerset Map ref 1D2 | SAT NAV TA20 3QA

Five Acres Caravan Club Site
Beetham, Chard, Somerset TA20 3QA
t (01460) 234519 **e** enquiries@caravanclub.co.uk
w **caravanclub.co.uk**

(69)	£11.80–£30.80
(69)	£11.80–£30.80
69 touring pitches	

Pleasant and peaceful site. Busy market town nearby. Chard resevoir nearby, great for birdwatching and walking. **directions** A303, 5.25 miles past roundabout at end of Ilminster bypass, left at crossroads lane signposted Crickleaze. Site on left. **open** March to October **payment** credit/debit cards, cash, cheques

General

BREAN, Somerset Map ref 1D1 | SAT NAV TA8 2RB

Holiday Resort Unity
Coast Road, Brean Sands, Brean TA8 2RB
t (01278) 751235 **f** (01278) 752006 **e** admin@hru.co.uk
w **hru.co.uk** ONLINE MAP GUEST REVIEWS ONLINE BOOKING LAST MINUTE OFFERS

	£8.00–£34.00
	£8.00–£34.00
(69)	£8.00–£32.00
(169)	£280.00–£910.00
385 touring pitches	

Pitches for caravans, motorhomes and tents. Lodges, villas, caravans and tents for hire. Entertainment, pools with 4 waterslides. Fun Park, children's club, fishing, golf. Prices from £8.00 per night. **directions** Off Junction 22 of M5. Follow Brown and White Tourist Board Signs from motorway towards Burnham On Sea and North heading for Berrow and Brean. **open** Feb to Nov plus New Year **payment** credit/debit cards

General ⬤ Leisure

BREAN, Somerset Map ref 1D1 | SAT NAV TA8 2SE

Northam Farm Holiday Park
South Road, Brean TA8 2SE
t (01278) 751244 **f** (01278) 751150 **e** enquiries@northamfarm.co.uk
w **northamfarm.co.uk** ONLINE MAP

(350)	£9.75–£25.25
(350)	£9.75–£25.25
(150)	£9.75–£21.25
450 touring pitches	

An attractive touring park situated 200m from a sandy beach. 30-acre park offering children's outdoor play areas, fishing lake, diner, take-away, mini-supermarket, launderette, dog walks, hardstanding and grass pitches. **directions** M5 jct 22. Follow signs to Burnham-on-Sea, Brean. Continue through Brean and Northam Farm is on the right, 0.5 mile past Brean Leisure Park. **open** March to October **payment** credit/debit cards, cash

General Leisure

CHEDDAR, Somerset Map ref 1D1 | SAT NAV BS27 3DB

Broadway House Holiday Park
Axbridge Road, Cheddar, Somerset BS27 3DB
t 0844 272 9501 **f** (01934) 744950 **e** enquiries@broadwayhousepark.co.uk
w **broadwayhousepark.co.uk** ONLINE MAP ONLINE BOOKING LAST MINUTE OFFERS

419 touring pitches

A fun-packed holiday destination just minutes from Cheddar offering super on-site facilities including a large bar and restaurant, heated outdoor pool and a wide choice of activities to choose from. **directions** M5 jct 22. Eight miles. Midway between Cheddar and Axbridge on A371. **open** March to November **payment** credit/debit cards, cash, cheques

General Leisure

CROWCOMBE, Somerset Map ref 1D1

SAT NAV TA4 4AW

Quantock Orchard Caravan Park
Flaxpool, Crowcombe, Taunton, Somerset TA4 4AW
t (01984) 618618 **f** (01984) 618618 **e** member@flaxpool.freeserve.co.uk
w **quantock-orchard.co.uk** ONLINE MAP GUEST REVIEWS LAST MINUTE OFFERS

(31)	£14.00–£29.00
(19)	£14.00–£29.00
(19)	£14.00–£29.00
(9)	£35.00–£85.00

68 touring pitches

Award-winning campsite with superb panoramic views of the Quantock Hills; open all year, fully heated toilet and shower block; tastefully landscaped with several stunning holiday homes for hire. **directions** On the A358 between Williton and Taunton. Behind Flaxpool Garage. **open** All year **payment** credit/debit cards, cash

General ⚡ 🗎 🐾 🏋 🐕 🏠 ☼ 🍴 ⚡ 🕐 🚻 📶 Leisure ▶ ∪ 🚴 ⚓ ⚡ 🎣 🔍 🏔

DONIFORD, Somerset Map ref 1D1

SAT NAV TA23 0UD

Sunnybank Holiday Park
Sunny Bank Holiday Caravan Park, Watchet TA23 0UD
t 0844 272 9505 **f** (01984) 632237 **e** enquiries@sunnybankpark.co.uk
w **sunnybankpark.co.uk** ONLINE MAP ONLINE BOOKING LAST MINUTE OFFERS

(15)	£200.00–£510.00

Nestled in the Quantock Hills in beautiful Somerset offering pure relaxation in an area of natural beauty with first-class on-site facilities including an outdoor heated pool and sun terrace. **directions** From M5 towards Minehead, follow signs to Doniford. At the bottom of the hill, turn right and Sunnybank is 100 meters down the lane. **open** except for 3rd January to 4th February **payment** credit/debit cards, cash, cheques

General 🗎 🐾 🏋 🍴 🏠 ☼ Leisure ▶ ∪ 🚴 ⚓ 🎣 🏔

DULVERTON, Somerset Map ref 1D1

SAT NAV TA22 9HL

Exmoor House Caravan Club Site
Dulverton, Somerset TA22 9HL
t (01398) 323268 **e** enquiries@caravanclub.co.uk
w **caravanclub.co.uk**

THE CARAVAN CLUB

(67)	£13.50–£32.79
(67)	£13.50–£32.79

67 touring pitches

Very quiet and secluded, in the heart of Lorna Doone country. Shops and pubs within walking distance. Explore this walker's paradise. **directions** From M5 jct 27, B3222 to Dulverton, left over river bridge, 200 yds on. Note: 2 narrow hump bridges on B3222, approach carefully. **open** March to November **payment** credit/debit cards, cash, cheques

General 🗎 🐾 🍴 🏠 ⚡ 🕐 🚻 📶 Leisure ⚓

DULVERTON, Somerset Map ref 1D1

SAT NAV TA22 9BE

Lakeside Caravan Club Site
Higher Grants, Exebridge, Dulverton, Somerset TA22 9BE
t (01398) 324068 **e** enquiries@caravanclub.co.uk
w **caravanclub.co.uk**

THE CARAVAN CLUB

(80)	£15.30–£35.51
(80)	£15.30–£35.51

80 touring pitches

Lakeside has splendid new facilities and all pitches (now level) boast superb views of surrounding hills and the Exe Valley. Within easy reach of the National Park. **directions** From A396 site on left within 2.5 miles. **open** March to November **payment** credit/debit cards, cash, cheques

General 🗎 💧 🐾 🍴 🏠 🗑 ⚡ 🕐 📶 Leisure ⚓ 🔍 🏔

MINEHEAD, Somerset Map ref 1D1

SAT NAV TA24 5SH

enjoyEngland.com
★★★★
HOLIDAY VILLAGE

Butlins Minehead

Warren Road, Minehead TA24 5SH
t 0845 070 4736 e butlins.webmaster@bourne-leisure.co.uk
w **butlins.com/resorts/minehead/index.aspx**
ONLINE MAP ONLINE BOOKING LAST MINUTE OFFERS

SPECIAL PROMOTIONS
See butlins.com for our
latest offers and prices.

If you're a fan of rolling hills with natural beauty, Minehead in Somerset could be just the place for you!

Superb live entertainment and a fantastic range of facilities and activities; sub tropical waterworld, funfair, all weather sports areas, children's play areas and clubs, bars and restaurants.

Butlins Minehead offers the perfect blend of nature and adventure. Get out and about to explore the stunning Exmoor National Park, have a go at coast-steering or take a Land Rover safari, or relax with a historic wander around Dunster Castle, swing by the local golf course or just stroll along the sandy beach. Bliss!

open All year
payment credit/debit cards, cheques

directions Heading south on the M5, follow the signposts for Junction 24, Bridgewater. Take the A38, then the A39 to Minehead. Heading north, take the M5 to Taunton (Junction 25), and then the A358 and A39 to Minehead. Head for the seafront – you can't miss us!

General ⚷ 🖥 ♿ 🛏 ☼ ✕ Leisure ▶ ∪ 🚲 ♪ 🏹 🎣 🍽 🎵 🔍 ⛰

POOLE, Somerset Map ref 1D1

SAT NAV TA21 9HN

Cadeside Caravan Club Site

Nynehead Road, Wellington, Somerset TA21 9HN
t (01823) 663103 e enquiries@caravanclub.co.uk
w **caravanclub.co.uk**

Well screened rural site. 10 mins from Wellington. Good base for exploring the beautiful Dorset coast. **directions** M5 via jct 26 onto A38 (signposted Wellington). Roundabout turn onto B3187 (signposted Wellington) at roundabout turn right (signposted Nynehead, Poole). Site on right. **open** All year **payment** credit/debit cards, cash, cheques

🚐 (16) £10.00–£18.00
🚏 (16) £10.00–£18.00
16 touring pitches

General 📞 ⊙ Leisure ▶

PORLOCK, Somerset Map ref 1D1

SAT NAV TA24 8HT

Burrowhayes Farm Caravan & Camping Site & Riding Stables

West Luccombe, Porlock, Minehead TA24 8HT
t (01643) 862463 e info@burrowhayes.co.uk
w **burrowhayes.co.uk**

🚐 (54) £12.00–£22.00
🚏 (54) £12.00–£22.00
Å (66) £12.00–£20.00
📷 (19) £190.00–£450.00
120 touring pitches

Popular family site in delightful National Trust setting on Exmoor, just 2 miles from the Coast. Surrounding moors and woods provide a walker's paradise. Children can play and explore safely. Riding stables offer pony-trekking for all abilities. Heated shower block with disabled and baby-changing facilities, laundrette and pot wash.

open Mid-March to end of October
payment credit/debit cards, cash, cheques

directions From Minehead, A39 towards Porlock; 1st left after Allerford to Horner and West Luccombe; Burrowhayes is 0.25 miles along on right before hump-backed bridge.

General 🖥 ⊙ ⌖ 🐾 🏍 🔥 ☼ 🖾 📞 ⊙ 🍴 🗺 Leisure ∪ 🚲 ✦

PORLOCK, Somerset Map ref 1D1

SAT NAV TA24 8ND

Porlock Caravan Park

High Bank, Porlock TA24 8ND
t (01643) 862269 f (01643) 862269 e info@porlockcaravanpark.co.uk
w **porlockcaravanpark.co.uk**

Delightful high-quality park situated within walking distance of quaint village of Porlock. Luxury holiday homes for hire. Touring caravans, motor homes and tents welcome. **directions** A39 from Minehead, in Porlock village take B3225 to Porlock Weir, site signposted. **open** March to October **payment** credit/debit cards, cash, cheques

🚐 £12.00–£19.50
🚏 £12.00–£19.50
Å £13.00–£20.00
📷 (9) £320.00–£545.00
40 touring pitches

General 🖥 ⊙ ⌖ 🏍 🔥 ☼ 📞 🍴 🗺 Leisure ∪ ✦

PRIDDY, Somerset Map ref 2A2

SAT NAV BA5 3BP

Cheddar Camping and Caravanning Club Site
Mendip Heights, Townsend, Priddy Wells, Somerset BA5 3BP
t (01749) 870241 **f** (01749) 870368 **e** cheddar@campingandcaravanningclub.
co.uk **w** **campingandcaravanningclub.co.uk/cheddar** ONLINE MAP GUEST REVIEWS

🚐	£23.00–£30.00
🚃	£23.00–£30.00
▲	£23.00–£30.00
90 touring pitches	

Tents, Caravans & Motorhomes welcome. Outstanding Natural Beauty – the Mendip Hills. Midway between Cheddar Gorge and Wells, there are many attractions in this area of Somerset. **directions** From A39/B3135 junction it is 4.5 miles to left turn to site, the second turning to Priddy. **open** 1 March - 15 November **payment** credit/debit cards, cash, cheques

General 📷 📶 🐕 🚿 🏕 ☀ 🔌 🚽 🛒 📶 Leisure ∪ ⌒ ⛰

ROOKS BRIDGE, Somerset Map ref 1D1

SAT NAV BS26 2TA

Acacia Farm Campsite
Acacia Farm, Bristol Road A38, Rooks Bridge, Axbridge BS26 2TA
t (01934) 750314 **e** info@acaciafarmsomerset.co.uk
w **acaciafarmsomerset.co.uk**

🚐 (5)	£10.00
🚃 (5)	£12.00
▲ (10)	£6.00
5 touring pitches	

Acacia Farm is a 5cl Camping and Caravan Club site in small hamlet of Rooksbridge in beautiful countryside. Excellent location from M5 and discovering the land of the Summer people. **directions** M5 Jct 22 10 mins. A38 signpost Bristol Airport, pass Wellington Pub & PO on your left, Acacia Farm is 400 yards on the right. **open** All year **payment** cash, cheques

General 🐕 🏕 ☀ 🚐 🔌 🛒 Leisure ▶ ∪ 🚲 ⌒

TAUNTON, Somerset Map ref 1D1

SAT NAV TA3 5NW

Ashe Farm Caravan and Campsite
Ashe Farm Caravan and Campsite, Thornfalcon, Taunton TA3 5NW
t (01823) 443764 **e** info@ashefarm.co.uk
w **ashefarm.co.uk** ONLINE MAP

🚐 (20)	£11.00–£14.00
🚃 (10)	£11.00–£14.00
▲ (10)	£11.00–£13.00
🏠 (3)	£175.00–£225.00
30 touring pitches	

Quiet farm site, lovely views, easy access. Central for touring. Easy reach coast and hills. Family run and informal. **directions** Leave M5 at Jnt 25, take A358 eastwards for 2.5 miles, turn right at Nags Head pub towards West Hatch. Site 0.25 mile on RHS. **open** 1st April to 31st October **payment** cash, cheques

General 📷 🐕 🏕 ☀ 🚐 🔌 🛒 Leisure ▶ ∪ ⚲ ⌒ ⛰

TWERTON-ON-AVON, Somerset Map ref 2B2

SAT NAV BA2 9JF

Newton Mill Holiday Park
Newton Road, Bath BA2 9JF
t 0844 272 9503 **e** enquiries@newtonmillpark.co.uk
w **newtonmillpark.co.uk** ONLINE MAP ONLINE BOOKING LAST MINUTE OFFERS

203 touring pitches	

Ideally located in rural Somerset just three miles from Bath, boasting a superb bar and restaurant in the parks charming old Mill House along with award-winning facilities, the perfect getaway. **directions** On A4 towards Bristol, take exit signposted Newton St Loe at roundabout by the Globe pub. Site is 1 mile on left. **open** All year **payment** credit/debit cards, cash, cheques

General 🔥 📷 📶 🐕 🚿 🏕 ☀ 🔲 🚐 🔌 🛒 📶 ✕ Leisure ▶ ∪ 🚲 ⌒ 🍽 🍺 ⛰

WATCHET (4 MILES), Somerset Map ref 1D1

SAT NAV TA4 4DY

HOLIDAY & TOURING PARK

⚐ (20)	£13.50–£30.00
⛺ (20)	£13.50–£30.00
⚑ (20)	£13.50–£30.00
⛺ (2)	£365.00–£593.00
⛺ (17)	£252.00–£563.00

Saint Audries Bay Holiday Club
West Quantoxhead, Minehead TA4 4DY
t (01984) 632515 **f** (01984) 632785 **e** info@staudriesbay.co.uk
w **staudriesbay.co.uk** ONLINE MAP GUEST REVIEWS

Family-owned and run, award-winning Park near Exmoor and Minehead, in beautiful surroundings on the Somerset coast. Fantastic views and beach access. Bed & Breakfast, Self catering & Pitches.

open All year except Xmas and New Year
payment credit/debit cards, cash, cheques

directions From M5 (north) J23, Bridgwater, A39 (15 miles). From M5 (south) J25, Taunton, A358 then A39 (15 miles).

General ⌂☺♿⌖⚡◉⏻☀⛢♨⚲♀✕ Leisure ⚲☂♟♪♣⛰

WATERROW, Somerset Map ref 1D1

TOURING & CAMPING PARK

⚐ (38)	£15.00–£24.00
⛺ (38)	£15.00–£24.00
⚑ (7)	£15.00–£24.00
⛺ (1)	£295.00–£425.00
45 touring pitches	

Waterrow Touring Park
Wiveliscombe, Nr Taunton, Somerset TA4 2AZ
t (01984) 623464 **e** waterrowpark@yahoo.co.uk
w **waterrowpark.co.uk**

Gently sloping, grassy site with hardstandings situated in beautiful river valley. Ideal base from which to explore this unspoilt area. Elizabethan cottage and one holiday caravan for rent. Adults only. **directions** M5 Junction 25, A358 round Taunton. B3227 through Wiveliscombe to Waterrow. Park 500 yds after Rock Inn. DO NOT FOLLOW SAT NAV DIRECTIONS **open** All year **payment** credit/debit cards, cash, cheques

General ☺♿⌖⏻☀♨⚲♀⚐ Leisure ☂♪

WESTON-SUPER-MARE, Somerset Map ref 1D1

SAT NAV BS22 9UJ

HOLIDAY, TOURING & CAMPING PARK

⚐ (90)	£10.00–£25.00
⛺ (90)	£10.00–£25.00
⚑ (30)	£10.00–£25.00
120 touring pitches	

Country View Holiday Park
29 Sand Road, Sand Bay, Weston-super-Mare BS22 9UJ
t (01934) 627595 **e** info@cvhp.co.uk
w **cvhp.co.uk**

Country View is surrounded by countryside and just 200yds from Sand Bay Beach. Heated pool, Bar, Shop and Children's Play Area. Fantastic toilet and shower facilities. Holiday Homes for sale. **directions** Exit 21 of M5 follow signs for Sand Bay along Queensway into Lower Norton Lane and take right into Sand Road. **open** March to January **payment** credit/debit cards, cash, cheques

General ☺⌖⏻☀♨⚲♀⚐ Leisure ☂♣⚓♪⚲☂♣⛰

WESTON-SUPER-MARE, Somerset Map ref 1D1 SAT NAV BS24 0JQ

Dulhorn Farm Holiday Park

Weston Road, Lympsham, Weston Super Mare Somerset BS24 0JQ
t (01934) 750298 **f** (01934) 750913 **e** dfhp@btconnect.com
w dulhornfarmholidaypark.co.uk

enjoyEngland.com ★★★★ TOURING & CAMPING PARK

(100)	£16.00–£22.00
(100)	£16.00–£22.00
(60)	£8.00–£22.00
(4)	£150.00–£420.00
(1)	£200.00–£420.00

100 touring pitches

A family site on a working farm set in the countryside, approximately four miles from the beach, midway between Weston and Burnham. Ideal for touring. Easily accessible from M5. **directions** M5 Junction 22, then North on A38, at next roundabout A370 towards Weston-Super-Mare, 1.5 miles on left. **open** March to October **payment** credit/debit cards, cash, cheques

General **Leisure**

WINCANTON, Somerset Map ref 2B3 SAT NAV BA9 8BJ

Wincanton Racecourse Campsite

Old Hill, Wincanton BA9 8BJ
t (01963) 34276 **e** enquiries@caravanclub.co.uk
w caravanclub.co.uk

THE CARAVAN CLUB

enjoyEngland.com ★★★ TOURING & CAMPING PARK

(57)	£10.70–£28.00
(57)	£10.70–£28.00

57 touring pitches

Attractive park in open countryside. Set in beautiful landscape of the Blackmore Vale. Shaftesbury and Sherbourne nearby. **directions** From A303, onto B3081 (signposted Racecourse). Follow B3081 for 4.5 miles. Site on right. **open** March to October **payment** credit/debit cards, cash, cheques

General **Leisure**

WINSFORD, Somerset Map ref 1D1 SAT NAV TA24 7JL

Halse Farm Caravan & Tent Park

Halse Farm Caravan & Tent Park, Winsford, Exmoor, Somerset TA24 7JL
t (01643) 851259 **e** brit@halsefarm.co.uk
w halsefarm.co.uk ONLINE MAP

enjoyEngland.com ★★★★ TOURING & CAMPING PARK

	£14.00–£18.00
(22)	£14.00–£18.00
(22)	£14.00–£18.00

44 touring pitches

Exmoor National Park, small, peaceful, working farm with spectacular views. Walkers and country lovers paradise. David Bellamy Gold Conservation Award. One mile to Winsford with shop, Thatched pub, Tea gardens. **directions** Signposted from A396. In Winsford turn left and bear left past Royal Oak Inn. One mile up hill. Entrance immediately after cattle grid on left. **open** 16 March to 31 October. **payment** credit/debit cards, cash, cheques

General **Leisure**

YEOVIL, Somerset Map ref 2A3 SAT NAV BA22 7JH

Long Hazel Park

High Street, Sparkford, Yeovil, Somerset BA22 7JH
t (01963) 440002 **e** longhazelpark@hotmail.com
w longhazelpark.co.uk ONLINE MAP

enjoyEngland.com ★★★★ HOLIDAY, TOURING & CAMPING PARK

(30)	£16.00–£20.00
(30)	£16.00–£20.00
(20)	£16.00–£20.00
(1)	£350.00–£800.00

50 touring pitches

WALKERS WELCOME · CYCLISTS WELCOME

Adult Only Park just off A303T. Level, landscaped grounds. Hardstandings, disabled facilities. Lodges for sale/hire. Pub/restaurant, shop, services, bus stop 200m. Public transport/rail link to Olympic sailing in Weymouth 2012. **directions** From Hazlegrove Services follow brown and white tourist signs into High Street. We are on the left-hand side just past the 30mph speed limit signs. **open** All year **payment** cash, cheques

General **Leisure**

CLATFORD, Wiltshire Map ref 2B2

SAT NAV SN8 4ND

Postern Hill Caravan and Camping Site

Postern Hill, Marlborough, Wiltshire, England SN8 4ND
t (01672) 515195 **e** posternhill.site@forestholidays.co.uk
w forestholidays.co.uk ONLINE MAP GUEST REVIEWS

🚐	£11.00–£22.00
🚗	£11.00–£22.00
⛺	£11.00–£22.00

170 touring pitches

Located in the Savernake Forest, which is privately owned and run by The Forestry Commission. The luscious green canopy of oak trees makes the woodland ideal for walking and cycling. **directions** Grid Ref: OS173 199 683 Attractions nearby: Stonehenge, Longleat Safari & Adventure Park **open** All year **payment** credit/debit cards, cash

General 🗓 ✕ 🏢 🎠 🗘 🚻

LACOCK, Wiltshire Map ref 2B2

SAT NAV SN15 2LP

Piccadilly Caravan Park Ltd

Folly Lane (West), Lacock, Chippenham SN15 2LP
t (01249) 730260 **e** piccadillylacock@aol.com

🚐	(39)	£17.00–£19.00
🚗	(39)	£17.00–£19.00
⛺	(4)	£17.00–£19.00

43 touring pitches

This well-maintained and peaceful site stands in open countryside 0.5 miles from the historic National Trust village of Lacock. **directions** Turn off A350 between Chippenham and Melksham, into Folly Lane West signposted Gastard and with Caravan symbol. **open** April to October **payment** cash, cheques

General 🗓 ✕ 🏢 🎠 ☼ 🖥 🗘 🚻 Leisure 🏊 ⛰

WARMINSTER, Wiltshire Map ref 2B2

SAT NAV BA12 7NL

Longleat Caravan Club Site

Longleat, Warminster, Wiltshire BA12 7NL
t (01985) 844663 **e** enquiries@caravanclub.co.uk
w caravanclub.co.uk

THE
CARAVAN
CLUB

🚐	(165)	£16.60–£38.90
🚗	(165)	£16.60–£38.90

165 touring pitches

Close to Longleat House, this is the only site where you can hear lions roar at night! Cafes, pubs and restaurants within walking distance. **directions** A362, signposted Frome, 0.5 miles left at roundabout onto Longleat Estate. Through toll booths, follow caravan signs for 1 mile. **open** March to November **payment** credit/debit cards, cash, cheques

General 🗓 📶 ✕ 🏢 🎠 ☼ 🖥 🗘 🚻 🚐 Leisure 🏊 ⛰

Looking for something else?

You can also buy a copy of our popular guide 'Self Catering' including self-catering holiday homes, approved caravan holiday homes, boat accommodation and holiday cottage agencies in England 2012.

Now available in good bookshops and online at
visitbritainshop.com

£8.99

There are hundreds of "Green" places to stay and visit in England from small bed and breakfasts to large visitor attractions and activity holiday providers. Businesses displaying this logo have undergone a rigorous verification process to ensure that they are sustainable (green) and that a qualified assessor has visited the premises.

We have indicated the accommodation which has achieved a Green award... look out for the 🌱 symbol in the entry.

South East

Berkshire, Buckinghamshire, Hampshire,
Isle of Wight, Kent, Oxfordshire, Surrey, Sussex

Want to relax in beautiful parks, ancient cathedrals, stately homes and rolling countryside? In the South East you can.

Feel the need to explore historic castles, admire stunning architecture, and fine dine your evenings away? No problem. From Oxford's spires, via Berkshire, Buckinghamshire, Surrey and Hampshire to the idyllic Isle of Wight, and from Kent's cathedral cities to the stunning East Sussex coast, there's a lifetime of attractions to explore.

History and Heritage

Throughout the ages, the South East has played an important role in protecting Britain from attack. Delve into the history of 1066 and the Battle of Hastings at Battle Abbey and Pevensey Castle. Dover Castle and its wartime tunnels are a must visit. There are so many incredible cathedrals and castles to see in the South East, you simply have to make a list: Arundel, Winchester, Rochester, Canterbury, Dover, Hever, Windsor, and Leeds. If sharp-toothed pre-history is more your thing, then the Isle of Wight is dinosaur central.

Arts and Culture

You can feel the creative energy flowing throughout the South East. For contemporary art try Eastbourne's Towner, Chichester's Pallant House Gallery and Southampton City Art Gallery; for old masters visit Oxford's Ashmolean, the world's first public museum. In 2011, Canterbury's The New Marlowe theatre opens to deliver the biggest and best productions whilst nurturing new talent. And for an unforgettable cinema experience head to Brighton's Duke of York.

Food and Drink

With orchards, fish-filled waters and open countryside, the South East is not short of inspirational ingredients or the chefs to cook them. Science and cooking combine with extraordinary results at Heston Blumenthal's Fat Duck in Bray in Berkshire and at the nearby Waterside Inn, Alain Roux also delivers culinary excellence– both restaurants maxed out with three Michelin stars. Why not wash things down with a glass of sparkling wine at Tenterden Vineyard or a pint at Britain's oldest brewer, Shepherd Neame.

Sports

Cowes on the Isle of Wight is an international sailing hotspot and comes alive for the summer regatta. For blazers, boat races and champagne try the Royal Regatta at Henley-on-Thames. If you want to get in the water yourself, then kayak the beautiful Seven Sisters Country Park. Or if you fancy a flutter on the horses then take your pick from the world-famous Ascot, Royal Windsor and Newbury racecourses, not forgetting Glorious Goodwood raceweek.

Music and Nightlife

With such a vibrant, young crowd of tourists and university students, it's no wonder that Brighton's music and nightlife scene is second only to London's. The Hanover area has a pub virtually at the end of every street. Gigs at Concorde 2 and Freebutt have seen many huge acts before they broke, and Brighton Centre, Komedia and Brighton Dome (where Abba won the Eurovision Song Contest in 1974) are where bigger established acts play.

Shopping

Antique-hunters should be kept blissfully busy in Tunbridge Wells and Hastings, whereas aspiring hipsters must hit Brighton's North Laine for ultra-cool boutiques, record shops and retro fashion. Bookworms should lose themselves in England's largest second-hand book shop, Baggins in Rochester.

Family Fun

Take your pick of fabulous beaches, discover your inner-Tarzan at Go Ape! or meet the dinosaurs that roamed freely around the Isle of Wight. Booklovers should take the Great Expectations Boat Ride at Dickens World or explore Oxford's Harry Potter film locations. With serious speed and face-melting G-force, Thorpe Park is perfect for thrill-seekers whereas younger kids will love the blockbusting entertainment on offer at LEGOLAND Windsor.

Handy Hints

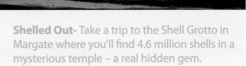

Speed Visit - Running out of time but want to see all the sights? 'The Golden Tours' excursion takes in the highlights of Canterbury, Dover and Leeds Castle in just one day.

With Great Expectation - Fans of Charles Dickens can visit the South East, with much of his life played out in cities like Rochester in Kent and Portsmouth in Hampshire.

Shelled Out- Take a trip to the Shell Grotto in Margate where you'll find 4.6 million shells in a mysterious temple – a real hidden gem.

Leisurely Pace - For the ultimate in luxury transport take an Orchard Poyle Horse-Drawn Carriage along the Long Walk and through Windsor Park – the views of the castle are divine.

OUT & ABOUT IN THE SOUTH EAST

Day 1 - Intellectual Pursuits

- Explore Oxford's 38 colleges for architectural and educational excellence; they are open in the afternoon
- Wander around the University's Ashmolean Museum and see works by Michelangelo and Picasso
- Visit Blenheim Palace the birthplace of Winston Churchill

Day 2 - Key to England

- Take a pilgrimage to St. Thomas Becket's shrine at Canterbury Cathedral
- Let Chaucer's colourful characters bring the 14th century to life at The Canterbury Tales
- Wander along the famous white cliffs and explore the majestic Dover Castle

Day 3 - Coast with the Most

- Admire the art exhibitions at Towner in Eastbourne
- Walk along Beachy Head for stunning coastal scenery
- Shop 'til you drop in Brighton's trendy North Laine and Lanes

Day 4 - Bargain Hunt

- Discover the past and admire the architecture at Rochester Cathedral and Castle
- Browse to your heart's content at Baggins, England's largest second-hand book shop
- Rummage for antiques in the spa town of Royal Tunbridge Wells

Day 5 - Pit Stop

- Mountain bike around the ancient New Forest, watch out for the ponies
- Visit the Beaulieu National Motor Museum
- Grab some retail therapy in Southampton before hitting the city's bars

Day 6 - The Wight Stuff

- Ride the Needles Park Chairlift then jump on a boat for a trip around the Needle Rocks
- Explore the exhibits at Dinosaur Isle then go fossil-hunting along the southern beaches
- Stretch your legs on one of the many footpaths across the island

Day 7 - Blockbuster

- Explore the Queen's favourite retreat, Windsor Castle
- Soar 50 metres above historic Windsor on the Royal Windsor Wheel
- Thrill-seekers and LEGO fans should hit LEGOLAND Windsor

Where to Go

 Attractions with this sign participate in the **Places of Interest Quality Assurance Scheme**.

 Attractions with this sign participate in the **Visitor Attraction Quality Assurance Scheme**.

Both schemes recognise high standards in all aspects of the visitor experience (see page 6)

ENTERTAINMENT & CULTURE

Beaulieu National Motor Museum
Hampshire SO42 7ZN
(01590) 612123
www.beaulieu.co.uk
Beaulieu featuring the world famous National Motor Museum, Palace House home of the Montagu family and Abbey Ruins containing an exhibition of monastic life.

City Sightseeing Windsor and Eton
Berkshire SL4 1NJ
(01708) 866000
www.city-sightseeing.com
Enjoy the dignified tranquillity of Windsor, including Windsor Castle, home of the British monarchy for centuries, and Eton College.

Dinosaur Isle
Sandown, Isle of Wight PO36 8QA
(01983) 404344
http://www.dinosaurisle.com
In a spectacular pterosaur shaped building on Sandown's blue flag beach walk back through fossilised time and meet life sized replica dinosaurs

Museum of English Rural Life
Reading, Berkshire RG1 5EX
(0118) 378 8660
www.merl.org.uk
MERL houses one of England's most fascinating collections relating to life and work in the countryside over the last 200 years.

REME Museum of Technology
Reading, Berkshire RG2 9NJ
(0118) 976 3375
www.rememuseum.org.uk
The museum shows the developing technology used by the Royal Electrical and Mechanical Engineers in maintaining and repairing the army's equipment since 1942.

Roald Dahl Museum and Story Centre
Great Missenden, Buckinghamshire HP16 0AL
(01494) 892192
www.roalddahlmuseum.org
Where Roald Dahl (1916-1990) lived and wrote many of his well-loved books.

FAMILY FUN

Aerial Extreme Milton Keynes
Buckinghamshire MK15 0DS
0845 652 1736
www.aerialextreme.co.uk/courses/willen-lake
Amaze yourself as you take each of the challenges head on.

Bekonscot Model Village and Railway
Beaconsfield, Buckinghamshire HP9 2PL
(01494) 672919
www.bekonscot.com
Use your imagination in this unique world of make-believe that has delighted generations of visitors.

Blackgang Chine
Chale, Isle of Wight PO38 2HN
(01983) 730330
www.blackgangchine.com
Set in Over 40 acres of spectacular cliff-top gardens.

Gulliver's Land
Milton Keynes, Buckinghamshire MK15 0DT
(01908) 609001
www.gulliversfun.co.uk
Family theme park with 40 rides aimed at children between 2 and 12 years.

Go Ape! High Wire Forest Adventure - Bracknell
Berkshire RG12 7QW
0845 643 9215
www.goape.co.uk
Go Ape! and tackle a high-wire forest adventure course of rope bridges, Tarzan swings and zip slides up to 35 feet above the forest floor.

LEGOLAND® Windsor
Berkshire SL4 4AY
0870 504 0404
www.legoland.co.uk
With over 55 interactive rides and attractions, there's just too much to experience in one day!

The Look Out Discovery Centre
Bracknell, Berkshire RG12 7QW
(01344) 354400
www.bracknell-forest.gov.uk/be
A hands-on, interactive science exhibition with over 80 exhibits, set in 1,000 hectares of Crown woodland.

Thorpe Park
Chertsey, Surrey KT16 8PN
0871 663 1673
www.thorpepark.com
New for 2010, prepare for SAW Alive, the world's most extreme live action horrow maze.

FOOD & DRINK

Denbies Wine Estate
Dorking, Surrey RH5 6AA
(01306) 876616
www.denbiesvineyard.co.uk
Established in 1986, Denbies Wine Estate is England's largest single estate vineyard with 265 acres of vines.

HERITAGE

1066 Battle Abbey and Battlefield
East Sussex TN33 0AD
(01424) 775705
www.english-heritage.org.uk/
daysout/properties/1066-battle-of-
hastings-abbey-and-battlefield/
An abbey founded by William the Conqueror on the site of the Battle of Hastings.

Bateman's
Etchingham, East Sussex TN19 7DS
(01435) 882302
www.nationaltrust.org.uk/batemans/
A 17thC Ironmaster's house which was the home of Rudyard Kipling between 1902-35. His study and Rolls Royce can be seen. Garden with working watermill..

Blenheim Palace
Woodstock, Oxfordshire OX20 1PX
(01993) 811091
www.blenheimpalace.com
Birthplace of Sir Winston Churchill and home to the Duke of Marlborough, Blenheim Palace, one of the finest baroque houses in England, is set in over 2,000 acres of landscaped gardens.

Brighton Pier
East Sussex BN2 1TW
(01273) 609361
www.brightonpier.co.uk
A Victorian pier with various food and drink outlets, fairground attractions and Palace of Fun arcade.

Chichester Cathedral
West Sussex PO19 1RP
(01243) 782595
www.chichestercathedral.org.uk
A magnificent Cathedral with treasures ranging from medieval stone carvings to world famous 20th Century artworks.

Didcot Railway Centre
Oxfordshire OX11 7NJ
(01235) 817200
www.didcotrailwaycentre.org.uk
Living museum recreating the golden age of the Great Western Railway. Steam locomotives and trains, Brunel's broad gauge railway, engine shed and small relics museum.

Frogmore House
Windsor, Berkshire SL4 1NJ
(020) 7766 7305
www.royalcollection.org.uk
Late 17th-century royal residence, particularly associated with Queen Charlotte and Queen Victoria.

Guildford Cathedral
Surrey GU2 7UP
(01483) 547860
http://www.guildford-cathedral.org
New Anglican cathedral, the foundation stone of which was laid in 1936. Notable sandstone interior and marble floors. Restaurant and shops.

Hever Castle and Gardens
Edenbridge, Kent TN8 7NG
(01732) 865224
www.hevercastle.co.uk
Romantic 13th century moated castle, once Anne Boleyn's childhood home. Magnificently furnished interiors, spectacular award winning gardens. Miniature Model House Exhibition, Yew Maze, unique Splashing Water Maze.

Kent & East Sussex Railway
Tenterden, Kent TN30 6HE
(01580) 765155
http://www.kesr.org.uk
England's finest rural light railway enables visitors to experience travel and service from a bygone age aboard beautifully restored Victorian coaches and locomotives.

Loseley Park
Guildford, Surrey GU3 1HS
(01483) 405112
http://www.loseley-park.com
A beautiful Elizabethan mansion, is set in stunning gardens and parkland. Built in 1562 it has a fascinating history and contains a wealth of treasures.

Osborne House
East Cowes, Isle of Wight PO32 6JX
(01983) 200022
www.english-heritage.org.uk/
daysout/properties/osborne-house
Step into Queen Victoria's favourite country home and experience a world unchanged since the country's longest reigning monarch died here just over 100 years ago.

Oxford Castle Unlocked
Oxfordshire OX1 1AY
(01865) 260666
www.oxfordcastleunlocked.co.uk
For the first time in 1000 years, the secrets of Oxford Castle have been ' unlocked', revealing episodes of violence, executions, great escapes, betrayal and even romance. Visit Oxford Castle and uncover the secrets for yourself.

Petworth House and Park
West Sussex GU28 0AE
(01798) 342207
www.nationaltrust.org.uk/petworth
Discover the National Trust's finest art collection displayed in a magnificent 17th century mansion within a beautiful 700-acre park. Petworth House contains works by artists such as Van Dyck, Reynolds and Turner.

Portsmouth Historic Dockyard
Hampshire PO1 3LJ
(023) 9272 8060
www.historicdockyard.co.uk
Be a part of your history at Portsmouth Historic Dockyard.

Rochester Castle
Kent ME1 1SW
(01634) 335882
www.visitmedway.org/site/
attractions/rochester-castle-p44583
One of the finest keeps in England. Also the tallest, partly built on the Roman city wall. Good views from the battlements over the River Medway.

Shanklin Chine
Shanklin Isle of Wight PO37 6BW
(01983) 866432
www.shanklinchine.co.uk
Historic gorge with dramatic waterfalls and nature trail.

Spinnaker Tower
Portsmouth, Hampshire PO1 3TT
(023) 9285 7520
www.spinnakertower.co.uk
The Spinnaker Tower is a national icon. It is a striking viewing tower on the south coast offering the public spectacular views from 3 platforms.

The Historic Dockyard Chatham
Kent ME4 4TZ
(01634) 823807
www.thedockyard.co.uk
A unique, award winning maritime heritage destination with a fantastic range of attractions, iconic buildings and historic ships to explore, plus a fabulous programme of touring exhibitions at No.1 Smithery.

Waddesdon Manor
Aylesbury, Buckinghamshire HP18 0JH
(01296) 653226
www.waddesdon.org.uk
This National Trust property houses the Rothschild Collection of art treasures and wine cellars. It also features spectacular grounds with an aviary, parterre and woodland playground, licensed restaurants, gift and wine shops.

Windsor Castle
Berkshire SL4 1NJ
(020) 7766 7304
http://www.royalcollection.org.uk
The oldest and largest inhabited castle in the world and The Queen's favourite weekend home.

NATURE & WILDLIFE

Arundel Wetland Centre
West Sussex BN18 9PB
(01903) 883355
www.wwt.org.uk/visit/arundel
WWT Arundel Wetland Centre is a 65-acre reserve in an idyllic setting, nestled at the base of the South Downs National Park.

Bedgebury National Pinetum & Forest
Cranbrook, Kent TN17 2SL
(01580) 879820
www.forestry.gov.uk/bedgebury
Visit the world's finest conifer collection at Bedgebury National Pinetum.

British Wildlife Centre
Lingfield, Surrey RH7 6LF
(01342) 834658
www.britishwildlifecentre.co.uk
The best place to see and learn about Britain's own wonderful wildlife, with over forty different species including deer, foxes, otters, badgers, pine martens and red squirrels.

Chiltern Sculpture Trail
Watlington, Oxfordshire
(01865) 778918
www.chilternsculpturetrail.co.uk
Woodland trail with sculpture sited around the forest. Artists work at the site during some months of the year.

Denmans Garden
Fontwell, West Sussex BN18 0SU
(01243) 542808
www.denmans-garden.co.uk
Beautiful 4 acre garden designed for year round interest through use of form, colour and texture. Beautiful plant centre, award winning and fully licensed Garden Cafe.

Drusillas Park
Alfriston, East Sussex BN26 5QS
(01323) 874100
www.drusillas.co.uk
Widely regarded as the best small zoo in the country Drusillas Park offers an opportunity to get nose to nose with nature with hundreds of exotic animals from monkeys and crocodiles to penguins and meerkats.

Exbury Gardens and Steam Railway
Beaulieu, Hampshire SO45 1AZ
(023) 8089 1203
www.exbury.co.uk
World famous woodland garden, home to the Rothschil Collection of rhododendrons, azaleas, camellias, rare trees and srubs, with its own steam railway.

Fishers Adventure Farm Park
Billingshurst , West Sussex RH14 0EG
(01403) 700063
www.fishersfarmpark.co.uk
Award-winning Adventure Farm Park and open all year. Ideally suited for ages 2-11 years. Huge variety of animals, rides and attractions from the skating rink, to pony rides, toboggan run, bumper boats, theatre shows and much much more!

Marwell Wildlife
Winchester, Hampshire SO21 1JH
(01962) 777407
www.marwell.org.uk
A visit to Marwell Wildlife is a chance to get close to the wonders of the natural world – and play a big part in helping to save them.

Great Dixter House and Gardens
Rye, East Sussex TN31 6PH
(01797) 252878
www.greatdixter.co.uk
An example of a 15thC manor house with antique furniture and needlework. The house is restored and the gardens were designed by Lutyens.

Pashley Manor Gardens
Wadhurst, East Sussex TN5 7HE
(01580) 200888
www.pashleymanorgardens.com
Pashley Manor Gardens offer a blend of romantic landscaping, imaginative plantings and fine old trees, fountains, springs and large ponds with an exciting programme of special events for garden and art lovers.

Paultons Family Theme Park
Romsey, Hampshire SO51 6AL
(023) 8081 4455
www.paultonspark.co.uk
A great family day out with over 60 different attractions and rides included in the price!

RHS Garden Wisley
Woking, Surrey GU23 6QB
0845 260 9000
www.rhs.org.uk/wisley
Stretching over 240 acres of glorious garden.

RSPB Pulborough Brooks
West Sussex RH20 2EL
(01798) 875851
www.rspb.org.uk/pulboroughbrooks
Set in the scenic Arun Valley with views to the South Downs, the two mile circular nature trail leads around this beautiful reserve.

Stowe Landscape Gardens
Buckinghamshire MK18 5DQ
(01280) 822850
www.nationaltrust.org.uk/stowegardens
Over forty temples and monuments, laid out against an inspiring backdrop of lakes and valleys.

Ventnor Botanic Gardens
St. Lawrence, Isle of Wight PO38 1UL
(01983) 855397
www.botanic.co.uk
The Botanic Garden on the Isle of Wight is a place where the pleasure of plants can be enjoyed to the fullest.

OUTDOOR ACTIVITIES

French Brothers Ltd
Windsor, Berkshire SL4 5JH
(01753) 851900
www.boat-trips.co.uk
Large range of public trips on weather-proof vessels from Windsor, Runnymede and Maidenhead.

Guildford Boat House
Surrey GU1 3XJ
(01483) 504494
www.guildfordboats.co.uk
Regular trips operate from Guildford along this tranquil stretch of the River Wey.

Xscape
Milton Keynes, Buckinghamshire MK9 3XS
0871 200 3220
www.xscape.co.uk
Xscape, Milton Keynes offers a unique combination of extreme sports and leisure activities for all ages.

Events 2012

Eastbourne Festival
Eastbourne
www.eastbournefestival.co.uk
April - May

End of the Pier Film Festival
Worthing
www.eotpfilmfestival.co.uk
April - May

Tulip Festival at Pashley Manor
Wadhurst
www.pashleymanorgardens.com
April - May

Glyndebourne Festival
Lewes
www.glyndebourne.com
May - August

Surrey County Show
Guildford
www.surreycountyshow.co.uk
28th May

Brighton Fringe Festival
Brighton
www.brightonfestivalfringe.org.uk
May

English Wine Week
Dorking
www.englishwineweek.co.uk
May - June

Windsor Castle Royal Tattoo
Windsor
www.windsortattoo.com
May

Alton Summer Beer Festival
Alton
www.altonbeerfestival.co.uk
June

Agricultural Show
Haywards Heath
www.seas.org.uk
June

Chichester Festivities
Chichester
www.chifest.org.uk
June - July

Henley Royal Regatta
Henley-upon-Thames
www.hrr.co.uk
June - July

Investec Derby Festival
Epsom
www.epsomderby.co.uk
June

Isle of Wight Festival
Newport
www.isleofwightfestival.com
June

Jane Austen Regency Festival
Alton
www.janeaustenregencyweek.co.uk
June

Bexhill Rowing Regatta
Bexhill-on-Sea
www.bexhillrowingclub.com
July

Glorious Goodwood
Chichester
www.goodwood.com
July

Lammas Festival
Eastbourne
www.lammasfest.org
July

Reading Real Ale and Jazz Festival
Reading
www.raaj.info
July

Arundel Festival
Arundel
www.arundelfestival.co.uk
August

Cowes Week
Cowes
www.cowesweek.co.uk
August

Isle of Wight Garlic Festival
Newchurch
www.garlic-festival.co.uk
August

Petersfield Festivities
Petersfield
www.petersfieldevents.co.uk
August

RAF Shoreham Airshow
Shoreham-by-Sea
www.shorehamairshow.com
August

Reading Festival
Reading
www.readingfestival.com
25th-27th August

V Festival
Chelmsford
www.vfestival.com
August

Worthing International Birdman Competition
Worthing
www.worthingbirdman.co.uk
August

England's Medieval Festival
Hailsham
www.mgel.com
September

Eastbourne Beer Festival
Eastbourne
www.eastbournebeerfestival.co.uk
October

Tourist Information Centres

When you arrive at your destination, visit an Official Partner Tourist Information Centre for quality assured help with accommodation and information about local attractions and events, or email your request before you go. To find a Tourist Information Centre by region look at http://www.enjoyengland.com under Destination Finder.

ASHFORD	18 The Churchyard	01233 629165	tourism@ashford.gov.uk
AYLESBURY	The Kings Head	01296 330559	tic@aylesburyvaledc.gov.uk
BANBURY	Castle Quay Shopping Centre	01295 753752	banbury.tic@cherwell-dc.gov.uk
BICESTER	Bicester Visitor Centre	01869 369055	bicestervisitorcentre@valueretail.com
BRIGHTON	Royal Pavilion Shop	03003 000088	brighton-tourism@brighton-hove.gov.uk
BURFORD	The Brewery	01993 823558	burford.vic@westoxon.gov.uk
CANTERBURY	12/13 Sun Street	01227 378100	canterburyinformation@canterbury.gov.uk
CHICHESTER	29a South Street	01243 775888	chitic@chichester.gov.uk
COWES	9 The Arcade	01983 813818	info@islandbreaks.co.uk
DOVER	The Old Town Gaol	01304 205108	tic@doveruk.com
GRAVESEND	Towncentric	01474 337600	info@towncentric.co.uk
GUILDFORD	14 Tunsgate	01483 444333	tic@guildford.gov.uk
HASTINGS	Queens Square	01424 451111	hic@hastings.gov.uk
LEWES	187 High Street	01273 483448	lewes.tic@lewes.gov.uk
MAIDSTONE	Town Hall, Middle Row	01622 602169	tourism@maidstone.gov.uk
MARGATE	12-13 The Parade	0870 2646111	visitorinformation@thanet.gov.uk
MARLOW	31 High Street	01628 483597	tourism_enquiries@wycombe.gov.uk
NEWBURY	The Wharf	01635 30267	tourism@westberks.gov.uk
NEWPORT	The Guildhall	01983 813818	info@islandbreaks.co.uk
OXFORD	Oxford Information Centre	01865 252200	tic@oxford.gov.uk
PORTSMOUTH	Clarence Esplanade	023 9282 6722	vis@portsmouthcc.gov.uk
PORTSMOUTH	The Hard	023 9282 6722	vis@portsmouthcc.gov.uk
RICHMOND	Old Town Hall	020 8940 9125	info@visitrichmond.co.uk
ROCHESTER	95 High Street	01634 843666	visitor.centre@medway.gov.uk
ROMSEY	Heritage & Visitor Centre	01794 512987	romseytic@testvalley.gov.uk

ROYAL TUNBRIDGE WELLS	The Old Fish Market	01892 515675	touristinformationcentre@tunbridgewells.gov.uk
RYDE	81-83 Union Street	01983 813818	info@islandbreaks.co.uk
RYE	4/5 Lion Street	01797 229049	ryetic@tourismse.com
SANDOWN	8 High Street	01983 813818	info@islandbreaks.co.uk
SHANKLIN	67 High Street	01983 813818	info@islandbreaks.co.uk
SOUTHAMPTON	9 Civic Centre Road	023 8083 3333	tourist.information@southampton.gov.uk
SWANLEY	Library & Information Centre	01322 614660	touristinfo@swanley.org.uk
WINCHESTER	Guildhall	01962 840500	tourism@winchester.gov.uk
WINDSOR	Royal Windsor Shopping Centre	01753 743900	windsor.tic@rbwm.gov.uk
WITNEY	26A Market Square	01993 775802	witney.vic@westoxon.gov.uk
WOODSTOCK	Oxfordshire Museum	01993 813276	woodstock.vic@westoxon.gov.uk
WORTHING	Chapel Road	01903 221066	tic@worthing.gov.uk
WORTHING	Marine Parade	01903 221066	tic@worthing.gov.uk
YARMOUTH	The Quay	01983 813818	info@islandbreaks.co.uk

Regional Contacts and Information

For more information on accommodation, attractions, activities, events and holidays in South East England, contact the regional or local tourism organisations. Their websites have a wealth of information and many produce free publications to help you get the most out of your visit.

The following publications are available from Tourism South East by logging on to www.visitsoutheastengland.com or by calling (023) 8062 5400

E-Brochures
Family Fun
Time for Us

South East England – We know just the place...

If you have
access needs...

Guests with hearing, visual or mobility needs can feel confident about booking accommodation that participates in the National Accessible Scheme (NAS).

Look out for the NAS symbols which are included throughout the accommodation directory. Using the NAS could help make the difference between a good holiday and a perfect one!

You can also search for NAS rated accommodation at **enjoyengland.com/access** or buy a copy of the new OpenBritain guide, available from Tourism for All - tel 0845 124 9971

Where to Stay

Entries appear alphabetically by town name in each county. A key to symbols appears on page 6. Maps start on page 298. Further listings of VisitEngland assessed accommodation appear on the CD at the back of this guide.

HURLEY, Berkshire Map ref 2C2

SAT NAV SL6 5NE

Hurley Riverside Park

Hurley SL6 5NE
t (01628) 824493 **f** (01628) 825533 **e** info@hurleyriversidepark.co.uk
w **hurleyriversidepark.co.uk** ONLINE MAP GUEST REVIEWS ONLINE BOOKING LAST MINUTE OFFERS

⊄ (138) £14.00–£24.00
🚐 (138) £14.00–£24.00
⛺ (62) £12.00–£22.00
🏠 (10) £300.00–£480.00
200 touring pitches

SPECIAL PROMOTIONS
Short breaks available to prebook March-May and September-October and at any time at one weeks notice.

Family-run Park alongside the River Thames. Ideal for visiting LEGOLAND Windsor, Henley & Oxford. Nature trail, riverside picnic grounds & slipway. Top 100 Parks, David Bellamy Gold & Special Distinction Awards. Tourers, Tents & Motorhomes. Electric, Multi-Service & Hardstanding pitches. Caravan Holiday Home and ReadyTent hire. Showers, shop, Wi-Fi.

open March to October
payment credit/debit cards, cash, cheques

directions M4 J8/9 or M40 J4, onto A404(M), third exit to Henley (A4130). Past Hurley Village, turn right into Shepherds Lane.

General 🗑 📶 🐕 🛒 📷 ☀ 💤 🍴 🏧 🚿 🏕 Leisure ▶ ∪ ⌥ ⛰

Looking for something else?

You can also buy a copy of our popular 'B&B' guide including guest accommodation, B&B's, guest houses, farmhouses, inns, and campus and hostel accommodation in England 2012.

Now available in good bookshops and online at **visitbritainshop.com**   **£8.99**

READING, Berkshire Map ref 2C2

★★★
TOURING &
CAMPING PARK

Wellington Country Park - Touring Caravan & Campsite
Odiham Road, Riseley, Nr Reading RG7 1SP
t (0118) 932 6444 **f** (0118) 932 6445 **e** info@wellington-country-park.co.uk
w **wellington-country-park.co.uk** ONLINE MAP

🚐 (57) £25.00–£33.50
🚐 (57) £25.00–£33.50
⛺ (15) £22.50–£27.50
57 touring pitches

Set within beautiful woodlands, fees include 2 people and FREE entry to Country Park with nature trails, animal farm, play areas, miniature railway, sand pits, crazy golf. Events all year. **directions** Hampshire/Berkshire border between Reading/Basingstoke. M4 junction 11 A33 towards Basingstoke. M3 junction 5 B3349 Reading. Sat Nav enter B3349 or Odiham Road, Riseley. **open** March to November **payment** credit/debit cards, cash, cheques

General 🗄 🐕 🎱 📶 📷 ☼ 🍴 🛗 🚿 ✗ **Leisure** ∪ 🚲 ⚠

SEER GREEN, Buckinghamshire Map ref 2D2   SAT NAV HP9 2QZ

★★★★
TOURING &
CAMPING PARK

Highclere Farm Camp Site
Newbarn Lane, Beaconsfield HP9 2QZ
t (01494) 874505 **f** (01494) 875238 **e** Highclerepark@aol.com
w **highclerefarmpark.co.uk**

🚐 (60) £15.00–£23.00
🚐 (60) £15.00–£23.00
⛺ (35) £12.00–£25.00
95 touring pitches

A Peaceful well kept family run site backing onto woodland with modern facilities. London, Wembley via nearby station. Windsor Legoland and many local attractions easily accessible. **directions** M40 junction 2, follow signs towards Amersham A355 approx 1 mile, turn right to Seer Green 2nd left then site is 1.5miles from village. **open** March 1st - 31st January **payment** credit/debit cards, cash, cheques

General ♿ 🗄 👷 🐕 📶 📷 ☼ 🍴 🛗 🚿 ⚑ **Leisure** ► 🚲 ⚠

SHOREFIELD Hampshire

DISCOVER RELAX EXPLORE UNWIND ENJOY

Have you heard about Shorefield Holidays?

All four of our touring parks are set in peaceful, unspoilt parkland in the beautiful South Coast area.
There are pitches available for touring caravans, motorhomes or tents.
There are comprehensive leisure facilities available and great entertainment for the whole family.
Pamper yourself in our 'Reflections' Day Spa at Shorefield Country Park, explore the New Forest National Park, or relax on Bournemouth's sandy beaches.
For full details, ask for our brochure or browse online.

SHOREFIELD
HOLIDAYS LIMITED

Tel 0844 391 3332
holidays@shorefield.co.uk
www.shorefield.co.uk   Ref: VBT

HAMPSHIRE
Lytton Lawn Touring Park
Milford on Sea, SO41 0TX
Forest Edge Holiday Park
St. Leonards, BH24 2SD

DORSET
Merley Court Touring Park
Wimborne, BH21 3AA
Swanage Coastal Park
Swanage, BH19 2RS

For **key to symbols** see page 6

ASHURST, Hampshire Map ref 2C3
SAT NAV SO40 7AR

Ashurst Caravan and Camping Site
Lyndhurst Road, Ashurst, Lyndhurst SO40 7AR
t (02380) 292097 **e** ashurst.site@forestholidays.co.uk
w campingintheforest.co.uk ONLINE MAP ONLINE BOOKING

£13.50–£29.00
£13.50–£29.00
£13.50–£29.00
280 touring pitches

Our Ashurst site is set in the middle of a woodland glade, with direct access to the Forest with its footpaths and cycle paths. **directions** Ashurst Campsite lies 2.5 miles North East of Lyndhurst on the A35. **open** 14th April - 26th September **payment** credit/debit cards, cash, cheques

General

BROCKENHURST, Hampshire Map ref 2C3
SAT NAV SO42 7QD

Aldridge Hill Caravan and Camping Site
Brockenhurst, Hampshire, England SO42 7QD
t (01590) 623152 **e** aldridgehill.site@forestholidays.co.uk
w campingintheforest.co.uk ONLINE MAP ONLINE BOOKING

£12.25–£13.50
£12.25–£13.50
£12.25–£13.50
200 touring pitches

Enjoy Hampshire Camping and Caravan holidays at the Aldridge Hill Caravan and Campsite, located about a mile north-west of the village of Brockenhurst. **directions** Please be aware that there are width limits on Meerut Road (the turning before the B3055) and also from the A35 into Rhinefield **open** Open 26 May - 6 June & 23 June - 5 September **payment** credit/debit cards, cash, cheques

General

BROCKENHURST, Hampshire Map ref 2C3

Hollands Wood Caravan and Camping Site
Lyndhurst Road, Brockenhurst, Hampshire SO42 7QH
t (01590) 622967 **e** Hollands.Wood@forestholidays.co.uk
w campingintheforest.co.uk ONLINE MAP ONLINE BOOKING

£14.00–£29.00
£14.00–£29.00
£14.00–£29.00
600 touring pitches

An abundance of oak trees covers our large site at Hollands Wood. Popular with families, groups and young people. **directions** Please do not use our post code in your sat nav as it will take you to a different campsite. **open** 14th April - 26th September **payment** credit/debit cards, cash, cheques

General

BROCKENHURST, Hampshire Map ref 2C3
SAT NAV SO42 7QL

Roundhill Caravan and Camping Site
Beaulieu Road, Brockenhurst, Hampshire SO42 7QL
t (01590) 624344 **e** Roundhill.site@forestholidays.co.uk
w campingintheforest.co.uk ONLINE MAP ONLINE BOOKING

£13.00–£26.00
£13.00–£26.00
£13.00–£26.00
500 touring pitches

Enjoy the luxury of space at our heathland site of Roundhill, near the southern edge of the National Park. **directions** From Lyndhurst take the A337 towards Lymington, turn left at Brockenhurst on to the B3055 and turn right into the site after approximately 1.5 miles. **open** 14th April - 26th September **payment** credit/debit cards, cash, cheques

General

CHRISTCHURCH, Hampshire Map ref 2B3

Holmsley Caravan and Camping Site
Forest Road, Thorny Hill, Bransgore, Christchurch BH23 7EQ
t (01425) 674502 e holmsley.site@forestholidays.co.uk
w **campingintheforest.co.uk** ONLINE MAP ONLINE BOOKING

⌘	£13.00–£28.00
⛟	£13.00–£28.00
⛺	£13.00–£28.00

600 touring pitches

An old World War 2 Airfield on the edge of the New Forest, Holmsley is the perfect base for a family holiday. **directions** Please contact us for directions **open** 14th April - 31st October **payment** credit/debit cards, cash, cheques

General 🗐 🛉 🐾 🗲 ⫘ 🝔 🗪 🖰 🍴 🆎

FORDINGBRIDGE, Hampshire Map ref 2B3

Sandy Balls Holiday Centre
Godshill, Fordingbridge SP6 2JY
t (01425) 653042 f (01425) 653067 e post@sandyballs.co.uk
w **sandyballs.co.uk** GUEST REVIEWS ONLINE BOOKING LAST MINUTE OFFERS

⌘ (225)	£15.00–£50.00
⛟ (225)	£15.00–£50.00
⛺ (138)	£10.00–£35.00
🛏 (111)	£149.00–£1399.00
⛺ (27)	£99.00–£899.00

225 touring pitches

SPECIAL PROMOTIONS
Visit our website for the latest special offers and exclusive Premier Club discounts and promotions.

Five-star Sandy Balls Holiday Centre has woodland lodges nestled in the stunning New Forest National Park. It is the perfect getaway for families, couples and friends for short breaks or longer. Its superb facilities include family-friendly Pizza in the Piazza, a leisure club and lots of activities for all ages.

open All year
payment credit/debit cards, cash, cheques

directions Sandy Balls is situated at the western end of Godshill village, a little more than a mile from Fordingbridge on the B3078.

General 🗲 🗐 🖐 🛉 🐾 ⫘ 🝔 ☼ 🗪 🖰 🍴 🆎 ✕ Leisure ▶ ∪ 🚲 🏊 🎾 🏐 🍷 🎵 🎣 🎠

Looking for something else?

You can also buy a copy of our popular guide 'Hotels' including country house and town house hotels, metro and budget hotels, serviced apartments and restaurants with rooms in England 2012.

Now available in good bookshops and online at
visitbritainshop.com   **£7.99**

GOSPORT, Hampshire Map ref 2C3 SAT NAV PO13 9BG

Kingfisher Caravan Park

Browndown Road, Stokes Road, Gosport, Lee-On-The-Solent PO13 9BG
t (023) 9250 2611 f (023) 9258 3583 e info@kingfisher-caravan-park.co.uk
w **kingfisher-caravan-park.co.uk**

⌂ (120)	£20.00–£25.00
⛺ (120)	£20.00–£25.00
▲ (120)	£15.00–£35.00
🚐 (30)	£240.00–£485.00

120 touring pitches

SPECIAL PROMOTIONS
Weekend breaks (3 nights minimum) from £200.00 when available.

Family-run park, very close to the sea, with views across the Solent to the Isle of Wight. Clubhouse, Restaurant, Shop, Launderette, Children's Room. Caravans for hire and for sale.

open All year
payment credit/debit cards, cash, cheques

directions M27 Junction 11, A32 towards Gosport.

General ⟨symbols⟩ Leisure ⟨symbols⟩

HAMBLE, Hampshire Map ref 2C3 SAT NAV SO31 4HR

Riverside Holidays

Satchell Lane, Hamble, Southampton SO31 4HR
t (023) 8045 3220 f (023) 8045 3611 e enquiries@riversideholidays.co.uk
w **riversideholidays.co.uk** ONLINE MAP LAST MINUTE OFFERS

⌂ (77)	£15.00–£32.00
⛺ (77)	£15.00–£32.00
▲ (77)	£13.00–£27.00
🏠 (8)	£361.00–£878.00
🚐 (14)	£279.00–£897.00

77 touring pitches

Quiet park overlooking marina and River Hamble, on edge of picturesque sailing village with many pubs/restaurants. Caravan holiday homes and pine lodges for hire, plus camping and touring facilities. **directions** Leave M27 at junction 8, follow signs for Hamble. Pass Tesco, continue over two mini roundabouts. Through traffic lights and take left into Satchell Lane. **open** All year **payment** credit/debit cards, cash, cheques

General ⟨symbols⟩ Leisure ⟨symbols⟩

Looking for something else?

You can also buy a copy of our popular guide 'Self Catering' including self-catering holiday homes, approved caravan holiday homes, boat accommodation and holiday cottage agencies in England 2012.

Now available in good bookshops and online at
visitbritainshop.com   **£8.99**

HAYLING ISLAND, Hampshire Map ref 2C3

SAT NAV PO11 0PB

RATING APPLIED FOR

⚑ (250) £119.00–£249.00

SPECIAL PROMOTIONS
Prices are per person for half board shortbreaks. We have great value kids' prices available and under 2s are FREE!

Mill Rythe Holiday Village

16 Havant Road, Hayling Island, Hampshire PO11 0PB
t (02392) 460044 f (02392) 460055 e millrythe.holidays@away-resorts.com
w **mill-rythe.com** ONLINE MAP ONLINE BOOKING LAST MINUTE OFFERS

You'll find this friendly holiday village nestled away on the western side of Chichester Harbour. With beautiful beaches, great on-park facilities and activities, unforgettable evening entertainment and world famous local attractions, it's the perfect base for a great British short-break. Full and half board, adult exclusive and family breaks available.

open All year except Xmas and New Year
payment credit/debit cards, cash, cheques

directions From the A27, take the A3023 sign posted Hayling Island. After around 3 miles turn left into the road signposted Mill Rythe.

General ⌖ ▣ ⍟ ⌕ ⍾ ☼ ✕ Leisure ⚲ ⚵ ⤳ ⚘ ⚲ ⛾ ♫ ⚓ ⌂

LYNDHURST, Hampshire Map ref 2C3

SAT NAV SO43 7FZ

TOURING & CAMPING PARK

🚐 £10.50–£16.00
🚑 £10.50–£16.00
▲ £10.50–£16.00
240 touring pitches

Denny Wood and Matley Wood Caravan and Camping Site

Beaulieu Road, Lyndhurst, Hampshire SO43 7FZ
t (02380) 293144 e denny&matley.wood@forestholidays.co.uk
w **campingintheforest.co.uk** ONLINE MAP ONLINE BOOKING

Scattered oak trees surround the peaceful grassy site at Denny Wood. Half a mile away, Matley Wood is a secluded site nestled in a peaceful woodland location. **directions** Please contact us for directions **open** 14th April - 26th September **payment** credit/debit cards, cash, cheques

General ⛺

LYNDHURST, Hampshire Map ref 2C3

SAT NAV SO43 7HH

TOURING & CAMPING PARK

🚐 £10.50–£19.00
🚑 £10.50–£19.00
▲ £10.50–£19.00
480 touring pitches

Ocknell and Longbeech Caravan and Camping Site

Fritham, Lyndhurst, Hampshire SO43 7HH
t (02380) 812740 e Ocknell.site@forestholidays.co.uk
w **campingintheforest.co.uk** ONLINE MAP ONLINE BOOKING

At the northern edge of the New Forest, Ocknell and Longbeech are approximately a mile apart. There is no electricity at either site, although there are toilets at Ocknell. **directions** Please note that many Sat Nav systems will direct you to Fritham village if you use our postcode. **open** 14th April - 26th September **payment** credit/debit cards, cash, cheques

General ⛏ ⍟ ⛺

NEW MILTON, Hampshire Map ref 2B3

SAT NAV BH25 5NH

Glen Orchard Holiday Park
Walkford Lane, New Milton BH25 5NH
t (01425) 616463 **f** (01425) 638655 **e** enquiries@glenorchard.co.uk
w **glenorchard.co.uk** LAST MINUTE OFFERS

⊞ (19)   £200.00–£650.00

Small family park in secluded, landscaped setting close to beaches, forest, riding, golf and fishing. Convenient for Bournemouth, Christchurch, Lymington, Southampton and Isle of Wight. **directions** A35 Lyndhurst to Bournemouth approximately 10 miles, at Hinton left into Ringwood Road after 0.75 mile Walkford Road, after 0.75 mile left into Walkford Lane. **open** March to October **payment** credit/debit cards, cash, cheques

General 🔌 🖥 ⏱ 🅿 ☼   **Leisure** ┣ ∪ 🚲 ✦ 🎣 ⚲

NEW MILTON, Hampshire Map ref 2B3

SAT NAV BH25 5WA

Setthorns Caravan and Camping Site
Wootton, New Milton, Hampshire BH25 5WA
t (01590) 681020 **e** setthorns.site@forestholidays.co.uk
w **campingintheforest.co.uk** ONLINE MAP ONLINE BOOKING

🚐   £12.00–£19.00
🚏   £12.00–£19.00
▲   £12.00–£19.00
237 touring pitches

If you're looking for a traditional camping holiday, Setthorns is the spot for you. **directions** Some Sat Nav systems will guide you to New Milton if you enter our postcode. **open** All year **payment** credit/debit cards, cash, cheques

General 🍴 💬 ☎ 🆗

RINGWOOD, Hampshire Map ref 2B3

SAT NAV BH24 2SB

Shamba Holidays
230 Ringwood Road, St Leonards, Ringwood BH24 2SB
t (01202) 873302 **f** (01202) 873392 **e** enquiries@shambaholidays.co.uk
w **shambaholidays.co.uk** ONLINE MAP LAST MINUTE OFFERS

🚐 (150)   £22.00–£32.00
🚏 (150)   £32.00
▲ (150)   £22.00–£32.00
150 touring pitches

Close to New Forest and Bournemouth with its fine beaches. Great for exploring Hampshire and Dorset. Modern toilet/shower facilities, heated indoor/outdoor pool, licensed clubhouse, games room, play area, takeaway, shop. **directions** Located off the main A31 Wimborne to Ringwood road, turn left at signboard into East Moors Lane. Approximately 1 mile on right-hand side. **open** March to October **payment** credit/debit cards, cash, cheques

General 🖥 🐕 🔧 ⏱ 🅿 ☼ 🍴 🆗 💬 ☎ 🆗 ✕   **Leisure** ┣ ∪ 🚲 ✦ ⚲ 🎣 ♟ 🍴 ⚲

ROMSEY, Hampshire Map ref 2C3

SAT NAV SO51 6FH

Hill Farm Caravan Park
Branches Lane, Sherfield English, Romsey SO51 6FH
t (01794) 340402 **f** (01794) 342358 **e** gjb@hillfarmpark.com
w **hillfarmpark.com** ONLINE MAP GUEST REVIEWS

🚐 (70)   £15.00–£35.00
🚏 (70)   £15.00–£35.00
▲ (30)   £15.00–£35.00
⊞ (6)   £280.00–£550.00
100 touring pitches

In Countryside on the edge of the New Forest, our quiet family-run site provides an ideal base for mature visitors and families with younger children to visit the area **directions** Directions given at time of booking. **open** Touring & Camping March to October, Statics February to December **payment** cash, cheques

General 🔌 🖥 ⏱ 🐕 🔧 🅿 ☼ 🔧 🍴 🆗 💬 ☎ 🆗 ✕   **Leisure** ┣ ∪ 🚲 ✦ ⚲

WINCHESTER, Hampshire Map ref 2C3   **SAT NAV SO21 1HL**

Morn Hill Caravan Club Site
Alresford Road, Winchester SO21 1HL
t (01962) 869877 **e** enquiries@caravanclub.co.uk
w caravanclub.co.uk

THE
CARAVAN
CLUB

(120)   £11.80–£30.80
(120)   £11.80–£30.80
120 touring pitches

Winchester is an old cathedral city of considerable charm with many ancient buildings. Oxford, Windsor, The New Forest and Stonehenge all within an hour's drive. **directions** M3 jct 10 A31 (signposted Alton). Left at roundabout signposted Easton. Immediate turn in front of pub, top of lane for Caravan Club. **open** April to November **payment** credit/debit cards, cash, cheques

General   Leisure

ISLE OF WIGHT

The best of all worlds
on the Island for all seasons

IslandView
Holidays

Great value holidays, the best modern facilities and the most beautiful Isle of Wight locations - Island View Holidays really does offer something for everyone. From family holidays full of fun to relaxing adults-only breaks, we have a choice of comfortable accommodation options to suit every budget, and all our sites offer pet-friendly holidays.

Rookley
Country Park   ★★★★★

Family caravans & bungalows sleeping from 2-8 people, set in 22 acres of landscaped grounds and lakes, with an unrivalled range of facilities.

Hillgrove
St. Helens   ★★★★★

Set in six acres of gently sloping lawns and only a short walk to the beach. Activities include an outdoor heated swimming pool and amusement arcade.

Field Lane
St. Helens   ★★★★★

In seven acres of well-tended grounds, you can enjoy truly tranquil surroundings, safe car-free playing fields or the beach moments away.

bookings +44 (0) 1983 721606   info@islandviewholidays.co.uk   www.islandviewholidays.co.uk

Looking for something else?

You can also buy a copy of our popular 'B&B' guide including guest accommodation, B&B's, guest houses, farmhouses, inns, and campus and hostel accommodation in England 2012.

Now available in good bookshops and online at
visitbritainshop.com   **£8.99**

BEMBRIDGE, Isle of Wight Map ref 2C3

SAT NAV PO35 5PL

⊞ (200)	£4.00–£41.00
⊟ (25)	£4.00–£52.00
Å (200)	£4.00–£35.00
⊞ (5)	£396.00–£1350.00
⊠ (150)	£168.00–£957.00
⊡ (200)	£151.00–£1182.00

400 touring pitches

SPECIAL PROMOTIONS
Special offers are available
from time to time. Please
visit our website for full
details.

Whitecliff Bay Holiday Park

Hillway Road, Bembridge, Isle Of Wight PO35 5PL
t (01983) 872671 **f** (01983) 872941 **e** holiday.sales@whitecliff-bay.com
w **whitecliff-bay.com** ONLINE MAP ONLINE BOOKING LAST MINUTE OFFERS

Situated in an area of outstanding natural beauty, this park offers stunning sea - and countryside
views. There's a huge array of activities and facilities for all ages, including a secluded beach and
indoor and outdoor pools. A fantastic place for great-value family holidays throughout the year.

open April to end of October
payment credit/debit cards, cash, cheques,
euros

directions From A3055 turn onto B3395 at
Brading and follow signposts.

General ⚷ 🖸 ♿ 🐕 ⚏ 📵 📶 ☼ 🎱 ⛽ 🚲 ⛇ 🚻 ⓦ ✕   Leisure ► 🚴 ♪ 🎣 🎿 🍸 🎵 🔍 ⛰

FRESHWATER, Isle of Wight Map ref 2C3

SAT NAV PO40 9SH

⊟ (50)	£12.25–£18.50
Å (60)	£5.25–£6.00

60 touring pitches

Heathfield Farm Camping

Heathfield Road, Freshwater PO40 9SH
t (01983) 407822 **e** web@heathfieldcamping.co.uk
w **heathfieldcamping.co.uk** ONLINE MAP GUEST REVIEWS

Family camping in a quiet, rural area with sea and downland views
Located on the outskirts of Freshwater village, 2 miles from
Yarmouth ferry port and the Needles. **directions** Please contact us
for directions **payment** credit/debit cards, cash, cheques

General ⚷ 🖸 ♿ 🐕 📶 📵 ☼ ⛇ 🚲 ⛽ 🚻 ⓦ   Leisure ∪ 🚴 ⛰

NITON, Isle of Wight Map ref 2C3

SAT NAV PO38 2NS

⊡ (7)	£180.00–£330.00

Meadow View Caravan Site

Newport Road, Niton, Ventnor, Isle of Wight PO38 2NS
t (01983) 730015 / 07977 856795 **e** info@meadowviewniton.co.uk
w **meadowviewniton.co.uk**

Small family run site with panoramic views over surrounding
countryside adjacent to owners working farm of cattle and sheep. 2
mins village, friendly pubs within walking distance. **directions** See
website or call for details. **open** Open April to November **payment**
cash, cheques

General 🖸 🐕 📵 ☼   Leisure ► 🚴 ♪ 🔍 ⛰

RYDE, Isle of Wight Map ref 2C3
SAT NAV PO33 1QL

Whitefield Forest Touring Park
Brading Road, Ryde PO33 1QL
t (01983) 617069 **e** pat&louise@whitefieldforest.co.uk
w whitefieldforest.co.uk

(50)	£15.00–£20.40
(50)	£15.00–£20.40
(50)	£15.00–£20.40
100 touring pitches	

Award winning, family-run touring park located in the tranquil setting of Whitefield Forest. All pitches are level and spacious, with new amenities block including baby, family and disabled facilities. **directions** Just off A3055 follow to Brading, at Tesco's roundabout straight accross, site approx half mile on left hand side. **open** 30 March to 01 October **payment** credit/debit cards, cash, cheques

General ⚲ 🖥 ♿ 🐕 ⚡ ⌂ ☼ 🚿 🅿 🛁 📷 **Leisure** ▶ ∪ ◢ ⚠

SANDOWN, Isle of Wight Map ref 2C3
SAT NAV PO36 0JP

Cheverton Copse Holiday Park Ltd
Scotchells Brook Lane, Sandown, Isle of Wight PO36 0JP
t (01983) 403161 **f** (01983) 408942 **e** holidays@chevertoncopse.com
w chevertoncopse.com ONLINE MAP GUEST REVIEWS LAST MINUTE OFFERS

(1)	£510.00–£895.00
(57)	£270.00–£795.00

Set in 4 acres of safe and attractive parkland, only 1.75 miles from Sandown Bay. Quietly resting among the trees, Cheverton Copse is within easy reach of Sandown and Shanklin. **directions** Please contact us for directions **open** 20th March to 6th November **payment** credit/debit cards, cheques

General ⚲ 🖥 ♿ 📷 ☼ **Leisure** 🏇 ◢ ♟ 🎵 ⚓ ⚠

ST HELENS, Isle of Wight Map ref 2C3
SAT NAV PO33 1YN

Carpenters Farm Campsite
Carpenters Road, St Helens PO33 1YN
t (01983) 874557 **e** info@carpentersfarms.co.uk
w carpentersfarm.co.uk LAST MINUTE OFFERS

(70)	£10.00–£17.00
(70)	£10.00–£17.00
(70)	£10.00–£17.00
70 touring pitches	

Farm campsite with beautiful views in picturesque rural setting, adjacent to RSPB Reserve and SSSI. Close to beaches and attractions. Relaxed atmosphere on site. Family groups and pets very welcome. **directions** Please contact us for directions **open** All year **payment** credit/debit cards, cash, cheques

General ⚲ 🖥 ♿ 🐕 ⚡ 📷 ☼ 🎮 ⚓ ⌂ 🅿 **Leisure** ▶ ∪ ◢ ⚠

ASHFORD, Kent Map ref 3B4
SAT NAV TN26 1NQ

Broadhembury Holiday Park (C & C)
Steeds Lane, Kingsnorth, Kent TN26 1NQ
t (01233) 620859 **f** (01233) 620918 **e** holidaypark@broadhembury.co.uk
w broadhembury.co.uk ONLINE MAP GUEST REVIEWS ONLINE BOOKING LAST MINUTE OFFERS

(60)	£16.00–£25.00
(60)	£16.00–£25.00
(50)	£16.00–£22.00
(5)	£290.00–£630.00
60 touring pitches	

In beautiful Kentish countryside. Fully accessible, heated facilities. Choose family park with children's facilities, or our quiet meadows for couples only to enjoy. Picturesque villages, walking, cycling, sandy beaches nearby. **directions** Junction 10 M20 take A2070 approx. 2 miles. Turn left 2nd roundabout following signs for Kingsnorth, park signposted from here. Left 2nd crossroads in village. **open** All year **payment** credit/debit cards, cash, cheques, euros

General ⚲ 🖥 ♿ 🐕 ⚡ 📷 ☼ 🎮 🚿 ⚓ ⌂ 🅿 📷 **Leisure** ▶ ∪ ◢ ♟ ⚠

SAT NAV CT7 0HD

BIRCHINGTON, Kent Map ref 3C3

Two Chimneys Caravan Park

Shottendane Road, Birchington CT7 0HD
t (01843) 843157 **f** (01843) 848099 **e** info@twochimneys.co.uk
w **twochimneys.co.uk** ONLINE MAP

🚐 (100) £14.50–£29.50
🚐 (50) £14.50–£29.50
⛺ (100) £14.50–£27.00
🏠 (10) £204.00–£682.00
250 touring pitches

A friendly, family-run country site near sandy beaches. Spacious, level pitches. Modern wc/shower and laundry facilities including disabled. Children's play and ball-games areas. Holiday Hire Available. Caravan Storage. **directions** A2 then A28 to Birchington. Turn right into Park Lane, bear left into Manston Road, left at crossroads (B2049), site on right. **open** Easter to October **payment** credit/debit cards, cash, cheques

General 🔲 🏕 🏠 ☀ 📞 🅿 🚻 💬 Leisure ∪ ⚲ 🐎 ♪ ⚑ ⚑ 🍴 🔍 ⚲

BIRCHINGTON (3 MILES), Kent Map ref 3C3

SAT NAV CT7 0NH

St Nicholas Camping Site

Streete Farm House, Court Road, St Nicholas-at-Wade, Birchington, Kent CT7 0NH
t (01843) 847245

🚐 (12) £20.00–£22.00
🚐 (8) £20.00–£22.00
⛺ (55) £16.00–£19.00
75 touring pitches

The site - flat, grassy and well-sheltered - is on the outskirts of the village, close to the village shop. The resort of Thanet is within easy reach. **directions** The site is signposted from the A299 and A28. **open** Easter to 31st October **payment** cash, cheques

General 🐕 🏠 ☀ 📞 🅿 🚻 Leisure ⚲

CANTERBURY, Kent Map ref 3B3

SAT NAV CT4 5PL

Yew Tree Park

Stone Street, Canterbury CT4 5PL
t (01227) 700306 **f** (01227) 700306 **e** info@yewtreepark.com
w **yewtreepark.com** ONLINE MAP LAST MINUTE OFFERS

🚐 (20) £14.00–£22.30
🚐 (5) £14.00–£22.30
⛺ (20) £14.00–£22.30
🏠 (8) £210.00–£530.00
45 touring pitches

Picturesque country park close to Canterbury, centrally located for exploring Kent. Naturally landscaped touring and camping facilities. Holiday apartments, lodge and static units. Outdoor heated pool. **directions** On B2068, 4 miles south of Canterbury, 9 miles north of M20, jct 11, then turn by Chequers Inn. Park entrance on left hand side. **open** March to October **payment** credit/debit cards, cash, cheques

General 🔲 📶 🏠 ☀ 📞 🅿 🚻 💬 Leisure ⚲ ⚲

FOLKESTONE, Kent Map ref 3B4

SAT NAV CT18 7BG

Black Horse Farm Caravan Club Site

385 Canterbury Road, Densole, Folkestone, Kent CT18 7BG
t (01303) 892665
w **caravanclub.co.uk**

THE
CARAVAN
CLUB

🚐 (118) £13.50–£32.79
🚐 (118) £13.50–£32.79
🚐
118 touring pitches

This is a quiet and relaxed country site, ideally suited for families wishing to visit the many interesting local attractions including the historic city of Canterbury. **directions** From M20 jct 13 on A260 to Canterbury, 2 miles from junction with A20, site on left 200 yds past Black Horse Inn. **open** All year **payment** credit/debit cards, cash, cheques

General 🔲 📶 🐕 🏠 ☀ 📞 🅿 🚻 💬 Leisure ⚑ ♪ ⚲

HOLLINGBOURNE, Kent Map ref 3B3

SAT NAV ME17 1XH

Bearsted Caravan Club Site
Ashford Road, Hollingbourne, Maidstone, Kent ME17 1XH
t (01622) 730018
w caravanclub.co.uk

THE CARAVAN CLUB

🚐 (69) £15.30–£35.51
🚏 (69) £15.30–£35.51
69 touring pitches

Set in tranquil surroundings, near to historic Leeds Castle. Maidstone and North Kent Coast nearby. Shopping, local treats and fun family attractions. **directions** Leave M20 at junction 8 and at roundabout turn into road signposted Bearsted, Maidstone. Site on left in 0.5 miles. **payment** credit/debit cards, cash, cheques

General 🔲 ⓦ 🐕 🛏 📷 ☼ 🔌 ⊕ 🚽 WP **Leisure** ▶ 🚣 ⚲

KINGSDOWN, Kent Map ref 3C4

SAT NAV CT14 8EU

Kingsdown Park Holiday Village
Upper Street, Kingsdown, Deal CT14 8EU
t (01304) 361205 **f** (01304) 380125 **e** info@kingsdownpark.co.uk
w kingsdownpark.net ONLINE MAP ONLINE BOOKING LAST MINUTE OFFERS

🏠 (50) £245.00–£739.00

This picturesque park provides the perfect base for exploring Kent. Comfortable lodges and excellent leisure facilities ensure you are not disappointed. **directions** Please contact us for directions **open** March to October and 20 December to 3 January **payment** credit/debit cards, cash, cheques

General 🔌 🔲 ⓦ 📷 ☼ ✕ **Leisure** ▶ ∪ ⚲ 🚲 🚣 🎾 ⚲ 🏋 ⚲

MARDEN, Kent Map ref 3B4

SAT NAV TN12 9ND

Tanner Farm Park
Tanner Farm, Goudhurst Road, Marden TN12 9ND
t (01622) 832399 **f** (01622) 832472 **e** enquiries@tannerfarmpark.co.uk
w tannerfarmpark.co.uk ONLINE BOOKING

🚐 (47) £13.50–£24.00
🚏 (33) £13.50–£24.00
⛺ (20) £13.00–£24.00
100 touring pitches

Secluded park on beautiful family farm. Ideal touring base for the area. Gold David Bellamy Conservation Award. Bed and breakfast also available. [Caravan Club AS.] **directions** From A21 or A229 onto B2079; midway between Marden and Goudhurst. **open** All year **payment** credit/debit cards, cash, cheques

General 🔌 🔲 ⓦ 🐕 🛏 📷 ☼ 🔌 ⊕ 🚽 WP **Leisure** 🚣 ⚲ ⚲

BURFORD, Oxfordshire Map ref 2B1

SAT NAV OX18 4JJ

Burford Caravan Club Site
Bradwell Grove, Burford, Oxfordshire OX18 4JJ
t (01993) 823080 **e** enquiries@caravanclub.co.uk
w caravanclub.co.uk

THE CARAVAN CLUB

🚐 (119) £15.30–£35.51
🚏 (119) £15.30–£35.51
119 touring pitches

Attractive, spacious site opposite Cotswold Wildlife Park. Burford has superb Tudor houses, a museum and historic inns. A great base from which to explore the Cotswolds. **directions** From roundabout at A40/A361 junction in Burford, take A361 signposted Lechlade. Site on right after 2.5 miles. Site signposted from roundabout. **open** July to November **payment** credit/debit cards, cash, cheques

General 🔲 📷 ☼ 🔌 ⊕ 🚽 **Leisure** ▶ 🚣 ⚲

STANDLAKE, Oxfordshire Map ref 2C1

Hardwick Parks
The Downs, Standlake, Witney OX29 7PZ
t (01865) 300501 **f** (01865) 300037 **e** info@hardwickparks.co.uk
w **hardwickparks.co.uk** ONLINE MAP

🚐 (214) £20.25–£21.75
🚐 (214) £25.00
🅰 (214) £15.50–£18.00
🚎 £249.00–£521.00
214 touring pitches

Rural park near Witney with lakes and river. Licensed clubhouse, shower/toilet block and shop. Tents, caravans and motorhomes welcome. Holiday caravans for hire and sale. Watersports available. **directions** Four and a half miles from Witney, signposted from the A415. **open** April to October **payment** credit/debit cards, cash, cheques

General 🔌 📶 🐕 🎱 📱 📻 ☀ ⛽ 🚿 🍴 🚻 🔥 X **Leisure** 🚤 🍷

REDHILL, Surrey Map ref 2D2

Alderstead Heath Caravan Club Site
Dean Lane, Merstham, Redhill, Surrey RH1 3AH
t (01737) 644629
w **caravanclub.co.uk**

THE CARAVAN CLUB

🚐 (150) £13.50–£32.79
🚐 (150) £13.50–£32.79
150 touring pitches

Quiet site with views over rolling, wooded North Downs. Denbies Wine Estate nearby and 35 minutes from Central London. For day trips, try Chessington and the National Trust's Chartwell. **directions** M25 jct8, A217 towards Reigate, fork left after 300 yds. Left at T-junction onto A23. 0.5 miles, right onto B2031. Left into Dean Lane. **open** All year **payment** credit/debit cards, cash, cheques

General 🔌 📶 📱 📻 ☀ ⛽ 🚿 🔥 🚻 🌐 **Leisure** ⛰

BATTLE, Sussex Map ref 3B4

ROSE AWARD CARAVAN HOLIDAY PARK

Crowhurst Park
Telham Lane, Battle, East Sussex TN33 0SL
t (01424) 773344 **f** (01424) 775727 **e** enquires@crowhurstpark.co.uk
w **crowhurstpark.co.uk** ONLINE BOOKING LAST MINUTE OFFERS

🏠 (54) £192.00–£1175.00

Development of pine lodges within grounds of a 17th century country estate. Facilities include leisure club with indoor swimming pool, bar, restaurant and children's playground. David Bellamy Gold Conservation Award. **directions** Two miles south of Battle on A2100. **open** 1st March to 8th January **payment** credit/debit cards, cash, cheques

General ♿ 🔌 📶 🎱 📱 ☀ X **Leisure** ▶ ∪ 🎿 🚴 🚤 🎣 🍷 🎯 ⛰

BATTLE, Sussex Map ref 3B4

Normanhurst Court Caravan Club Site
Stevens Crouch, Battle, East Sussex TN33 9LR
t (01424) 773808 **e** enquiries@caravanclub.co.uk
w **caravanclub.co.uk**

THE CARAVAN CLUB

🚐 (149) £13.50–£32.79
🚐 (149) £13.50–£32.79
149 touring pitches

Located close to the 1066 Trail, great for walkers, nature lovers and families. The seaside towns of Eastbourne and Hastings are just a short drive away. **directions** From Battle, turn left onto A271. Site i 3 miles on left. **open** March to November **payment** credit/debit cards, cash, cheques

General 🔌 🐕 📱 📻 📱 🔥 🚿 🚻 🌐 **Leisure** ▶ 🚤 ⛰

BEXHILL-ON-SEA, Sussex Map ref 3B4

Kloofs Caravan Park
Sandhurst Lane, Whydown, Bexhill TN39 4RG
t (01424) 842839 **e** camping@kloofs.com
w kloofs.com

TOURING & CAMPING PARK

🚐	£25.00
🚐	£25.00
⚲	£25.00
50 touring pitches	

Freedom - All Weather, All Year. Fully serviced, hard or grass, extra large pitches. Ultra modern facilities, private washing, large showers, central heating, Cat 1 disabled. Quiet, rural, tranquil. **directions** A259 to Little Common roundabout, Turn north into Peartree Lane. Left at crossroads, Sandhurst Lane is 300m on left. **open** All year **payment** credit/debit cards, cash, cheques

General 🔌 🐕 🛱 📱 ☀ 🖳 🏧 📞 🅿 💻   **Leisure** ▶ ∪ ⟋ ⚠

Looking for something else?

You can also buy a copy of our popular guide 'Hotels' including country house and town house hotels, metro and budget hotels, serviced apartments and restaurants with rooms in England 2012.

Now available in good bookshops and online at
visitbritainshop.com   **£7.99**

For **key to symbols** see page 6

BOGNOR REGIS, Sussex Map ref 2C3
SAT NAV PO21 1JJ

enjoyEngland.com
★★★★
HOLIDAY VILLAGE

Butlins Bognor Regis
Upper Bognor Road, Bognor Regis, West Sussex PO21 1JJ
t 0845 070 4736 **e** butlins.holidays@bourne-leisure.co.uk
w butlins.com/resorts/bognor-regis/
ONLINE MAP ONLINE BOOKING LAST MINUTE OFFERS

SPECIAL PROMOTIONS
See butlins.com for our
latest offers and prices.

Our Bognor Regis Resort is officially one of Britain's sunniest locations. Sitting right on the West

Sussex coast and within just a couple of hours drive from London, it's the perfect getaway.
Superb live entertainment and a fantastic range of facilities and activities; sub tropical waterworld,
funfair, all weather sports areas, childrens play areas and clubs, bars and restaurants.

There's a relaxing spa, which is ideal for grown-ups seeking a pampering, and our new celebrity
restaurant Turner's - great if you're looking for top quality dining at an affordable price.

If you feel like discovering the area around our resort, the gorgeous beach and the South Downs
National Park and heritage sites are right on your doorstep.

open All year
payment credit/debit cards, cheques

directions We're easy to find. From the M3
head for the A27, then simply follow the A259
coast road and you can't miss us. We're just
one mile east of Bognor Regis on the
Littlehampton road near Felpham Village.

General 🐾 ▢ ⓦ 🅿 ☼ ✕ **Leisure** ▶ 🚲 ⌇ 🍷 ♫ ✎ ⋔

BOGNOR REGIS, Sussex Map ref 2C3 — SAT NAV PO21 3ER

Copthorne Caravans
Rose Green Road, Bognor Regis PO21 3ER
t (01243) 262408 **f** (01243) 262408 **e** holidays@copthornecaravans.co.uk
w **copthornecaravans.co.uk** ONLINE MAP ONLINE BOOKING

£185.00–£495.00

Copthorne Caravans is a small, family owned holiday park with Rose Award, holiday caravans for hire. Many places of interest are within easy reach, including the sea! Online Booking: www.copthornecaravans.co.uk **directions** We are two miles west of Bognor Regis and one mile from the beach. **open** 1st April to 31st October **payment** cash, cheques

General ⬜ ▯ ☼ **Leisure** ✦ ⌂

BOGNOR REGIS, Sussex Map ref 2C3 — SAT NAV PO22 9RP

Rowan Park Caravan Club Site
Rowan Way, Bognor Regis, West Sussex PO22 9RP
t (01243) 828515 **e** enquiries@caravanclub.co.uk
w **caravanclub.co.uk**

(94) £13.50–£32.79
(94) £13.50–£32.79
94 touring pitches

The town of Bognor Regis is a traditional seaside resort with many entertainments. Chichester Festival Theatre and Arundel, have a music and drama festival at the end of August. **directions** From roundabout on A29, 1 mile north of Bognor, turn left into Rowan Way, site 100 yds on right, opposite Halfords superstore. **open** March to November **payment** credit/debit cards, cash, cheques

General ⬜ ⚲ ▯ ▩ ☼ ▤ ▨ ◔ ⚑ ▱ **Leisure** ▶ ⟋ ⌂

BRACKLESHAM BAY, Sussex Map ref 2C3 — SAT NAV PO20 8JE

South Downs Holiday Village
Bracklesham Lane, Bracklesham Bay, Chichester PO20 8JE
t (01692) 582277 **e** info@richardsonsgroup.net
w **richardsonsholidayvillages.co.uk** LAST MINUTE OFFERS

£225.00–£500.00

South Downs Holiday Village is a small and friendly location for adults. Providing full board breaks with regular entertainment. Chalets are all ground floor. Hotel over two floors. **directions** Please contact us for directions **open** All year **payment** credit/debit cards, cash, cheques

General ▯ ▩ ✕ **Leisure** ⟋ ♟ ♫ ✦

BRIGHTON & HOVE, Sussex Map ref 2D3 — SAT NAV BN2 5TS

Sheepcote Valley Caravan Club Site
East Brighton Park, Brighton BN2 5TS
t (01273) 626546 **e** enquiries@caravanclub.co.uk
w **caravanclub.co.uk**

(269) £16.00–£38.90
(269) £16.00–£38.90
269 touring pitches

Located on the South Downs. 2 miles from Brighton, a lively town with a Marina, shops, pubs, restaurants, cinema and an exotic Royal Pavilion. **directions** M23/A23, join A27 (Lewes). B2123 (Falmer/Rottingdean). Right, onto B2123 (Woodingdean). At traffic lights, right (Warren Road). 1 mile, left (Wilson Avenue). **open** All year **payment** credit/debit cards, cash, cheques

General ⬜ ⚱ ⚲ ▯ ▩ ☼ ▤ ▨ ◔ ⚑ ▱ **Leisure** ▶ ⌂

CHICHESTER 5 MILES, Sussex Map ref 2C3

SAT NAV PO20 7HY

Bell Caravan Park

Bell Lane, Birdham, Chichester PO20 7HY
t (01243) 512264 **e** bellcaravanpark@hotmail.co.uk

🚐 £16.00
🚐 (15) £16.00
15 touring pitches

Quiet, sheltered Caravan park convenient for Chichester and the coast. With easy access to chichester marina. Country walks and cycle path. **directions** Take the A286 from Chichester. At Birdham village turn left at the roundabout into Bell Lane. Caravan Park is 500 hundred yards on the left. **open** March to October **payment** cash, cheques

General 🐕 🛏 🅿 ☼ 🚿 🔌 ⏱ 🚻 Leisure ▶ ∪ 🚲 ✈

EASTBOURNE, Sussex Map ref 3B4

SAT NAV BN24 5NG

Fairfields Farm Caravan & Camping Park

Eastbourne Road, Westham, Pevensey BN24 5NG
t (01323) 763165 **f** (01323) 469175 **e** enquiries@fairfieldsfarm.com
w fairfieldsfarm.com GUEST REVIEWS

🚐 (60) £17.00–£22.00
🚐 (60) £17.00–£22.00
▲ (60) £17.00–£22.00
60 touring pitches

SPECIAL PROMOTIONS
Special low season midweek offer: 3 nights for the price of 2. Contact us for more details.

A quiet country touring site on a working farm. Clean facilities, lakeside walk with farm pets and free fishing for campers. Close to the beautiful seaside resort of Eastbourne, and a good base from which to explore the diverse scenery and attractions of south east England.

open April to October
payment credit/debit cards, cash

directions From A27 Pevensey roundabout, travel through Pevensey towards castle, then through Westham. Turn left (B2191) towards Eastbourne. Over level crossing and we are on left.

General 🔲 🐕 🐾 🛏 ☼ 🖥 🚿 🔌 ⏱ 🚻 Leisure ✈

GORING-BY-SEA, Sussex Map ref 2D3

SAT NAV BN13 3RT

Northbrook Farm Caravan Club Site

Titnore Way, Worthing, West Sussex BN13 3RT
t (01903) 502962 **e** enquiries@caravanclub.co.uk
w caravanclub.co.uk

THE
CARAVAN
CLUB

🚐 (70) £10.70–£28.00
🚐 (70) £10.70–£28.00
70 touring pitches

Attractive, grassy site populated by lush trees. Spacious play area and activity field. Beach at Worthing nearby. **directions** From A24 follow signs for Chichester/Littlehampton. 4 miles on, far side of bridge, signposted Ferring and Goring. 0.75 miles left. **open** March to November **payment** credit/debit cards, cash, cheques

General 🐕 🛏 🖥 🔌 ⏱ 🚻 📷 Leisure ▶ ⛰

Littlehampton Caravan Club Site
Mill Lane, Wick, Littlehampton BN17 7PH
t (01903) 716176 **e** enquiries@caravanclub.co.uk
w caravanclub.co.uk

THE **CARAVAN CLUB**

🚐 (117)   £13.50–£32.79
🚃 (117)   £13.50–£32.79
117 touring pitches

Littlehampton has a beautiful natural harbour. Site within walking distance of town and beach. Waterside restaurants, golf course, museum and the Look and Sea Visitor Centre. **directions** Leave A27 onto A284 signposted Littlehampton. Site on left of Mill Lane. **open** April to January **payment** credit/debit cards, cash, cheques

General 🗄️ 🕭 🐾 🎣 🖂 🎡 📶 🕙 ⬛ **Leisure** ► ⤵ ⛰️

Bay View Park Ltd
Old Martello Road, Pevensey Bay, Pevensey BN24 6DX
t (01323) 768688 **f** (01323) 769637 **e** holidays@bay-view.co.uk
w bay-view.co.uk ONLINE MAP ONLINE BOOKING

🚐 (40)   £16.00–£23.00
🚃 (4)   £16.00–£23.00
▲ (50)   £16.00–£23.00
🏠 (9)   £209.00–£635.00
94 touring pitches

Family site on a private road next to the beach. Play area. New showers and laundry. Small, well-stocked shop. On site, par 3, 9 hole golf course and refreshments. **directions** On A259 coast road between Pevensey Bay and Eastbourne. **open** March to October **payment** credit/debit cards, cash, cheques

General ♿ 🗄️ 🕭 🐾 🚲 🎣 🖂 ☼ 🍴 🎡 🕙 ⬛ 📶 **Leisure** ► 🐎 ⤵ ⛰️

ROSE **AWARD** CARAVAN HOLIDAY PARK

Green Lawns Holiday Park
Paddock Lane, Selsey, Chichester, West Sussex PO20 9EJ
t (01243) 606080 **f** (01243) 606068 **e** holidays@bunnleisure.co.uk
w bunnleisure.co.uk ONLINE MAP LAST MINUTE OFFERS

🏠 (1)   £690.00–£1650.00
🏠 (20)   £185.00–£999.00

Offers leafy lanes, duck ponds and open green spaces for privacy, peace and quiet but with access to all Bunn Leisure's facilities and a courtesy bus to take you around. **directions** From A27 Chichester by-pass take B2145 to Selsey. Green Lawns is clearly signed on right once you are in town. **open** March to October **payment** credit/debit cards, cash

General 🗄️ 🕭 🐾 🚲 🎣 ☼ ✕ **Leisure** ► ∪ 🏊 🐎 ⤵ ⇲ ⇲ 🍴 🎵 ♦ ⛰️

Warner Farm Camping & Touring Park
Warner Lane, Selsey, Chichester, West Sussex PO20 9EL
t (01243) 604499 **f** (01243) 604499 **e** touring@bunnleisure.co.uk
w warnerfarm.co.uk ONLINE MAP LAST MINUTE OFFERS

🚐 (80)   £20.00–£45.00
🚃 (50)   £20.00–£45.00
▲ (120)   £18.00–£33.00
250 touring pitches

Great value, quality, fun filled family camping & touring holidays. Well maintained Standard, Electric & Full Service pitches. Stay here & enjoy all Bunn Leisure's great facilities and entertainment. **directions** From A27 Chichester by-pass take B2145 to Selsey. Warner Farm is clearly signed on the right once you are in town. **open** March to October **payment** credit/debit cards, cash

General 🗄️ 🕭 🐾 🚲 🎣 ☼ 🖂 🎡 🕙 ⬛ 📶 ✕ **Leisure** ► ∪ 🏊 🐎 ⤵ ⇲ ⇲ 🍴 🎵 ♦ ⛰️

SELSEY, Sussex Map ref 2C3

SAT NAV PO20 9BH

West Sands Holiday Park
Mill Lane, Selsey, Chichester, West Sussex PO20 9BH
t (01243) 606080 **f** (01243) 606068 **e** holidays@bunnleisure.co.uk
w **bunnleisure.co.uk** ONLINE MAP LAST MINUTE OFFERS

(5) £440.00–£1600.00
(37) £185.00–£999.00

The liveliest of our parks on the South Coast offering family fun in fantastic seaside location. Famous for the best entertainment with top acts and live performances. Plus Kid's entertainment. **directions** From A27 Chichester by-pass take B2145 to Selsey. West Sands is clearly signed on right once you are in the town. **open** March to October **payment** credit/debit cards, cash

General ▯ ☺ ★ ☎ ▦ ⋒ ☼ ✕ Leisure ▶ ∪ ⚲ ♫ ♪ ☞ ☜ ☂ ♪ ♫ ✪ ⋔

SELSEY, Sussex Map ref 2C3

SAT NAV PO20 9EJ

White Horse Holiday Park
Paddock Lane, Selsey, Chichester, West Sussex PO20 9EJ
t (01243) 606080 **f** (01243) 606068 **e** holidays@bunnleisure.co.uk
w **bunnleisure.co.uk** ONLINE MAP LAST MINUTE OFFERS

(20) £185.00–£999.00

With its coveted award for its traditional atmosphere it is perfect for families. Offering a relaxed holiday, though never far from all the facilities and entertainment. **directions** From A27 Chichester bypass take B2145 to Selsey. White Horse is clearly signed on the right once you are in town. **open** March to October **payment** credit/debit cards, cash

General ▯ ☺ ★ ☎ ▦ ⋒ ☼ ✕ Leisure ▶ ∪ ⚲ ♫ ☞ ☜ ☂ ♪ ✪ ⋔

WASHINGTON, Sussex Map ref 2D3

SAT NAV RH20 4AJ

Washington Caravan & Camping Park
London Road, Washington, West Sussex RH20 4AJ
t (01903) 892869 **f** (01903) 893252 **e** washingtoncampsite@yahoo.co.uk
w **washcamp.com**

(21) £19.00
(5) £19.00
(80) £19.00
21 touring pitches

The park is set in beautifully landscaped grounds beneath the South Downs affording the right atmosphere for an enjoyable stay. Well situated for visiting places of interest. **directions** Please contact us for directions **payment** credit/debit cards, cash, cheques

General ▯ ★ ☎ ⋒ ♫ ☕ ♁ Leisure ∪

Looking for something else?

You can also buy a copy of our popular guide 'Self Catering' including self-catering holiday homes, approved caravan holiday homes, boat accommodation and holiday cottage agencies in England 2012.

Now available in good bookshops and online at
visitbritainshop.com

£8.99

So much to see, so little time - how do you choose?

Make the most of your leisure time; look for attractions with the Quality Marque.

VisitEngland operates the Enjoy England Visitor Attraction Quality Assurance Scheme.

Annual assessments by trained impartial assessors test all aspects of the customer experience so you can visit with confidence.

For ideas and inspiration visit www.enjoyengland.com/attractions

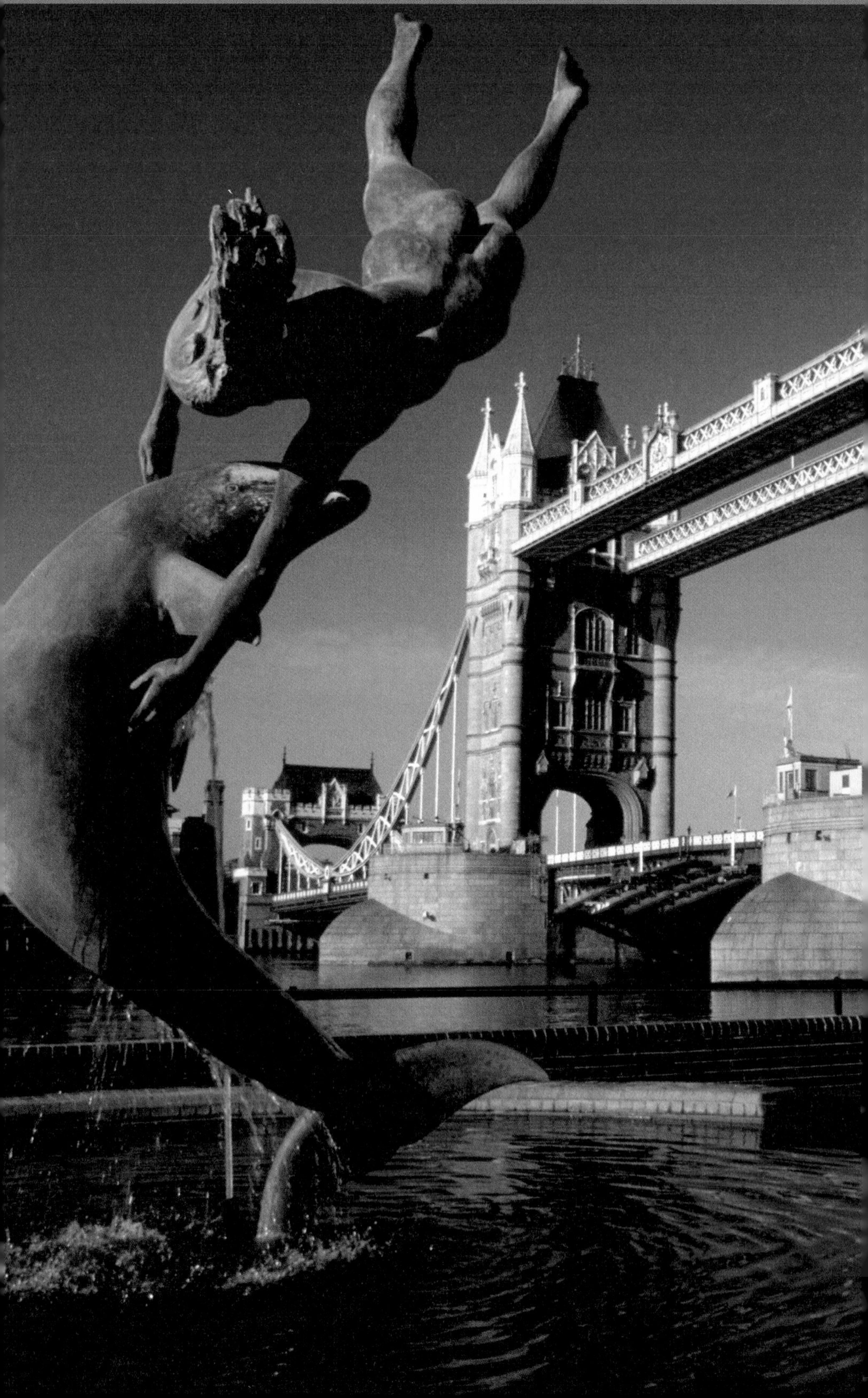

London

Arguably, the greatest city in the world, London is home to the Queen, and volumes of history and world-famous architecture. With a plethora of free museums and art galleries, there is always something amazing to see and do.

It's impossible to walk 100 metres in London without stumbling across a famous monument or place of historical significance. Oh, and the shopping and culture can rival anywhere.

History and Heritage

Since the Roman encampment of Londinium in AD43, the city has survived everything from the Black Death to the Blitz. In 1666 the Great Fire nearly wiped out the city altogether, but this gave Sir Christopher Wren the opportunity to show off his architectural skills including his masterpiece St Paul's Cathedral. It's impossible to distil all of London past into words – the only thing to do is experience it for yourself.

Arts and Culture

With its huge Turbine Hall, the Tate Modern is the place to experience modern and contemporary art - you can see work by Picasso, Dalí, and Pollock all for free. Or see the best of British at the National Portrait Gallery. And for an aural treat, take those ears off to a musical in the West End or Opera at the majestic Covent Garden.

The Queen's Diamond Jubilee celebrations marking 60 years of the Queen's reign will centre around an extended weekend on 2nd - 5th June 2012, with events all over the city including a river pageant featuring a flotilla of 1,000 boats, a televised concert from Buckingham Palace, and a carriage procession through London to St Paul's Cathedral.

Food and Drink

You can always splash out for afternoon tea at the Ritz where a cellist soundtracks every delicious bite. For a taste of the real London though take a trip to Brick Lane and sample a curry. Gordon Ramsay's ability to cook as well as he can swear means his Royal Hospital Restaurant is worthy of its three Michelin stars and your attention.

Shopping

Be warned, when your kids enter Hamleys there's every chance they will explode – the Regent Street toy shop is chock-full of childish delights. The luxury department store, Harrods, has a similar effect on grown-ups. For street performers and quality produce look no further than Covent Garden and for ultra-cool boutiques Carnaby Street has been at the centre of things since the swinging sixties.

Family Fun

Anyone who says science is boring has never been to the Science Museum where you can enjoy the hands-on exhibits that help bring the theories to life. Things go bump in the daytime at London Dungeons which are packed full of spooky attractions. Or head

to London Zoo at feeding time for an unforgettable experience. Drink in tranquil views over the city from the London Eye. Then head past the Houses of Parliament to Buckingham Palace..

Sports

Will we finally get a UK Wimbledon champ? Don't miss the chance of seeing it happen at the greatest grass tennis tournament in the world. You can catch Gerrard, Rooney and co. at Wembley, the home of English football, or watch international cricket at the Oval and Lords.

But the main event of 2012 will be the Olympic and Paralympic Games. An unbeatable opportunity to see world class athletes at some of London's most iconic venues including Horse Guards Parade, Wembley Stadium, Lords and Hyde Park. In addition, London will also have some fantastic new sporting venues for the Games: the VeloPark, the Aquatics Centre, the Basketball Arena, and of course, the Olympic Stadium. The games open on 27 July 2012 with a fantastic Opening Ceremony, but visitors can also enjoy a tour of the stunning Olympic Park as it prepares.

Music and Nightlife

For clubbing look no further than Fabric and Ministry of Sound – institutions in the global dance scene, they play host to the world's superstar DJs. Ronnie Scott's legendary Soho venue has been showcasing virtuoso musicians from across the world for over 50 years and is well worth a visit.

Handy Hints

Late Bird - Get cheap theatre tickets at the ticket booths in Leicester Square.

On foot - Walk! London's a great city to explore on foot and its centre is smaller than you think.

Train - Buy an Oyster card for cheaper, easier travel on buses and the Tube.

Freebies - Make the most of London's many free museums and galleries.

OUT & ABOUT IN LONDON

Day 1 - London's West End

- For the ultimate in retail therapy hit Oxford Street, Regent Street and Carnaby Street
- See an exhibition at the Photographer's Gallery
- Enjoy a musical in the West End

Day 2 - Explore Westminster

- Marvel at the architecture at Westminster Cathedral
- Explore the Houses of Parliament on a tour
- Visit Churchill's War Rooms

Day 3 - Cheap Treats

- Hit the Science Museum, Natural History Museum and the V&A
- Take a stroll around Hyde Park
- Visit the Diana memorial play park at Kensington Gardens

Day 4 - Greenwich Time

- Jump on a boat trip to Greenwich
- Hit the Royal Observatory and stand on the Greenwich Meridian Line
- Visit the National Maritime Museum

Day 5 - East-Enders

- Explore the evolution of interior design at the Geffrye Museum
- Sample a nice and spicy curry in Brick Lane
- Have a good rummage at Spitalfields Market

Day 6 - Bloomsbury and Covent Garden

- Explore the wealth of antiquities at the British Museum
- Check out the shops and performers at Covent Garden
- Experience a show at the Royal Opera House

Day 7 - Southbank Show

- Get all James Bond with a speedboat trip along the river Thames
- Visit Tate Modern and marvel at the huge Turbine Room as well as work by Warhol
- Take a trip on the London Eye and drink in those views

Where to Go

 Attractions with this sign participate in the **Places of Interest Quality Assurance Scheme**.

 Attractions with this sign participate in the **Visitor Attraction Quality Assurance Scheme**.

Both schemes recognise high standards in all aspects of the visitor experience (see page 6)

ENTERTAINMENT & CULTURE

Apsley House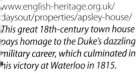
Westminster W1J 7NT
(020) 7499 5676
www.english-heritage.org.uk/
daysout/properties/apsley-house/
*This great 18th-century town house
pays homage to the Duke's dazzling
military career, which culminated in
his victory at Waterloo in 1815.*

**BBC Television Centre
Tours**
**Hammersmith and Fulham
W12 7RJ**
(03709) 011227
www.bbc.co.uk/tours/
televisioncentre.shtml
*"On the award-winning tour of BBC
Television Centre you will see what
happens inside the most famous TV
headquarters in the world!"*

British Museum
Camden WC1B 3DG
(020) 7323 8299
www.thebritishmuseum.ac.uk
*Founded in 1753, the British Museum's
remarkable collections span over two
million years of human history and
culture, all under one roof.*

**Down House - Home of
Charles Darwin**
Bromley BR6 7JT
(01689) 859119
www.english-heritage.org.uk/daysout/
properties/home-of-charles-darwin-
down-house/
*The family home and workplace of
Charles Darwin.*

**Estorick Collection of
Modern Italian Art**
Islington N1 2AN
(020) 7704 9522
www.estorickcollection.com
*World-famous collection of Italian
Futurists, Modigliani, Morandi and
others in a beautiful Georgian house.
Also temporary exhibitions, events,
library and shop.*

**Greenwich Heritage
Centre**
Greenwich SE18 4DX
(020) 8854 2452
www.greenwich.gov.uk
*Local history museum with displays
of archaeology, natural history and
geology. Also temporary exhibitions,
schools service, sales point and
Saturday club.*

**London Transport
Museum**
Westminster WC2E 7BB
(020) 7379 6344
http://www.ltmuseum.co.uk
*The history of transport for everyone,
from spectacular vehicles, special
exhibitions, actors and guided tours to
film shows, gallery talks and children's
craft workshops.*

Lord's Tour
Westminster NW8 8QN
(020) 7616 8595
www.lords.org/history/tours-of-lords/
*Guided tour of Lord's Cricket Ground
including the Long Room, MCC
Museum, Real Tennis Court, Mound
Stand and Indoor School.*

Imperial War Museum
Southwark SE1 6HZ
(020) 7416 5320
www.iwm.org.uk
*This award-winning museum tells the
story of conflict involving Britain and
the Commonwealth since 1914. See
thousands of imaginatively displayed
exhibits, from art to aircraft, utility
clothes to U-boats.*

Museum of London
City of London EC2Y 5HN
(020) 7001 9844
www.museumoflondon.org.uk
*Step inside Museum of London for an
unforgettable journey through the
capital's turbulent past.*

National Gallery
Westminster WC2N 5DN
(020) 7747 2888
www.nationalgallery.org.uk
*The National Gallery houses one of
the greatest collections of Western
European painting in the world.
Discover inspiring art by Botticelli,
Caravaggio, Leonardo da Vinci,
Monet, Raphael, Rembrandt, Titian,
Vermeer and Van Gogh.*

Natural History Museum
**Kensington and Chelsea
SW7 5BD**
(020) 7942 5000
www.nhm.ac.uk
*The Natural History Museum reveals
how the jigsaw of life fits together.
Animal, vegetable or mineral, the best
of our planet's most amazing treasures
are here for you to see - for free.*

117

National Maritime Museum
Greenwich SE10 9NF
(020) 8858 4422
www.nmm.ac.uk
Britain's seafaring history housed in an impressive modern museum. Themes include exploration, Nelson, trade and empire, passenger shipping, luxury liners, maritime London, costume, art and the sea, the future and environmental issues.

National Portrait Gallery
Westminster WC2H 0HE
(020) 7306 0055
www.npg.org.uk
The National Portrait Gallery houses the world's largest collection of portraits. Visitors come face to face with the people who have shaped British history from Elizabeth I to David Beckham. Entrance is free.

Royal Air Force Museum
Hendon
Barnet NW9 5LL
(020) 8205 2266
www.rafmuseum.org
Take off to the Royal Air Force Museum and flypast the history of aviation with an exciting display of suspended aircraft, touch screen technology, simulator rides, hands-on section, film shows, licensed restaurant.

Science Museum
Kensington and Chelsea SW7 2DD
0870 870 4868
www.sciencemuseum.org.uk
The Science Museum is world-renowned for its historic collections, awe-inspiring galleries, family activities and exhibitions - and it's FREE!

Southbank Centre
Lambeth SE1 8XX
0871 663 2501
www.southbankcentre.co.uk
A unique arts centre with 21 acres of creative space, including the Royal Festival Hall, Queen Elizabeth Hall and The Hayward.

St Bartholomew's Hospital Archives and Museum
City of London EC1A 7BE
(020) 7601 8152
www.bartsandthelondon.nhs.uk/aboutus/st_bartholomews_hospital.asp
The museum tells the inspiring story of Bart's Hospital. Founded nearly 9 centuries ago, it is one of the oldest hospitals in Britain.

Tate Britain
Westminster SW1P 4RG
(020) 7887 8888
www.tate.org.uk
Tate Britain presents the world's greatest collection of British art in a dynamic series of new displays and exhibitions.

Tate Modern
Southwark SE1 9TG
(020) 7887 8888
www.tate.org.uk/modern
The national gallery of international modern art and is one of London's top free attractions. Packed with challenging modern art and housed within a disused power station on the south bank of the River Thames.

Tower Bridge Exhibition
Southwark SE1 2UP
(020) 7403 3761
www.towerbridge.org.uk
Inside Tower Bridge Exhibition you will travel up to the high-level walkways, located 140 feet above the Thames and witness stunning panoramic views of London before visiting the Victorian Engine Rooms.

Victoria and Albert Museum
Kensington and Chelsea SW7 2RL
(020) 7942 2000
www.vam.ac.uk
The V&A is the world's greatest museum of art and design, with collections unrivalled in their scope and diversity.

Wallace Collection
Westminster W1U 3BN
(020) 7563 9551
www.wallacecollection.org
The Wallace Collection is a national museum, displaying superb works of art in an historic London town house.

Wembley Stadium Tours
Brent HA9 0WS
0844 800 2755
www.wembleystadium.com/wembleystadiumtour/default.aspx
Until your dream comes true, there's only one way to experience what it's like winning at Wembley - take the tour.

Wimbledon Lawn Tennis Museum
Merton SW19 5AG
(020) 8944 1066
www.wimbledon.org
A fantastic collection of memorabilia dating from 1555, including Championship Trophies, Art Gallery, and special exhibitions, reflecting the game and championships of today.

FAMILY FUN

Chessington World of Adventures
Kingston upon Thames KT9 2NE
0870 444 7777
www.chessington.com
Explore Chessington - it's a whole world of adventures! Soar on the Vampire rollercoaster or discover the mystery of Tomb Blaster. Take a walk on the wild side in the Trails of the Kings or visit the park's own SEA LIFE Centre.

London Eye
Lambeth SE1 7PB
0870 500 0600
www.londoneye.com
Get the best view of London when you visit The London Eye, a top London attraction and the world's largest observation wheel.

Royal Observatory Greenwich
Greenwich SE10 9NF
(020) 8858 4422
www.nmm.ac.uk/places/royal-observatory/
Stand on the Greenwich Meridian Line, Longitude Zero, which divides East and West. Watch the time-ball fall at 1 o'clock. Giant refracting telescope.

HERITAGE

Chiswick House
Hounslow W4 2RP
(020) 8995 0508
www.english-heritage.org.uk/daysout/properties/chiswick-house/
The celebrated villa of Lord Burlington with impressive grounds featuring Italianate garden with statues, temples, obelisks and urns.

Churchill Museum and Cabinet War Rooms
Westminster SW1A 2AQ
(020) 7930 6961
www.iwm.org.uk
Learn more about the man who inspired Britain's finest hour at the highly interactive and innovative Churchill Museum, the world's first major museum dedicated to life of the 'greatest Briton'. Step back in time and discover the secret.

Eltham Palace
Greenwich SE9 5QE
(020) 8294 2548
www.elthampalace.org.uk
A spectacular fusion of 1930s Art Deco villa and magnificent 15th century Great Hall. Surrounded by period gardens.

Hampton Court Palace
Richmond upon Thames
KT8 9AU
0870 752 7777
http://www.hrp.org.uk
This magnificent palace set in delightful gardens was famously one of Henry VIII's favourite palaces.

HMS Belfast
Southwark SE1 2JH
(020) 7940 6300
http://www.iwm.org.uk
HMS Belfast, launched 1938, served throughout WWII, playing a leading part in the destruction of the German battle cruiser Scharnhorst and in the Normandy Landings.

Kensington Palace State Apartments
Kensington and Chelsea
W8 4PX
0870 751 5170
http://www.hrp.org.uk
Home to the Royal Ceremonial Dress Collection, which includes some of Queen Elizabeth II's dresses worn throughout her reign, as well as 14 of Diana, Princess of Wales' evening dresses.

Kenwood House
Camden NW3 7JR
(020) 8348 1286
http://www.english-heritage.org.uk/daysout/properties/kenwood-house/
Beautiful 18th century villa with fine interiors, and a world-class collection of paintings. Also fabulous landscaped gardens and an award-winning restaurant.

Queen Elizabeth's Hunting Lodge
Waltham Forest E4 7QH
(020) 8529 6681
www.cityoflondon.gov.uk
Timber-framed hunting grandstand built in 1543 for Henry VIII. It still stands in a beautiful part of Epping Forest overlooking the old hunting field for which it was designed.

Southwark Cathedral
Southwark SE1 9DA
(020) 7367 6700
www.southwark.anglican.org/cathedral
Oldest Gothic church in London (c1220) with interesting memorials connected with the Elizabethan theatres of Bankside.

Somerset House
Westminster WC2R 1LA
(020) 7845 4670
www.somerset-house.org.uk
This magnificent 18thC building houses the celebrated collections of the Courtauld Institute of Art Gallery, Gilbert Collection and Hermitage Rooms.

Tower of London
Tower Hamlets EC3N 4AB
0870 756 6060
www.hrp.org.uk
The Tower of London spans over 900 years of British history. Fortress, palace, prison, arsenal and garrison, it is one of the most famous fortified buildings in the world, and houses the Crown Jewels, armouries, Yeoman Warders and ravens.

NATURE & WILDLIFE

London Wetland Centre
Richmond upon Thames
SW13 9WT
(020) 8409 4400
www.wwt.org.uk
The London Wetland Centre is a unique wildlife visitor attraction just 25 minutes from central London. Run by the Wildfowl and Wetlands Trust (WWT), it is acclaimed as the best urban site in Europe to watch wildlife.

ZSL London Zoo
Westminster NW1 4RY
(020) 7722 3333
www.londonzoo.co.uk
Come face to face with some of the hairiest, scariest, tallest and smallest animals on the planet - right in the heart of the capital.

OUTDOOR ACTIVITIES

Bateaux London Restaurant Cruisers
Westminster WC2N 6NU
(020) 7695 1800
www.bateauxlondon.com
Bateaux London offers lunch and dinner cruises, combining luxury dining, world-class live entertainment and five-star customer care.

London Eye River Cruise Experience
Lambeth E1 7PB
0870 500 0600
www.londoneye.com
See London from a different perspective and enjoy a unique 40 minute circular sightseeing cruise on the river Thames.

Events 2012

Head of the River Race
Various Locations
www.horr.co.uk
April

London Independent Film Festival
Various Locations
www.londonindependent.org
April

The London Book Fair
Earl's Court
www.londonbookfair.co.uk
16th - 18th April

Virgin London Marathon
London
www.virginlondonmarathon.com
22nd April

Queen's Diamond Jubilee
Various Locations
www.culture.gov.uk/diamondjubilee
2nd - 5th June

Hampton Court Flower Show
East Molesey
www.rhs.org.uk/Shows-Events
July

Wireless Festival
London
www.wirelessfestival.co.uk
July

Great British Beer Festival
London
gbbf.camra.org.uk/home
August

London Olympics
Various Locations
www.london2012.com
27th July - 12th August

One Love Festival
Hainault Forest Country Park
www.onelovefestival.co.uk
August

Notting Hill Carnival
London
www.thenottinghillcarnival.com
26th-27th August

The Mayor's Thames Festival
London
www.thamesfestival.org
September

Tourist Information Centres

When you arrive at your destination, visit an Official Partner Tourist Information Centre for quality assured help with accommodation and information about local attractions and events, or email your request before you go. To find a Tourist Information Centre by region look at http://www.enjoyengland.com under Destination Finder.

CITY OF LONDON	St Paul's Churchyard		stpauls.informationcentre@cityoflondon.gov.uk
GREENWICH	46 Greenwich Church Street	0870 608 2000	tic@greenwich.gov.uk
LEWISHAM	Lewisham Library	020 8297 8317	tic@lewisham.gov.uk

Regional Contacts and Information

For more information on accommodation, attractions, activities, events and holidays in London, contact Visit London. When you arrive at your destination, visit an Official Partner Tourist Information Centre for quality assured help, or email your request before you go.

The publications listed are available from the following organisations:

Go to **visitlondon.com** for all you need to know about London. Look for inspirational itineraries with great ideas for weekends and short breaks.

Or call 0870 1 LONDON (0870 1 566 366) for:

• **A London visitor information pack**

• **Visitor information on London**
Speak to an expert for information and advice on museums, galleries, attractions, riverboat trips, sightseeing tours, theatre, shopping, eating out and much more! Or simply go to visitlondon.com

• **Accommodation reservations**

Ratings you can trust

Wherever you see a quality rating sign, you can be sure that one of VisitEngland's professional assessors has been there before you, checking the place on your behalf – and will be there again, because every place with a national rating is assessed annually.

The star ratings reflect the quality that you're looking for when booking accommodation. All properties have to meet an extensive list of minimum requirements to take part in the scheme. From there, increased levels of quality apply. For instance, you'll find acceptable quality at one star, good quality at three star and exceptional quality at five star establishments.

Quite simply, the more stars, the higher the overall level of quality you can expect to find. Establishments at higher rating levels also have to meet some additional requirements for facilities.

Many self-catering establishments have a range of accommodation units in the building or on the site, and in some cases the individual units may have different star ratings. In such cases, the entry shows the range available.

 VisitEngland's unique Gold Awards are given in recognition of exceptional quality in self-catering accommodation. The assessors make recommendations for Gold Awards during the assessments. They will look at the quality provided in all areas, in particular housekeeping, hospitality, bedrooms and bathrooms, to see if it meets the highest quality for the star level achieved.

While star ratings are based on a combination of quality, range of facilities and level of service offered, Gold Awards are based solely on quality.

Where to Stay

Entries appear alphabetically by town name in each county. A key to symbols appears on page 6. Maps start on page 298. Further listings of VisitEngland assessed accommodation appear on the CD at the back of this guide.

LONDON E4, Inner London

SAT NAV E4 7RA

Lee Valley Campsite

Sewardstone Road, Chingford, London E4 7RA
t (020) 8529 5689 f (020) 8559 4070 e scs@leevalleypark.org.uk
w **leevalleypark.org.uk/wheretostay** ONLINE MAP GUEST REVIEWS

(65)	£12.90–£19.20
(65)	£12.90–£19.20
(35)	£12.90–£19.20
(17)	£25.00–£45.00
65 touring pitches	

An ideal holiday venue that lets you mix the pleasure of the countryside with the excitement of central London. With excellent facilities including an on-site shop and children's play area.

open Open 1 March - 31 January
payment credit/debit cards, cash, cheques

directions M25 jct 6, follow signs to Chingford. Turn left at the roundabout and the campsite is 2 miles on the right.

General ▢ ⊁ ⊾ ⑪ ⋔ ☼ ▨ ⇄ ⊕ ⏻ ☗ ⊚ Leisure ∪ ⌇ ⋀

Looking for something else?

You can also buy a copy of our popular 'B&B' guide including guest accommodation, B&B's, guest houses, farmhouses, inns, and campus and hostel accommodation in England 2012.

Now available in good bookshops and online at **visitbritainshop.com** **£8.99**

Official tourist board guide **Camping, Touring & Holiday Parks**

LONDON N9, Inner London

Lee Valley Camping and Caravan Park

Meridian Way, Edmonton, London N9 0AR
t (020) 8803 6900 **f** (020) 8884 4975 **e** leisurecomplex@leevalleypark.org.uk
w **leevalleypark.org.uk/wheretostay** ONLINE MAP

(100)	£12.90–£19.20
(100)	£12.90–£19.20
(60)	£12.90–£19.20
(12)	£25.00–£45.00
100 touring pitches	

SPECIAL PROMOTIONS
Please note different rates apply during the London 2012 events. Please visit the website for more details.

An ideal site for those who want to enjoy peace and quiet and visiting the sites within the Lee Valley Regional Park. Or alternatively ideal for those of you wishing to experience the excitement of visiting the various sites and attractions in Central London are less than an hour away.

open All year except Xmas and New Year
payment credit/debit cards, cash, cheques, euros

directions Leave M25 at J25, follow signs for City. Turn left for Freezywater at traffic lights, follow signs for Lee Valley Leisure Complex.

General 🗐 ⚛ 🐕 🏋 📖 🌣 🔌 🛏 🚰 Leisure ► ∪ ⤴ ⛰

LONDON SE2, Inner London

Abbey Wood Caravan Club Site

Federation Road, London SE2 0LS
t (020) 8311 7708
w **caravanclub.co.uk** ONLINE MAP

(210)	£16.00–£38.90
(210)	£16.00–£38.90
210 touring pitches	

With mature tree screening and spacious grounds, this gently sloping, secure site is the ideal base for exploring the capital. Nearby Greenwich also offers its own blend of fascinating attractions. **directions** On M2 turn off at A221. Then turn right into McLeod Road, right into Knee Hill. The site is the 2nd turning on the right. **open** All year **payment** credit/debit cards, cash, cheques

General 🗐 ⚛ 🐕 📖 🌣 ⊡ 🚲 🔌 🛏 🚰 Leisure ⛰

LONDON SE19, Inner London

Crystal Palace Caravan Club Site

Crystal Palace Parade, London SE19 1UF
t (020) 8778 7155 **f** (020) 8676 0980 **e** enquiries@caravanclub.co.uk
w **caravanclub.co.uk**

(126)	£16.00–£38.90
(126)	£16.00–£38.90
126 touring pitches	

A busy but friendly site on the edge of a pleasant park with many attractions for children. In close proximity to all of London's attractions. **directions** Turn off the A205, South Circular Road at West Dulwich into Croxted Road. The site is adjacent to the BBC television mast. **open** All year **payment** credit/debit cards, cash, cheques

General 🗐 ⚛ 🐕 📖 🌣 ⊡ 🔌 🛏 🚰

East of England

Bedfordshire, Cambridgeshire, Essex,
Hertfordshire, Norfolk, Suffolk

Jutting out of the East of England is the Anglo-Saxon kingdom known as East Anglia. Today fragmented into Norfolk, Suffolk, Bedfordshire, Cambridgeshire, Essex and Hertfordshire, it's known as the 'breadbasket of England'.

This region offers idyllic Broads, dramatic fens, rolling downs, a traditional coastline and some of Britain's finest gardens and wildlife habitats. If you like fine food, empty spaces and a taste of what England used to look like, make a beeline east.

History and Heritage

Three major events have shaped the ancient kingdom: the medieval Saxon invasion by the Angles (who named the place back in the 5th Century), the Viking invasion of the 8th Century, and World War Two. Sutton Hoo's Saxon treasures are housed in a brilliant museum near Woodbridge, Norwich is the most complete medieval city in England, and the 124 airfields that made up 'Little America' during WW2 are dotted throughout the region. The Aviation Museum at Duxford - home to some working Spitfires - is the one-stop-shop for all WW2 memorabilia.

Arts and Culture

"I see Gainsborough in every hedge and hollow tree," said John Constable of Suffolk's landscape, neatly linking the two artists to this beautiful county. Visit the beautiful Flatford Mill, scene of arguably Constable's most famous painting The Hay Wain, or try Ipswich's Christchurch Mansion, home to the largest collection of the artist's work. Norfolk's arts and culture scene is vibrant, with the Norfolk and Norwich Festival featuring world-class music and performing arts.

Food and Drink

Caley's Cocoa Café in the 14th Century Norwich Guildhall is home to arguably the best hot chocolate in England, though lovers of a stronger drink might prefer a visit to the Adnams Brewery in Southwold, or Greene King's Visitor Centre in Bury St Edmunds. Even stronger tastes can brave an intense mustard hit at the Coleman's Mustard Shop in Norwich, or try all three in a local pub on any given Sunday. The Norfolk Food Festival does exactly as one might expect in a region of local jam, pickle and ale makers, and is endorsed by no less a foodie goddess than Delia Smith herself.

Sports

East Anglia is also the global-centre for thoroughbred buying, though if you haven't the riches to bag a descendent of Red Rum you can always visit the world-famous National Stud in the horse racing capital of Newmarket to see how it's done. The area has more than its fair share of golf courses and for the less proficient plenty of Crazy Golf, particularly at coastal towns including the fun-packed Great Yarmouth and Southend.

Music and Nightlife

Throughout East Anglia there is a marvellous choice of pubs (many with live music), restaurants and clubs. Cambridge, mainly because of its student population, has a lively night scene. The 1300 seat, art-deco Theatre Royal, Norwich recently renovated and modernised stages popular performances including Opera and drama. The Comedy Store offers a unique cabaret style setting for some of the very best comedians.

Shopping

If it's quality farm produce you're after, there are plenty of local fairs, including the twice-monthly Stow Market, to rummage around. Norwich is home to Chapelfield shopping centre as well as lots of individual shops in and around the lanes. Head to historic St Albans for high street names, as well as many specialist shops offering antiques and books

Family Fun

Thetford Forest's mountain bike trails and Go Ape! rope walks are the perfect place for energetic nippers, and nearby Pleasurewood Hills in Lowestoft will get you a high five too. Nature-loving kids will love a trip to the Broads National Park, where The Canoe Man (aka ranger Mark Wilkinson) takes kids on a hushed, otter-spotting hunt through the reeds.

Handy Hints

Early Birds – Spot the sun peeping up on the horizon from Lowestoft Ness and you'll be the first person in the UK to do so. It's the eastern-most point of the country.

Pinkie in the Air – If you're enjoying an afternoon tea of cucumber sandwiches, tea and a Victoria Sponge in its birthplace, you're at Woburn Abbey.

Charming - England's smallest pub in Bury St Edmunds. And delightful Southwold pier.

Locked Out – Love the idea of a canal boat holiday but don't fancy going through a lock? The Norfolk Broads is a huge network of waterways, all lock-free.

OUT & ABOUT IN THE EAST OF ENGLAND

Day 1 - Fine Crockery and Spitfires

- See WW2's finest planes at the Duxford Aviation Museum
- Pop in to see the Queen at Sandringham near Norfolk
- Visit Colchester - the oldest town in England no less

Day 2 - Towers and Grand Designs

- Take a sneak at one of the three buildings featured on C4's Grand Designs TV show
- See the fairytale-like House-in-the-Clouds in Thorpeness
- The 12th century Framlingham Castle is a medieval masterpiece

Day 3 - Fish and Chips

- Wake up on the Sunrise Coast - from Lowestoft to Southwold - the eastern most point of the UK
- Try the Quantum Tunneling Telescope on Southwold Pier
- Hit Aldeburgh for Fish & Chips; sit on the sea wall scoffing

Day 4 - Get Wet

- Take a surf lesson on Cromer Beach - the closest real surfer's waves to London
- Try the White Water Rafting Centre at Lee Valley Regional Park
- Try kiteboarding at Hunstanton Beach, the UK home of the sport

Day 5 - Squeeze in some Wares

- The Nutshell, Bury St Edmunds, England's smallest pub
- Coleman's Mustard Shop, Norwich
- Adnams Brewery, home of the Ghost Ship Ale, Southwold

Day 6 - Adventure

- Ride Thetford Forest's mountain bike trails
- Join an Otter Hunt in the Broads National Park
- Get white knuckles on the rollercoasters at Pleasurewood Hills

Day 7 - Bridleways and Saddles

- Visit the National Stud, the global home of thoroughbred breeding
- Take in a horse race at Newmarket, where it all began
- Pony Trek through Walsingham

Where to Go

 Attractions with this sign participate in the **Places of Interest Quality Assurance Scheme**.

Attractions with this sign participate in the **Visitor Attraction Quality Assurance Scheme**.

Both schemes recognise high standards in all aspects of the visitor experience (see page 6)

ENTERTAINMENT & CULTURE

Central Museum and Planetarium
Southend-on-Sea, Essex SS2 6ES
(01702) 434449
www.southendmuseums.co.uk
An Edwardian building housing displays of archaeology, natural history, social and local history.

Gainsborough's House
Sudbury, Suffolk CO10 2EU
(01787) 372958
www.gainsborough.org
Gainsborough's House is the only museum situated in the birthplace of a great British artist. The permanent collection is built around the works of Thomas Gainsborough.

Hitchin Museum and Art Gallery
Hertfordshire SG5 1EH
(01462) 434476
www.north-herts.gov.uk/art_museums_and_heritage.htm
Local history museum and art gallery which tells the story of Hitchin. Two art galleries. Victorian pharmacy, costume gallery, and more.

Imperial War Museum Duxford
Cambridge CB22 4QR
(01223) 835000
www.iwm.org.uk/duxford
With its air shows, unique history and atmosphere, nowhere else combines the sights, sounds and power of aircraft quite like Duxford.

National Horseracing Museum and Tours
Newmarket, Suffolk CB8 8JH
(01638) 667333
www.nhrm.co.uk
Discover the stories of racing from its early origins at Newmarket to its modern-day heroes

Norwich Castle Museum and Art Gallery
Norfolk NR1 3JU
(01603) 493625
www.museums.norfolk.gov.uk
Ancient Norman keep of Norwich Castle dominates the city and is one of the most important buildings of its kind in Europe.

Peterborough Museum and Art Gallery
Cambridgeshire PE1 1LF
(01733) 864663
www.peterborough.gov.uk/leisure_and_culture/museum_and_galleries.aspx
Discover the rich & varied history of the Peterborough area - from Jurassic Sea Monsters to Napoleonic Prisoners of War to the haunted Museum building.

Royal Gunpowder Mills
Waltham Abbey, Essex EN9 1JY
(01992) 707370
www.royalgunpowdermills.com
A spectacular 170-acre location for a day of family fun. Special events including Spitfire flypast, award winning Secret History exhibition, tranquil wildlife walks, guided land train tours and rocket science gallery.

FAMILY FUN

Adventure Island
Southend-on-Sea, Essex SS1 1EE
(01702) 443400
www.adventureisland.co.uk
One of the best value 'theme parks' in the South East with over 60 great rides and attractions for all ages. No admission charge you only 'pay if you play'.

Bodyflight Bedford
Clapham, MK41 6AE
0845 200 2960
www.bodyflight.co.uk
Indoor Skydiving! Learn to fly like a skydiver on a vertical column of air! Offering lessons for all abilities.

Go Ape! High Wire Forest Adventure - Thetford
Santon Downham, Suffolk IP27 0AF
0845 643 9215
www.goape.co.uk
Take to the trees and experience an exhilarating course of rope bridges, tarzan swings and zip slides...all set high above the forest floor.

Go Ape! High Wire Forest Adventure - Woburn Safari Park
Milton Keynes, Bedfordshire MK17 9QN
0845 643 9215
www.goape.co.uk
Take to the trees and experience an exhilarating course of rope bridges, tarzan swings and zip slides...all set high above the forest floor.

Sea-Life Adventure
Southend-on-Sea, Essex SS1 2ER
(01702) 442200
www.sealifeadventure.co.uk
With more than 30 display tanks and tunnels to explore, there are loads of fishy residents to discover at Sea-Life Adventure.

The National Stud
Newmarket, Cambridgeshire CB8 0XE
(01638) 663464
www.nationalstud.co.uk
The beautiful grounds & facilities are a recognised tourist attraction in the eastern region.

HERITAGE

Audley End House and Gardens
Saffron Walden, Essex CB11 4JF
(01799) 522842
www.english-heritage.org.uk/audleyend
Audley End is one of England's most magnificent stately homes.

Blickling Hall, Gardens and Park
Norwich, Norfolk NR11 6NF
(01263) 738030
www.nationaltrust.org.uk/blickling
A Jacobean redbrick mansion with a garden, orangery, parkland and lake. Spectacular long gallery, plasterwork ceilings and fine collections of furniture, pictures and books. Walks.

Bressingham Steam and Gardens
Diss, Norfolk IP22 2AA
(01379) 686900
www.bressingham.co.uk
World-renowned gardener and horticulturalist Alan Bloom combined his passion for plants and gardens with his love of steam, to create a truly unique attraction at Bressingham.

Cathedral and Abbey Church of St Alban
St. Albans, Hertfordshire AL1 1BY
(01727) 860780
www.stalbanscathedral.org
St Alban is Britain's first Christian martyr and the Cathedral, with its shrine, is its oldest place of continuous worship.

Holkham Hall
Wells-next-the-Sea, Norfolk NR23 1AB
(01328) 710227
www.holkham.co.uk
Magnificent Palladian hall. Rolling parkland. A wealth of wildlife. The best beach in England.

Ickworth House, Park and Gardens
Bury St. Edmunds, Suffolk IP29 5QE
(01284) 735270
www.nationaltrust.org.uk/ickworth
Fine paintings, a beautiful collection of Georgian silver, an Italianate garden and stunning parkland.

Kings College Chapel
Cambridge CB2 1ST
(01223) 331212
www.kings.cam.ac.uk
It's part of one of the oldest Cambridge colleges sharing a wonderful sense of history and tradition with the rest of the University.

Knebworth House
Hertfordshire SG1 2AX
(01438) 812661
www.knebworthhouse.com
Historic house, home to the Lytton family since 1490.

Oliver Cromwell's House
Ely, Cambridgeshire CB7 4HF
(01353) 662062
www.olivercromwellshouse.co.uk
Visit the former Lord Protector's family's home and experience an exhibition on 17th Century life.

Sandringham
King's Lynn, Norfolk PE35 6EN
(01485) 545408
www.sandringhamestate.co.uk
H.M. The Queen. A fascinating house, an intriguing museum and the best of the Royal gardens.

Somerleyton Hall and Gardens
Lowestoft, Suffolk NR32 5QQ
(01502) 734901
www.somerleyton.co.uk
12 acres of landscaped gardens to explore including our famous 1864 Yew hedge maze. Guided tours of the Hall.

NATURE & WILDLIFE

Banham Zoo
Norwich, Norfolk NR16 2HE
(01953) 887771
www.banhamzoo.co.uk
Wildlife spectacular which will take you on a journey to experience tigers, leopards and zebra plus some of the world's most exotic, rare and endangered animals.

Colchester Zoo
Essex CO3 0SL
(01206) 331292
www.colchester-zoo.com
Enjoy daily displays, feed elephants and giraffes and see over 260 species in over 60 acres of parkland!

Fritton Lake Country World
Great Yarmouth, Norfolk NR31 9HA
(01493) 488288
A woodland and lakeside haven with a children's assault course, putting, an adventure playground, golf, fishing, boating, wildfowl, heavy horses, cart rides, falconry and flying displays.

The Raptor Foundation
Huntingdon, Cambridgeshire PE28 3BT
(01487) 741140
www.raptorfoundation.org.uk
Bird of prey centre, offering 3 daily flying displays with audience participation, gift shop, Silent Wings tearoom, Raptor crafts shop.

RHS Garden Hyde Hall
Chelmsford, Essex CM3 8AT
(01245) 400256
www.rhs.org.uk/hydehall
A garden of inspiration beauty with an eclectic range of horticultural styles from traditional to modern providing year round interest.

RSPB Minsmere Nature Reserve
Saxmundham, Suffolk IP17 3BY
(01728) 648281
www.rspb.org.uk/minsmere
One of the UK's premier nature reserves, offering excellent facilities for people of all ages and abilities.

WWT Welney Wetland Centre
Wisbech, Norfolk PE14 9TN
(01353) 860711
www.wwt.org.uk/welney
A wetland nature reserve of 1,000 acres attracting large numbers of ducks and swans in winter and waders in spring and summer plus a range of wild plants and butterflies.

ZSL Whipsnade Zoo
Dunstable, Bedfordshire LU6 2LF
(01582) 872171
www.zsl.org/zsl-whipsnade-zoo
ZSL Whipsnade Zoo is one of Europe's largest wildlife conservation parks.

Woburn Safari Park
Bedfordshire MK17 9QN
(01525) 290407
www.woburn.co.uk
Drive through the safari park with 30 species of animals in natural groups just a windscreen's width away.

Events 2012

East Anglian Dragon Boat Festival
Oulton Broad
www.dragonboatfestivals.co.uk
May

Hertfordshire County Show
Redbourn
www.hertsshow.com
May

King's Lynn May Garland Procession
King's Lynn
www.thekingsmorris.co.uk
May

Luton International Carnival
Luton
www.luton.gov.uk
May

Aldeburgh Festival of Music and the Art
Saxmundham
www.aldeburgh.co.uk
June

Cambridgeshire County Show
Royston
www.cambscountyshow.co.uk
June

East of England Show
Peterborough
www.eastofengland.org.uk
June

Royal Norfolk Show
Norwich
www.royalnorfolkshow.co.uk
June

Suffolk Show
Ipswich
www.suffolkshow.co.uk
June

St. Albans Festival
St. Albans
www.stalbans.gov.uk
June - July

Bedfordshire County Show
Biggleswade
www.shuttleworth.org
July

Cambridge Folk Festival
Cherry Hinton
www.cambridgefolkfestival.co.uk
July

Dunstable Downs Kite Festival
Dunstable
www.dunstablekitefestival.co.uk
July

Hitchin Festival
Hitchin
www.htci.org.uk
July

Latitude Festival
Southwold
www.mywebsite.co.uk
July

Rhythms of the World
Hitchin
www.rotw.org.uk
July

Chilli Festival
Stevenage
www.beningtonlordship.co.uk
August

Southend Carnival
Southend-on-Sea
www.southend-on-seacarnival.org.uk
August

Aldeburgh Food and Drink Festival
Saxmundham
www.aldeburghfoodanddrink.co.uk
September - October

Great Yarmouth Maritime Festival
Great Yarmouth
www.maritime-festival.co.uk
September

The Duxford Air Show
Cambridge
www.iwm.org.uk/duxford
September

Woburn Oyster Festival
Woburn
www.woburnoysterfestival.co.uk
September

Bedford Beer and Cider Festival
Bedford
www.northbedscamra.org.uk
October

World Conker Championship
Oundle
www.worldconkerchampionships.com
October

Tourist Information Centres

When you arrive at your destination, visit an Official Partner Tourist Information Centre for quality assured help with accommodation and information about local attractions and events, or email your request before you go. To find a Tourist Information Centre by region look at http://www.enjoyengland.com under Destination Finder.

ALDEBURGH	152 High Street	01728 453637	atic@suffolkcoastal.gov.uk
BEDFORD	St Pauls Square	01234 221712	TouristInfo@bedford.gov.uk
BISHOP'S STORTFORD	The Old Monastery	01279 655831	tic@bishopsstortford.org
BURY ST EDMUNDS	6 Angel Hill	01284 764667	tic@stedsbc.gov.uk
CAMBRIDGE	Wheeler Street	0871 226 8006	tourism@cambridge.gov.uk
COLCHESTER	1 Queen Street	01206 282920	vic@colchester.gov.uk
DISS	Meres Mouth	01379 650523	dtic@s-norfolk.gov.uk
ELY	Oliver Cromwell's House	01353 662062	tic@eastcambs.gov.uk
FELIXSTOWE	91 Undercliff Road West	01394 276770	ftic@suffolkcoastal.gov.uk
GREAT YARMOUTH	25 Marine Parade	01493 846345	dnh@great-yarmouth.gov.uk
HUNSTANTON	Town Hall	01485 532610	hunstanton.tic@west-norfolk.gov.uk
IPSWICH	St Stephens Church	01473 258070	tourist@ipswich.gov.uk
KING'S LYNN	The Custom House	01553 763044	kings-lynn.tic@west-norfolk.gov.uk
LAVENHAM	Lady Street	01787 248207	lavenhamtic@babergh.gov.uk
LETCHWORTH GARDEN CITY	33-35 Station Road	01462 487868	tic@letchworth.com
LOWESTOFT	East Point Pavilion	01502 533600	touristinfo@waveney.gov.uk
LUTON	Luton Central Library	01582 401579	tourist.information@luton.gov.uk
MALDON	Wenlock Way	01621 856503	tic@maldon.gov.uk
NEWMARKET	Palace House	01638 667200	tic.newmarket@forest-heath.gov.uk
NORWICH	The Forum	01603 213999	tourism@norwich.gov.uk
PETERBOROUGH	3-5 Minster Precincts	01733 452336	tic@peterborough.gov.uk
SAFFRON WALDEN	1 Market Place	01799 510444	tourism@uttlesford.gov.uk

SLEAFORD	Advice Centre, Money's Yard,	01529 414294	tic@n-kesteven.gov.uk
SOUTHEND-ON-SEA	Pier Entrance	01702 215620	vic@southend.gov.uk
SOUTHWOLD	69 High Street	01502 724729	southwold.tic@waveney.gov.uk
ST ALBANS	Town Hall	01727 864511	tic@stalbans.gov.uk
STOWMARKET	The Museum of East Anglian Life	01449 676800	tic@midsuffolk.gov.uk
SUDBURY	Town Hall	01787 881320	sudburytic@babergh.gov.uk
WITHAM	61 Newland Street	01376 502674	tic@witham.gov.uk
WOODBRIDGE	Station Buildings	01394 382240	wtic@suffolkcoastal.gov.uk

Regional Contacts and Information

For more information on accommodation, attractions, activities, events and holidays in East of England, contact the regional or local tourism organisations. Their websites have a wealth of information and many produce free publications to help you get the most out of your visit.

East of England Tourism

Tel: (01284) 727470
Email: info@eet.org.uk
Web: www.visiteastofengland.com

The comprehensive website is updated daily. Online brochures and information sheets can be downloaded including Whats's New; Major Events; Stars and Stripes (connections with the USA) and a range of Discovery Tours around the region.

Where to Stay

Entries appear alphabetically by town name in each county. A key to symbols appears on page 6. Maps start on page 298. Further listings of VisitEngland assessed accommodation appear on the CD at the back of this guide.

CAMBRIDGE, Cambridgeshire Map ref 2D1

SAT NAV CB1 8NQ

Cherry Hinton Caravan Club Site

Lime Kiln Road, Cherry Hinton, Cambridge, Cambridgeshire CB1 8NQ
t (01223) 244088 **f** (01223) 412546 **e** enquiries@caravanclub.co.uk
w caravanclub.co.uk

(60)   £15.90–£35.51
(60)   £15.90–£35.51
60 touring pitches

Set within a site of special scientific interest, bordered by a nature trail. 10 minute bus journey into Cambridge. Guided walks along the backs on the River Cam. **directions** M11 jct 9 onto A11. After 7 miles slip road signposted Fulbourn. Continue to roundabout signposted Cambridge. Left at lights. Left onto Lime Kiln Road.
open All year **payment** credit/debit cards, cash, cheques

General 🖥 ♿ 📶 📷 ☼ 🛒 🔌 🔄 🚿 🅿 **Leisure** ▶ ⚓

Looking for something else?

You can also buy a copy of our popular guide 'Hotels' including country house and town house hotels, metro and budget hotels, serviced apartments and restaurants with rooms in England 2012.

Now available in good bookshops and online at **visitbritainshop.com**   £7.99

CAMBRIDGE, Cambridgeshire Map ref 2D1

SAT NAV CB23 7DG

Highfield Farm Touring Park

Long Road, Comberton, Cambridge CB23 7DG
t (01223) 262308 **f** (01223) 262308 **e** enquiries@highfieldfarmtouringpark.co.uk
w **highfieldfarmtouringpark.co.uk** ONLINE MAP GUEST REVIEWS

🚐 (60) £13.00–£17.00
🚕 (60) £13.00–£17.00
🛖 (60) £11.00–£16.00
120 touring pitches

SPECIAL PROMOTIONS
Low-season rate for Senior
Citizens - 10% discount for
stay of 3 nights or longer.

A popular, family-run park with excellent facilities close to the university city of Cambridge and
Imperial War Museum, Duxford. Ideally situated for touring East Anglia within easy access of the
Cambridge park and rides. Please view our website for further information.

open April to October
payment cash, cheques, euros

directions A428 to Bedford. After 3 miles, left
at roundabout, follow sign to Comberton. From
M11 jct 12, A603 to Sandy. Then B1046 to
Comberton.

General 🗐 ⛺ 🐾 🎮 📷 ☼ 🖥 🚲 🍴 🎱 🚽 🚿 🖥 Leisure ► ∪ ♪ ⚲

HEMINGFORD ABBOTS, Cambridgeshire Map ref 3A2

SAT NAV PE28 9AJ

Quiet Waters Caravan Park

Hemingford Abbots, Huntingdon PE28 9AJ
t (01480) 463405 **f** (01480) 463405 **e** quietwaters.park@btopenworld.com
w **quietwaterscaravanpark.co.uk**

🚐 (20) £15.50–£19.50
🚕 (20) £15.50–£19.50
🛖 (20) £15.50–£19.50
🏠 (9) £295.00–£423.00
20 touring pitches

A quiet riverside park situated in centre of picturesque village.
Many local walks and cycle routes. Ideal for fishing from own
banks. Family run. **directions** Junction 25 off the A14. 13 miles
from Cambridge, 5 miles from Huntingdon. Nearest town St Ives 2
miles. **open** April to October **payment** credit/debit cards, cash,
cheques

General 🗐 ⛽ 🐾 🎮 📷 ☼ 🎱 🚽 🚿 Leisure ∪ ♪

HUNTINGDON, Cambridgeshire Map ref 3A2

SAT NAV PE28 0BB

Grafham Water Caravan Club Site

Church Road, Grafham, Huntingdon, Cambridgeshire PE28 0BB
t (01480) 810264 **e** enquiries@caravanclub.co.uk
w **caravanclub.co.uk**

THE CARAVAN CLUB

🚐 (69) £15.30–£35.50
🚕 (69) £15.30–£35.50
69 touring pitches

Attractive site half a mile north of Grafham Water. Heated outdoor
swimming pool and children's play area. Cycling, horse riding,
tennis and golf nearby. **directions** Turn left off A1 at roundabout in
Buckden onto B661; turn right and follow caravan signs. **payment**
credit/debit cards, cash, cheques

General 🗐 ⛽ 🐾 🎮 📷 🎱 🚽 🚿 🖥 Leisure ∪ ⚲ ♪ ⚲ ⚲

HUNTINGDON, Cambridgeshire Map ref 3A2 SAT NAV PE28 2AZ

Houghton Mill Caravan Club Site

Mill Street, Houghton, Huntingdon, Cambridgeshire PE28 2AZ
t (01480) 466716 **e** enquiries@caravanclub.co.uk
w caravanclub.co.uk

CARAVAN CLUB

(54) £15.30–£35.51
(54) £15.30–£35.51
54 touring pitches

Spectacular views across the river to the National Trust's Houghton Mill, the last working watermill on this river. There's an abundance of footpaths and bridleways. **directions** From Houghton village continue straight through market square into Mill Street, pass church on right. Site entrance on left before last house. **open** April to November **payment** credit/debit cards, cash, cheques

General Leisure

HUNTINGDON, Cambridgeshire Map ref 3A2 SAT NAV PE28 2AA

Wyton Lakes Holiday Park

Banks End, Wyton, Huntingdon PE28 2AA
t (01480) 412715 **f** (01480) 412715 **e** loupeter@supanet.com
w wytonlakes.com ONLINE MAP

(60) £17.00
(60) £17.00
(20) £14.00
80 touring pitches

Adults-only park. Some pitches beside the on-site carp and coarse-fishing lakes. River frontage. Close to local amenities. **directions** Exit 23 off A14. Follow signs A141 March. Go past 4 roundabouts. At 4th roundabout A1123 to St Ives. Park approx 1 mile on right. **open** April to October **payment** cash, cheques

General Leisure

PETERBOROUGH, Cambridgeshire Map ref 3A1 SAT NAV PE2 5UU

Ferry Meadows Caravan Club Site

Ham Lane, Peterborough, Cambridgeshire PE2 5UU
t (01733) 233526 **e** enquiries@caravanclub.co.uk
w caravanclub.co.uk

CARAVAN CLUB

(265) £15.30–£35.50
(265) £15.30–£35.50
265 touring pitches

Set in a country park with steam trains, cycle and walking trails. Enjoy sailing, windsurfing and coarse fishing or a visit to Peterborough. **directions** From any direction, on approaching Peterborough, follow the brown signs to Nene Park and Ferry Meadows. **open** All year **payment** credit/debit cards, cash, cheques

General Leisure

COLCHESTER, Essex Map ref 3B2 SAT NAV CO5 8UA

Cosways Holiday Park

Fen Lane, East Mersea, Colchester CO5 8UA
t (01206) 383252 **f** (01206) 383252 **e** holidays@cosways.co.uk
w cosways.co.uk LAST MINUTE OFFERS

(3) £235.00–£495.00

Quiet family Holiday Park in rural East Mersea. Outdoor heated swimming pool, shop, clubhouse, private beach, Holiday homes for sale & hire. Use of nearby fishing, golf and entertainment facilities. **directions** Exit A12 at J26, follow signs B1025 to Mersea. Cross the Causeway, turn left to East Mersea. Take second right past Dog & Pheasant pub. **payment** credit/debit cards, cash, cheques

General Leisure

MERSEA ISLAND, Essex Map ref 3B3

SAT NAV CO5 8SE

Waldegraves Holiday Park
Waldegraves Lane, West Mersea, Colchester CO5 8SE
t (01206) 382898 f (01206) 385359 e holidays@waldegraves.co.uk
w **waldegraves.co.uk** ONLINE MAP ONLINE BOOKING LAST MINUTE OFFERS

⏻ (60)	£16.00–£26.00
⏚ (60)	£16.00–£26.00
▲ (60)	£16.00–£26.00
⌂ (25)	£235.00–£495.00
60 touring pitches	

Ideal family park, grassland sheltered with trees and four fishing lakes, undercover golf driving range, pitch and putt, heated swimming pool, private beach, two play areas. Licensed bar and restaurant. **directions** Junction 26 off A12 join B1025 to Mersea Island cross the Strood take left fork to East Mersea. 2nd right. **open** March to November **payment** credit/debit cards, cash, cheques

General ▯ ⓦ ⛺ ⚞ ⬛ ⛺ ☼ 🔌 🛏 🛉 ✕   Leisure ▶ ♪ ⚓ 🍴 ♫ ◆ ⛰

Looking for something else?

You can also buy a copy of our popular guide 'Self Catering' including self-catering holiday homes, approved caravan holiday homes, boat accommodation and holiday cottage agencies in England 2012.

Now available in good bookshops and online at
visitbritainshop.com   **£8.99**

ST. LAWRENCE, Essex Map ref 3B3

St. Lawrence Holiday Park
10 Main Road, St. Lawrence Bay, Southminster CM0 7LY
t (01621) 779434 **f** (01621) 778311 **e** office@slcaravans.co.uk
w slcaravans.co.uk

St. Lawrence Holiday Home Park pride themselves on offering a peaceful tranquil setting that enables their guests to make the most of their precious holiday time, so much so, that some customers have been on the park for over fifty years!

Gary & Karen and the team always look forward to welcoming new customers and usually have a great range of caravans for sale to suit most tastes and budgets! Gary & Karen have always believed in the sustainability of the caravan holiday and this belief has been reinforced with the continuing support of many loyal customers.

Over the last ten years there has been major reinvestment and redevelopment of the Park with the installation a high speed Wi-Fi network, a launching ramp for the beach and expansion of the St. Lawrence Inn to include a children's room and an Indian restaurant, The Indian Ocean, offering fine cuisine and take-away menu. This quality graded Park was a finalist in the 2010 Caravan Park Essex Tourism awards.

directions On the A130 turn exit at Rettendon turnpike take A132 towards South Woodham Ferrers. Then the B1012 to Latchingdon, at the Church turn left into Bradwell Road, follow our brown Tourism, though Mayland and Steeple, turn left into Main Road. The Park is 1km on the right hand side

General 🏕 🐾 📻 💬 🔌 ✕ Leisure ▶ 🏌 🎱 🎵 🎤

BACTON, Norfolk Map ref 3C1

SAT NAV NR12 0JB

Castaways Holiday Park
Paston Road, Bacton-on-Sea, North Walsham NR12 0JB
t (01692) 650436 e anna.hollis@castawaysholidaypark.net
w **castawaysholidaypark.net** ONLINE MAP GUEST REVIEWS

A family run Holiday Park overlooking the sea incorporating Static Caravans, Pine Lodges and Apartments. Facilities include: Shop, Reception, Childrens Playground, Clubhouse with Entertainment, Amusement Arcade. Pets welcome. **directions** Please contact us for directions **open** All year **payment** credit/debit cards, cash, cheques

🏠 (3)	£200.00–£588.00
🚐 (5)	£170.00–£403.00
🏕 (34)	£120.00–£568.00

General 🔥🖥♿🅿️🚭🛒💷✕ Leisure ∪⚓🚴🌊🎾🍴🎵🎱🎢

BURGH ST. PETER, Norfolk Map ref 3C1

SAT NAV NR34 0BT

Waveney River Centre
Staithe Road, Burgh St. Peter, Norfolk NR34 0BT
t (01502) 677343 f (01502) 677566 e info@waveneyrivercentre.co.uk
w **waveneyrivercentre.co.uk** ONLINE MAP GUEST REVIEWS ONLINE BOOKING LAST MINUTE OFFERS

Multi-award winning Holiday Park & Marina on the Broads. Stunning views across marshes and river. The Park is a wildlife haven. Explore the river by day cruiser or canoe. **directions** A143 to Haddiscoe and follow brown signs to Waveney River Centre. Turn left into Burgh Road (2 miles) and travel 2.5 miles until you arrive. **open** All year **payment** credit/debit cards, cash, cheques

🚐 (17)	£14.00–£33.00
🚐 (14)	£14.00–£33.00
⛺ (35)	£8.00–£28.00
🏠 (13)	£275.00–£925.00
🏠 (3)	£275.00–£825.00
🏕 (2)	£225.00–£535.00

17 touring pitches

General 🖥♿🚭🛒🏠📷☀️🅿️🔄🍴✕ Leisure ►🚴🌊🎾🍴🎵🎱🎢

BURNHAM MARKET, Norfolk Map ref 3B1

SAT NAV PE31 8DD

Deepdale Backpackers and Camping
Deepdale Information Centre, Burnham Deepdale, Norfolk PE31 8DD
t (01485) 210256 f (01485) 210158 e info@deepdalebackpackers.co.uk
w **deepdalebackpackers.co.uk** ONLINE MAP GUEST REVIEWS LAST MINUTE OFFERS

Ecofriendly award winning hostel and camping on the beautiful north Norfolk coast. Offering private ensuite rooms, dorm beds, tipis, yurts, camping for tents and small campervans. **directions** Halfway between Hunstanton and Wells-next-the-Sea on the A149 coast road. Coasthopper bus service stops at Deepdale, connecting with trains and national coaches at King's Lynn. **open** All year **payment** credit/debit cards, cash, cheques

🚐 (82)	£4.50–£9.00
⛺ (82)	£4.50–£9.00

General 🔥🖥♿🚭🛒🏠📷☀️🔄🔄✕ Leisure ►🎾🚴🌊

Looking for something else?

You can also buy a copy of our popular 'B&B' guide including guest accommodation, B&B's, guest houses, farmhouses, inns, and campus and hostel accommodation in England 2012.

Now available in good bookshops and online at

visitbritainshop.com　　　　**£8.99**

CAISTER-ON-SEA, Norfolk Map ref 3C1   SAT NAV NR30 5HH

Eastern Beach Holiday Park

Manor Road, Caister-on-Sea, Great Yarmouth NR30 5HH
t (01493) 720367 e beach_h.penman@bt.connect.com
w **easternbeachcaravanpark.co.uk** ONLINE MAP ONLINE BOOKING LAST MINUTE OFFERS

🚐 (50)   £30.00–£100.00
🚆 (2)   £99.00–£525.00
🚉 (50)   £99.00–£525.00

SPECIAL PROMOTIONS
Short breaks from £99.00
first week of school holidays
£399.00 August bank
holiday £80.00 a night min
3 nights.

We are a independent 4 star park, over looking a golden stretch of beach, ideal setting for individuals and families who enjoy the seaside and norfolk broads with fishing, golf courses near by. On the park are bars, restaurant, games room arcade with bowling alley, childrens play area, and launderette.

open All year
payment credit/debit cards, cash, cheques

directions M11/A11/A12/A14 from London and south east, while the A47 and A14 serve the midlands and the north. from Great Yarmouth follow to Caister.

General 🗓 ⌂ 🐕 🏠 ☼ ✕   Leisure ▶ ∪ ⚓ 🍸 🎵 ✎ 🎢

CAISTER-ON-SEA, Norfolk Map ref 3C1   SAT NAV NR30 5DH

Wentworth Holidays

Bultitudes Loke, Caister on Sea, Great Yarmouth, Norfolk NR30 5DH
t (01493) 720382 f (01493) 377573 e donaldpeers@hotmail.co.uk
w **grasmere-wentworth.co.uk**

🚆 (12)   £155.00–£385.00

Wentworth is a small family run chalet site adjacent to Grasmere Caravan Park. All chalets are fully equipped including towels and bedding, also four wheelchair friendly units. **directions** From A149 Great Yarmouth enter at Stadium roundabout 1/2 mile concealed turning just after blue house on the left. **open** March-October **payment** credit/debit cards, cash, cheques

General 🗓 ☼

CROMER, Norfolk Map ref 3C1   SAT NAV NR11 7HN

Deer's Glade Caravan and Camping Park

Whitepost Road, Hanworth, Norwich NR11 7HN
t (01263) 768633 f (01263) 768328 e info@deersglade.co.uk
w **deersglade.co.uk** ONLINE MAP ONLINE BOOKING

🚐 (100)   £11.50–£15.50
🚲 (100)   £11.50–£15.50
⛺ (125)   £11.50–£15.50
125 touring pitches

A quiet, rural, family-run park in a lovely woodland clearing, in north Norfolk. Ideal for walking, fishing, cycling, spotting wildlife and visiting the north Norfolk coast and Norfolk Broads. **directions** Halfway between Aylsham and Cromer, turn off A140 towards Suffield Green. The park is half a mile on the right. **open** All year **payment** credit/debit cards, cash

General ⟲ 🗓 ⌂ 🐕 🛍 🏠 ☼ 🚰 🍴 ◻ 🚿 🛒   Leisure ∪ ⚑ ⚓ 🎢

CROMER, Norfolk Map ref 3C1

SAT NAV NR27 9NH

Seacroft Caravan Club Site

Runton Road, Cromer NR27 9NH
t (01263) 514938 e enquiries@caravanclub.co.uk
w **caravanclub.co.uk**

THE
CARAVAN
CLUB

(94) £16.50–£42.20
(94) £16.50–£42.20
94 touring pitches

Ideal site for a family holiday. Leisure complex including bar, restaurant and outdoor heated swimming pool. Golf, sea and fresh water fishing and birdwatching nearby. **directions** Turn left off A149 (Cromer-Sheringham). Site entrance on left in 1 mile. **open** April 2010 to January 2011 **payment** credit/debit cards, cash, cheques

General Leisure

GREAT HOCKHAM, Norfolk Map ref 3B1

Thetford Forest Camping and Caravan Club Site

Puddledock Farm, Great Hockham, Thetford, Norfolk IP24 1PA
t (01953) 498455 e thetford@thefriendlyclub.co.uk
w **campingandcaravanningclub.co.uk/thetfordforest** ONLINE MAP GUEST REVIEWS

The
Camping and
Caravanning
Club
The Friendly Club

£23.00–£26.00
£23.00–£26.00
£23.00–£26.00
150 touring pitches

Surrounded by natural history, home to rare butterflies and plants and you may spot red, roe or muntjac deer. Cycling routes, sculpture trails and Go Ape close by. **directions** From the A1075 (Thetford) look out for picnic spot then brown signs to the left. Do not use site postcode in Satnav. **open** All year **payment** credit/debit cards, cash, cheques

General Leisure

GREAT YARMOUTH, Norfolk Map ref 3C1

SAT NAV NR30 5DH

Grasmere Caravan Park

9 Bultitudes Loke, Caister on Sea, Great Yarmouth, Norfolk NR30 5DH
t (01493) 720382 f (01493) 377573 e donaldpeers@hotmail.co.uk
w **grasmere-wentworth.co.uk**

(40) £16.00–£20.00
(6) £16.00–£20.00
(1) £180.00–£395.00
(11) £120.00–£405.00
40 touring pitches

Grasmere is a family run business suitable for those looking for a quieter holiday. Touring pitches and Static vans are available for hire. **directions** From A149 Great Yarmouth enter at Stadium roundabout 1/2 mile concealed turning just after blue house on the left. **open** April to October **payment** credit/debit cards, cash, cheques

General Leisure

GREAT YARMOUTH, Norfolk Map ref 3C1

SAT NAV NR30 4AU

Great Yarmouth Racecourse Caravan Club Site

Jellicoe Road, Great Yarmouth, Norfolk NR30 4AU
t (01493) 855223 e enquiries@caravanclub.co.uk
w **caravanclub.co.uk**

THE
CARAVAN
CLUB

(115) £13.50–£32.79
(115) £13.50–£32.79
115 touring pitches

Spacious, level site in a very popular family resort offering wide, sandy beaches, countless seaside attractions and fishing, golf, sailboarding, ballroom dancing and bowls. **directions** Travel north on A149, left at lights into Jellicoe Road. Within 0.25 miles, left into racecourse entrance. **open** April to November **payment** credit/debit cards, cash, cheques

General Leisure

GREAT YARMOUTH, Norfolk Map ref 3C1   SAT NAV NR29 3NW

Summerfields Holiday Park
Beach Road, Scratby, Great Yarmouth NR29 3NW
t (01692) 582277 f (01493) 730292 e info@richardsonsgroup.net
w **richardsonsholidayparks.co.uk** ONLINE BOOKING LAST MINUTE OFFERS

£125.00–£550.00
£250.00–£550.00

Featuring an indoor heated pool with sauna, spa bath and solarium. Amusements and entertainment for children and adults. Chalet and caravan accommodation. Eight hundred yards from the beach. **directions** Please contact us for directions **payment** credit/debit cards, cash, cheques

General ⚓ ⚐ ▥ ⌂ ☼ ✕   Leisure ❦ ⚑ ♫ ⚓ ⟋⟍

HEMSBY, Norfolk Map ref 3C1   SAT NAV NR29 4HT

Hemsby Beach Holiday Park
Beach Road, Hemsby, Great Yarmouth NR29 4HT
t (01692) 582277 e info@richardsonsgroup.net
w **richardsonsholidayparks.co.uk** ONLINE BOOKING LAST MINUTE OFFERS

(200) £135.00–£550.00

Family holiday park with on-site facilities, children's club & daily entertainment. Just minutes from the sandy beach, arcades & diners on Beach Road. **directions** Please contact us for directions **open** April to October **payment** credit/debit cards, cash, cheques

General ⚓ ▣ ⚐ ▥   Leisure ❦ ⚑ ♫ ⚓ ⟋⟍

HEMSBY, Norfolk Map ref 3C1   SAT NAV NR29 4HR

Seacroft Holiday Village
Beach Road, Hemsby-on-Sea NR29 4HR
t (01692) 582277 e info@richardsonsgroup.net
w **richardsonsholidayvillages.co.uk** LAST MINUTE OFFERS

(250) £225.00–£350.00

Adult only catered site with on-site entertainment. Themed breaks include 60s, 70s, cabaret & comedy. Suitable for the modern 50 year old & the more mature holidaymaker. **directions** Please contact us for directions **open** Except January **payment** credit/debit cards, cash, cheques

General ▥ ✕   Leisure ❦ ⚑ ♫ ⚓

Looking for something else?

You can also buy a copy of our popular guide 'Hotels' including country house and town house hotels, metro and budget hotels, serviced apartments and restaurants with rooms in England 2012.

Now available in good bookshops and online at
visitbritainshop.com   **£7.99**

HUNSTANTON, Norfolk Map ref 3B1

SAT NAV PE36 5BB

🚐 (157) £17.00–£53.00
🚐 (50) £17.00–£53.00
⛺ (125) £17.00–£48.00
🏠 (156) £253.00–£1418.00
332 touring pitches

SPECIAL PROMOTIONS
Superb themed breaks every autumn. Beauty breaks, music weekends, Turkey and Tinsel breaks. Please check website for more details.

Searles Leisure Resort

South Beach Road, Hunstanton PE36 5BB
t (01485) 534211 f (01485) 533815 e bookings@searles.co.uk
w **searles.co.uk**
ONLINE MAP ONLINE BOOKING LAST MINUTE OFFERS

Creating happiness for all ages. Family-run, established for fifty years, Searles has something for everyone: superb range of accommodation, award winning touring park, bars, restaurants, entertainment, swimming pools, 27 holes golf, fishing lake and more - all 200yds from a sandy beach.

The ideal base for exploring the Norfolk coast. For family holidays in North Norfolk, Searles of Hunstanton is the undisputed market leader. At Searles you can expect excellent value accommodation, an award winning range of facilities and things to do, and exciting and varied entertainment for all the family.

There's no doubt that Searles has the widest and most varied choice of accommodation on the Norfolk coast. Choose between hi-spec leisure lodges, static caravan holiday homes, fully serviced pitches for tourers and motorhomes, or even a space to pitch your tent. For something completely different, how about a sumptuous room in our luxury Hunstanton hotel?

Whatever you fancy, whatever your budget, there's no better place to call home while you visit the beautiful North Norfolk coast.

open Touring all year, Holiday hire, Feb to Nov
payment credit/debit cards, cash, cheques

directions From King's Lynn take the A149 to Hunstanton. Upon entering Hunstanton follow B1161 to South Beach.

General 🔌🗄️♿🐕🎱🛏️☀️🍴🍽️🛒☕🚲♨️✕ **Leisure** ⛳🎯⚲♣️🎵🎣🐟🎱🎹🔍⛰️

MUNDESLEY, Norfolk Map ref 3C1   SAT NAV NR11 8BT

Mundesley Holiday Village
Paston Road, Norwich NR11 8BT
t (01263) 721553 **e** info@richardsonsgroup.net
w richardsonsholidayvillages.co.uk LAST MINUTE OFFERS

⚐ (180)   £225.00–£450.00

Adult only catered holiday village, providing a programme of entertainment & activities. Just a few minutes walk from Mundesley Beach & close to the seaside villages of Cromer & Sheringham. **directions** Please contact us for directions **payment** credit/debit cards, cash, cheques

General ▯ ✕ Leisure ☂ ♟ ♫ ✎

MUNDESLEY, Norfolk Map ref 3C1   SAT NAV NR11 8DF

Sandy Gulls Caravan Park
Cromer Road, Mundesley NR11 8DF
t (01263) 720513 **e** info@sandygulls.co.uk
w sandygulls.co.uk

⚐ (40)   £12.00–£25.00
⚐ (40)   £12.00–£25.00
⚐ (2)   £250.00–£465.00
40 touring pitches

SPECIAL PROMOTIONS
New holiday caravans for sale and hire.

The area's only cliff-top touring park. Located just south of Cromer. All pitches have panoramic sea views, electric/TV hook-ups. Free access to superb shower facilities. Miles of clean, sandy beaches and rural footpaths. Managed by the owning family for thirty years. Gold David Bellamy Conservation Award. Adults only.

open 1st March - 30th November
payment cash, cheques, euros

directions From Cromer drive south along coast road for 5 miles.

General ☇ ⬘ ▯ ⌂ ☼ ⌨ ⬚ ☎ Leisure ▶ ∪ ♪

NORWICH, Norfolk Map ref 3C1   SAT NAV NR12 0EW

Cable Gap Holiday Park
Coast Road, Bacton, Norfolk NR12 0EW
t (01692) 650667 **e** holiday@cablegap.co.uk
w cablegap.co.uk ONLINE MAP LAST MINUTE OFFERS

⚐ (1)   £374.00–£622.00
⚐ (19)   £178.00–£616.00

Cable Gap Holiday Park is a friendly family run 5 Star Park providing first class facilities. A Silver David Bellamy, our caravans are Rose Awarded. **directions** Follow B1150 from Norwich or B1159 from Cromer. **open** March to November **payment** credit/debit cards, cash, cheques

General ⬘ ▤ ♿ ☇ ▯ ⌂ ☼ Leisure ▶ ∪ ⚲ ♪

NORWICH, Norfolk Map ref 3C1

SAT NAV NR12 0JB

Red House Chalet and Caravan Park

Paston Road, Bacton, Norfolk NR12 0JB
t (01692) 650815 f (01502) 537460 e redhousechalets@tiscali.co.uk
w **redhousechalets.co.uk** LAST MINUTE OFFERS

(18)	£225.00–£380.00
(8)	£235.00–£430.00

Peaceful family run park with beautiful sea views and private access to a tranquil sandy beach. Deluxe caravan holiday homes & chalets for hire. Close to Norfolk Broads & shops. **directions** Situated on main B1159 coast road within the village of Bacton. Red House offers ideal base location sightseeing Norfolk Broads and coastal region. **open** All year **payment** credit/debit cards, cash, cheques, euros

General 🔥 🖃 🐕 🐾 ☼ **Leisure** 🎣 🍴 🔍

SANDRINGHAM, Norfolk Map ref 3B1

SAT NAV PE35 6EZ

The Sandringham Estate Caravan Club Site

Glucksburgh Woods, Sandringham, Norfolk PE35 6EZ
t (01553) 631614 e enquiries@caravanclub.co.uk
w **caravanclub.co.uk**

THE
CARAVAN
CLUB

(136)	£16.00–£38.90
(136)	£16.00–£38.90
136 touring pitches	

One of The Club's most prestigious sites. Take a walk to Sandringham House, enjoy the Country Fair. Kids will love the nature trails, land train ride and adventure playground. **directions** A149 from King's Lynn (signposted Hunstanton). 2 miles right onto B1439 (signposted West Newton). Site on left. **open** All year **payment** credit/debit cards, cash, cheques

General 🖃 💧 🐕 📵 ☼ 🔲 💡 🚰 🚾 **Leisure** ⛰

SCRATBY, Norfolk Map ref 3C1

SAT NAV NR29 3QT

Beachside Holidays (Norfolk)

Wakefield Court, California, Great Yarmouth, Norfolk NR29 3QT
t (01493) 730279 e holidays@theseaside.org
w **beachside-holidays.co.uk** ONLINE MAP GUEST REVIEWS ONLINE BOOKING LAST MINUTE OFFERS

(1)	£225.00–£695.00
(6)	£175.00–£595.00

Exclusive position, in our idyllic garden setting, overlooking the sea betwixt Great Yarmouth and the Norfolk Broads. VisitEngland 4 star Excellent Quality in Tourism Assessment directly overlooking Norfolks sandy beach. **directions** From Great Yarmouth, follow A149, then B1159, at Scratby turn right into Beach Road. Follow into Rottenstone Lane & we are 50m on left. **open** All year **payment** credit/debit cards, cash, cheques

General 🖃 🐕 ☼ **Leisure** ▶ ∪ ⛲ 🎣

SHADWELL, Norfolk Map ref 3B2

SAT NAV IP24 2RX

Thorpe Caravan & Camping Site

Shadwell, Thetford, Norfolk IP24 2RX
t (01842) 751042 e thorpe.woodland@forestholidays.co.uk
w **forestholidays.co.uk** ONLINE MAP GUEST REVIEWS

	£11.00–£18.50
	£11.00–£18.50
	£11.00–£18.50
460 touring pitches	

Enjoy the tranquility of Forest Holidays Thorpe Caravan Park and Campsite in Norfolk. Tucked away on the bank of the River Thet, ideal choice for a relaxing break in England. **directions** A1066 from Thetford, after 5 miles take the left fork with the caravan sign. 0.25 miles - left. Do not follow signs to Shadwell. **open** All year **payment** credit/debit cards, cash

General 🐕 📵 ☼ 🚰

SNETTISHAM, Norfolk Map ref 3B1

SAT NAV PE31 7RA

Diglea Caravan and Camping Park

Beach Road, Snettisham PE31 7RA
t (01485) 541367

🚐 (200)	£12.00–£20.00
🚎 (200)	£12.00–£20.00
⛺ (200)	£12.00–£20.00

200 touring pitches

Diglea is a friendly family run park in a rural setting, situated on the peaceful north Norfolk coast, a quarter of a mile from the beach and RSPB reserve. Just five miles from all the holiday attractions of Hunstanton and ten miles from the historic town of King's Lynn.

open Open beginning of April until the end of September
payment credit/debit cards, cash

directions From King's Lynn take the A149 Hunstanton road to Snettisham. Turn left at sign marked Snettisham beach. Park is 1.5 miles on left.

General 🗐 🛪 🏕 ☼ 🖵 🕒 🕯 Leisure ⤵ 🍷 ♫ 🎣

STANHOE, Norfolk Map ref 3B1

SAT NAV PE31 8PU

The Rickels Caravan and Camping Park

Bircham Road, Stanhoe, King's Lynn PE31 8PU
t (01485) 518671

🚐	£14.00–£16.00
🚎	£14.00–£16.00
⛺	£14.00–£16.00

26 touring pitches

The Rickels is a quiet, friendly, high-quality family-run park in 3 acres of grassland with a peaceful, relaxed atmosphere where you can enjoy a pleasant and restful holiday. Adults only. **directions** Please contact us for directions **open** April to end October **payment** cash, cheques

General 🗐 🛪 🏕 ☼ 🛎 🖵 🕒 🕯 🚾 Leisure 🚴 ⤵

SWAFFHAM, Norfolk Map ref 3B1

SAT NAV IP26 5BZ

The Covert Caravan Club Site

High Ash, Hillborough, Swaffham, Norfolk IP26 5BZ
t (01842) 878356 e enquiries@caravanclub.co.uk
w caravanclub.co.uk

THE
CARAVAN
CLUB

🚐 (90)	£10.70–£25.20
🚎 (90)	£10.70–£25.20

90 touring pitches

Secluded site in beautiful wooded countryside owned by the Forestry Commission. Ideal for the wildlife observer and good for walkers. Own sanitation required. **directions** Site entrance from A1065, 2 miles north of Mundford and 2.7 miles south of Hilborough. **open** TBA to November **payment** credit/debit cards, cash, cheques

General 🛪 🖵 🕒 🚾

WATTON, Norfolk Map ref 3B1

SAT NAV IP25 7EZ

Lowe Caravan Park
Ashdale, 134 Hills Road, Saham Hills, Thetford IP25 7EZ
t (01953) 881051 f (01953) 881051
w lowecaravanpark.co.uk

(20)	£13.00–£15.00
(6)	£13.00–£15.00
(4)	£250.00–£295.00
20 touring pitches	

SPECIAL PROMOTIONS
Static caravans short break available £50 per night minimum 3 nights stay. Country music once a month.

Small friendly caravan park more suited to the over 55's. Located in the heart of Norfolk, situated in the quiet village of Saham, two miles from the market town of Watton. We also have fully equipped static caravans for hire, all with own parking bays.

open All year except Xmas and New Year
payment cash, cheques

directions From Watton high street turning to Saham Hills. 2nd turning on right (Plough Boy Lane) at T-Junction. Turn right (Hills Road). First driveway on right.

General 🐕 🏕 ☼ 🚃 🖵 🕓 🚻   Leisure ▶ ✒

BUCKLESHAM, Suffolk Map ref 3C2

SAT NAV IP10 0BW

Westwood Caravan Park
Old Felixstowe Road, Bucklesham, Ipswich, Suffolk IP10 0BW
t (01473) 659637 e info@westwoodcaravanpark.co.uk
w westwoodcaravanpark.co.uk GUEST REVIEWS LAST MINUTE OFFERS

(90)	£15.00–£20.00
(90)	£15.00–£20.00
(90)	£15.00–£20.00
(1)	£210.00–£245.00
90 touring pitches	

Westwood Caravan Park is situated outside the village of Bucklesham, in the heart of the Suffolk countryside, yet easily accessible from the A12/A14. Superb shower and toilet facilities & Play-area/Games-room. **directions** Follow the A14 towards Felixstowe. After junction-58, take exit signposted Kirton. Follow the road for one and a half miles, park is on the right. **open** 1st March to 15th January **payment** credit/debit cards, cash

General 🔌 🖵 💡 🐕 🥾 🏕 ☼ 🚃 🕓 🚻 🖵   Leisure ∪ ✒ 🎣 ⛰

BUNGAY, Suffolk Map ref 3C1

SAT NAV NR35 1HG

Outney Meadow Caravan Park
Outney Meadow, Bungay NR35 1HG
t (01986) 892338
w outneymeadow.co.uk

(45)	£14.00–£17.00
(45)	£14.00–£17.00
(45)	£14.00–£17.00
45 touring pitches	

Easy walking distance to Bungay market town. Situated between the River Waveney (canoe trail) and golf course, ideal base for exploring the beautiful countryside. Fishing, bikes and canoes available. **directions** Please contact us for directions **open** March to October **payment** credit/debit cards, cash, cheques

General 🖵 🐕 🏕 ☼ 🖳 🚃 🖵 🕓 🚻 🖵   Leisure ▶ 🚲 ✒

FELIXSTOWE, Suffolk Map ref 3C2

SAT NAV IP11 2HB

Peewit Caravan Park

Walton Avenue, Felixstowe IP11 2HB
t (01394) 284511 **e** peewitpark@aol.com
w **peewitcaravanpark.co.uk** ONLINE MAP

⛺ (35)	£14.00–£25.00
🚐 (35)	£14.00–£25.00
⛺ (10)	£13.00–£30.00

45 touring pitches

Family run and operated, Peewit Caravan Park is an oasis of peace and tranquility. Situated just 900 metres from Felixstowe's seafront, a short walk from the Edwardian town centre. **directions** A14 to Port of Felixstowe Dock Gate 1 roundabout. Entrance 100 yds on left. Site 500 yds up driveway. **open** April to October **payment** credit/debit cards, cash, cheques

General ⊟ 🐕 ⓘ ⓡ ☼ ♿ ⊡ ⊙ ⓟ **Leisure** ► ⚓ ✈ ⚲

KESSINGLAND, Suffolk Map ref 3C2

SAT NAV NR33 7PJ

Heathland Beach Caravan Park

London Road, Kessingland NR33 7PJ
t (01502) 740337 **f** (01502) 742355 **e** heathlandbeach@btinternet.com
w **heathlandbeach.co.uk** ONLINE MAP GUEST REVIEWS ONLINE BOOKING

⛺	£20.00–£30.00
🚐	£20.00–£28.00
⛺	£10.00–£30.00
🏠 (6)	£310.00–£590.00

63 touring pitches

Heathland Beach is a spacious, award-winning, family-owned holiday park situated on a picturesque cliff overlooking the secluded beach at Kessingland. Heathland Beach abounds with excellent facilities. **directions** Off A12 onto B1437 between Kessingland and Lowestoft. **open** Easter to end of October **payment** credit/debit cards, cash, cheques

General ⚲ ⊟ ♀ 🐕 ⌚ ⓘ ⓡ ☼ ⊡ ♿ ⊙ ⓟ ⓦ **Leisure** ► ∪ ⚲ ✈ ⚲ ⓣ

LOWESTOFT, Suffolk Map ref 3C1

SAT NAV NR33 7BD

Beach Farm Residential and Holiday Park Limited

Arbor Lane, Pakefield, Lowestoft, Suffolk NR33 7BD
t (01502) 572794 **f** (01502) 537460 **e** beachfarmpark@aol.com
w **beachfarmpark.co.uk** ONLINE MAP LAST MINUTE OFFERS

⛺ (2)	£20.00–£24.00
🚐 (2)	£18.00–£22.00
⛺ (2)	£16.00–£28.00
🏠 (8)	£345.00–£569.00
🏠 (21)	£235.00–£469.00

2 touring pitches

Beach Farm is a friendly, peaceful family run park with Deluxe Caravan holiday homes, Country Lodges for hire and Park Homes for sale. Close to beach & large supermarket. **directions** Join A12 at large roundabout, Pakefield water tower from all directions and follow brown signs 'Beach Farm' to Arbor Lane exit then 100yds on right. **open** March 1st to January 2nd **payment** credit/debit cards, cash, cheques, euros

General ⚲ ⊟ ⓘ ⓡ ☼ ⊡ ♿ ⊙ ⓟ ✗ **Leisure** ► ∪ ⚓ ✈ ⓣ ⚲ ⚲

LOWESTOFT (3 MILES), Suffolk Map ref 3C1

SAT NAV NR33 7BQ

Pakefield Caravan Park

Arbor Lane, Pakefield, Lowestoft NR33 7BQ
t (01502) 561136 **f** (01502) 539264 **e** info@pakefieldcaravanpark.co.uk
w **pakefieldpark.co.uk** ONLINE MAP LAST MINUTE OFFERS

⛺ (12)	£16.00–£24.00
🚐	£16.00–£24.00
🏠 (12)	£117.00–£589.00

12 touring pitches

Set on the Sunrise coast, with fantastic sea views, this park is an ideal location to explore all that suffolk and the norfolk coast has to offer. **directions** From the A12 take the Pakefield exit and pass the water tower on left. Turn right Grayson Drive, then right down Grayson Avenue. **open** 1st March - 31st October **payment** credit/debit cards, cash, cheques

General ⚲ ⊟ ♀ 🐕 ⌚ ⓘ ⓡ ☼ ♿ ⊙ ⓟ ⓦ ✗ **Leisure** ► ✈ ⓣ ⚲ ♪ ⚲ ⚲

POLSTEAD, Suffolk Map ref 3B2   SAT NAV CO6 5BZ

Polestead Camping and Caravanning Club Site
Holt Road, Bower House Tye, Polstead, Suffolk CO6 5BZ
t (01787) 211969 e Polstead.Site@thefriendlyclub.co.uk
w **campingandcaravanningclub.co.uk/polstead** ONLINE MAP GUEST REVIEWS

🚐	£23.00–£26.00
🚙	£23.00–£26.00
⚊	£23.00–£26.00
50 touring pitches	

Set on the edge of a conservation area. There are plenty of opportunities for activity nearby or you may choose to relax and enjoy the beautiful Suffolk countryside. **directions** OS Map Reference: 155 - TL985403 Latitude: 52.0251 Longitude: 0.8937Railway: Sudbury 7 miles. **open** 14th February - 14th January **payment** credit/debit cards, cash, cheques

General 🖥 ♿ 🐕 🔌 🚿 ☀ 🔊 ⭕ 🚻 **Leisure** ⛰

Looking for something else?

You can also buy a copy of our popular guide 'Self Catering' including self-catering holiday homes, approved caravan holiday homes, boat accommodation and holiday cottage agencies in England 2012.

Now available in good bookshops and online at
visitbritainshop.com   **£8.99**

East Midlands

Derbyshire, Leicestershire & Rutland, Lincolnshire, Northamptonshire, Nottinghamshire

154 Where to Go   **157** Events   **160** Where to Stay

Taking in the counties of Derbyshire, Leicestershire, Lincolnshire, Northamptonshire, Nottinghamshire and Rutland, the East Midlands is a treasure trove of magnificent castles and stately homes, thriving cosmopolitan cities, historic market towns and dramatic, untouched countryside of the Peak District National Park.

Robin Hood loved the East Midlands, and once you visit, so will you.

History and Heritage

There's over a thousand years of history in the East Midlands, just waiting to be explored. Uncover the legend of the lost crown jewels; search for the servant of Satan turned to stone by an angel, or experience life in an authentic 19th century workhouse. Whether you are into country houses, or re-staged castle battles, ancient cathedrals and 500-year old walled gardens, the East Midlands is a fantastic place to get your hands on the intriguing past.

Arts and Culture

For world-class exhibitions in Lincolnshire, start your cultural journey at The Hub National Centre for Craft and Design before heading to The Collection to take in some ancient artifacts. With independent galleries showcasing local artists and venues offering everything from comedy to dance performances, the only problem is fitting it all in. For the best in international modern art, head to the Nottingham Contemporary before taking a tram to the nearby New Art Exchange, which is dedicated to African, African Caribbean and South Asian artists.

Food and Drink

The East Midlands is a true food lovers' paradise. From world renowned local delicacies such as Melton Mowbray Pork Pie, Stilton cheese and Bakewell Pudding to farm shops, gastro pubs and Michelin starred restaurants - there is something on offer for every palate. And for all this in one sumptuous place, check out the East Midlands Food and Drink Festival held in October.

Music and Nightlife

For a night on the tiles, Nottingham's trendy Lace Market and Old Market Square have old world charm with thumping fun that sums up a night out in the East Midlands. Lincoln's nightlife is also legendary, and rightfully so.

For a dose of culture, The Derby Playhouse and Guildhall Theatre and Leicester's De Montfort Hall host quality touring production, while the Drill Hall is Lincoln's upgraded multi-arts venue.

Shopping

With an eclectic mix of independent retailers, designer boutiques and high street brands, you'll want to carry some spare luggage when shopping in the East Midlands. Nottingham is a good place to start with the Paul Smith Flagship store an obvious entry point. The cities of Derby, Lincoln and Leicester also offer quality retail therapy, from huge malls to old Victorian market stalls.

Sports

The Peak District is prime walking and cycling country, with a mind bending and leg wobbling range of terrain, walks and trails suitable for all levels and ages. For the golfer there is also a huge choice of public and private courses just waiting to steal your golf balls. The East Midlands is England's spiritual home of motorsport with Silverstone and Donnington Park the jewels in the petrolhead's crown.

Family Fun

The East Midlands is bursting with great days out for the family – from high wire high jinks at Go Ape! to underground action in Nottingham's deep caves. There are butterfly farms and worlds of horses, a National Space Centre, and re-creations of Robin Hood's famous adventures. Cycle on well-marked trails, or let off steam on historical railways.

Handy Hints

Sky Ride – A cable car at Derbyshire's oldest attraction, the Heights of Abraham is a must.

Mountain Biking - Hope Valley and and Edale are the most popular centres for mountain biking in the Peak District.

Gardens - Head to Coton Manor, Easton Walled Gardens, Renishaw Hall and Teversal Manor for all sorts of arboreal delights.

Movie set - Chatsworth House was used in the 2006 movie Pride and Prejudice, and you can walk amongst the home and gardens in the steps of Mr Darcy.

Melton Mowbray Market - Head to this food epicenter, the market has been in existence for over 1000 years.

OUT & ABOUT IN THE EAST MIDLANDS

Day 1 - Film and TV

- Visit Chatsworth House, the backdrop for *Pride and Prejudice*
- Burghley House, which featured in *The Da Vinci Code* and *The Golden Age*
- Lincoln Cathedral is one of the finest medieval buildings in Europe and feature as Westminster Abbey in *The Da Vinci Code*

Day 2 - Robin Hood County

- Visit Nottingham Castle which boasts a museum that tells the story of Nottingham and the legend of Robin Hood
- Amble around Sherwood Forest and check out Major Oak, a massive tree at least 500 years old
- Visit Clumber Chapel - a Gothic cathedral in miniature

Day 3 - Peak District

- Buxton, famous for its spring water and a spa town since Roman times
- Bakewell to feast on an authentic Bakewell Pudding
- Walk, cycle or horse ride The Tissington Trail which runs from Ashbourne to Parsley Hay

Day 4 - For Foodies

- Grainstore Brewery in Oakham, the place to visit for English ales and ciders
- Hansen's Chocolate House, East Midland's producer of quality handmade chocolates
- The Hartington Creamery in Hartington, the oldest Stilton creamery in the UK

Day 5 - Culture Vulture

- Hit the New Art Exchange in Nottingham for African, Afro-Caribbean and south Asian arts
- The Fishmarket Gallery in Northampton is home to artists' studios, café bar and two independent gallery spaces
- Check out the famous Bathing Beauties beach huts in Lincolnshire - a gallery of permanent seaside architecture

Day 6 - Castles

- Take in great views of Castleton at Peveril Castle and learn of the colourful past from 1066
- Get close to one of the last surviving Magna Carta, now nearly 800 years old, at Lincoln Castle
- Tattershall Castle is a tour de force example of medieval brick architecture built in the 14th century

Day 7 - Wild and Wet

- Explore Rutland Water, Europe's largest man-made lake; the canals of Foxton Locks on a colourful narrow boat
- The National Watersports Centre at Holme Pierrepont - home to an international 2,000 metre regatta course, man-made white water slalom and water-ski lagoon history and perhaps a red squirrel

Where to Go

 Attractions with this sign participate in the **Places of Interest Quality Assurance Scheme**.

 Attractions with this sign participate in the **Visitor Attraction Quality Assurance Scheme**.

Both schemes recognise high standards in all aspects of the visitor experience (see page 6)

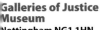

Derby Museum and Art Gallery
Derby DE1 1BS
(01332) 716659
www.derby.gov.uk/museums
Derby Museum and Art Gallery holds collections and displays relating to the history, culture and natural environment of Derby and its region.

Galleries of Justice Museum
Nottingham NG1 1HN
0115) 952 0555
www.galleriesofjustice.org.uk
You will be delving in to the dark and disturbing past of crime and punishment.

Mansfield Museum
Mansfield, Nottinghamshire NG18 1NG
(01623) 463088
www.mansfield.gov.uk/museum
Our dynamic museum and art gallerys permanent displays house a fascinating mix of local art and artefacts. Come and explore Mansfields social history or investigate 21st Century challenges facing our planet.

Newark Castle and Conflict
Newark, Nottinghamshire NG24 1BG
(01636) 655765
www.newark-sherwood.gov.uk
Newark Castle has been at the heart of the town for many centuries and has played an important role in historical events.

National Waterways Museum -Stoke Bruerne
Towcester, Northamptonshire NN12 7SE
(01604) 862229
www.nwm.org.uk
Stoke Bruerne is an ideal place to explore the story of our waterways.

Newark Air Museum
Nottinghamshire NG24 2NY
(01636) 707170
www.newarkairmuseum.org
The museum is open to the public every day except December 24th, 25th, 26th and January 1st.

Northampton Museum & Art Gallery
Northampton NN1 1DP
(01604) 838111
www.northampton.gov.uk/museums
Displays include footwear and related items, paintings, ceramics and glass and the history of Northampton.

Silk Mill - Derby's Museum of Industry and History
Derby DE1 3AF
(01332) 255308
www.derby.gov.uk/museums
The Silk Mill was completed around 1723 and the re-built Mill now contains displays on local history and industry.

FAMILY FUN

Foxton Locks
Market Harborough LE16 7RA
(01908) 302500
http://www.foxtonlocks.com
A great day out for all the family.

Gulliver's Theme Park
Matlock Bath, Derbyshire DE4 3PG
(01629) 580540
www.gulliversfun.co.uk
With more than 40 rides & attractions, Gulliver's provides the complete family entertainment experience. Fun & adventure with Gully Mouse, Dora the explorer, Diego and "The Lost World".

National Space Centre
Leicester LE4 5NS
0845 605 2001
www.spacecentre.co.uk
The award winning National Space Centre is the UK's largest attraction dedicated to space. From the moment you catch sight of the Space Centre's futuristic Rocket Tower, you'll be treated to hours of breathtaking discovery & interactive fun.

Sherwood Pines Forest Park
Edwinstowe, Nottinghamshire NG21 9JL
(01623) 822447
www.forestry.gov.uk
The largest forest open to the public in the East Midlands and centre for a wide variety of outdoor activities.

Wicksteed Park
Kettering, Northamptonshire NN15 6NJ
(01536) 512475
www.wicksteedpark.co.uk
Wicksteed Park remains Northamptonshire's most popular attraction and entertainment venue.

HERITAGE

78 Derngate
Northampton NN1 1UH
(01604) 603407
www.78derngate.org.uk
Charles Rennie Mackintosh transformed a typical terraced house into a startlingly modern house for local model maker W.J. Bassett-Lowke. It was his last major commission and his only work in England.

Althorp
Northampton NN7 4HQ
(01604) 770107
www.althorp.com
Come and visit one of England's finest country houses, home of the Spencer family for over 500 years and ancestral home of Diana, Princess of Wales.

Ashby de la Zouch Castle
Leicestershire LE65 1BR
(01530) 413343
www.english-heritage.org.uk/
daysout/properties/ashby-de-la-
zouch-castle
Visit the ruins of Ashby de la Zouch Castle where you will see the ruins of this historical castle, the original setting for many of the scenes of Sir Walter Scott's classic tale 'Ivanhoe'.

Belton House
Belton, Lincolnshire NG32 2LS
(01476) 566116
www.nationaltrust.org.uk/main/
w-beltonhouse
Belton,is a perfect example of an English Country House.

Belvoir Castle
Melton Mowbray, Leicestershire NG32 1PE
(01476) 871002
www.belvoircastle.com
Home to the Duke and Duchess of Rutland, Belvoir Castle offers stunning views of the Vale of Belvoir.

Bosworth Battlefield Heritage Centre
Market Bosworth, Leicestershire CV13 0AD
(01455) 290429
www.bosworthbattlefield.com
Delve into Leicestershire's fascinating history at Bosworth Battlefield Country Park - the site of the 1485 Battle of Bosworth.

Chatsworth
Bakewell, Derbyshire DE45 1PP
(01246) 582204
www.chatsworth.org
One of Britain's best loved historic houses and estates.

Creswell Crags
Chesterfield, Derbyshire S80 3LH
(01909) 720378
www.creswell-crags.org.uk
A world famous archaeological site, home to Britain's only known Ice Age cave art.

Doddington Hall
Lincoln LN6 4RU
(01522) 694308
www.doddingtonhall.com
A superb Elizabethan mansion by the renowned architect Robert Smythson. The hall stands today as it was completed in 1600 with walled courtyards, turrets and gatehouse.

Great Central Railway
Leicester LE11 1RW
(01509) 230726
www.gcrailway.co.uk
The Great Central Railway is Britain's only double track main line steam railway. Enjoy an exciting calendar of events, a footplate ride or dine in style on board one of the steam trains.

Haddon Hall
Bakewell, Derbyshire DE45 1LA
(01629) 812855
www.haddonhall.co.uk
Haddon Hall is conveniently situated on the A6 between Bakewell and Matlock, Derbyshire.

Hardwick Hall
Chesterfield, Derbyshire S44 5QJ
(01246) 850430
www.nationaltrust.org.uk/hardwick
Owned by the National Trust the Estate includes Hardwick Hall, Stainsby Mill and a Park. The Hall is one of Britain's greatest Elizabethan houses, the water-powered Mill is fully functioning, the Park has a fishing lake and circular walks.

Kedleston Hall
Derby DE22 5JH
(01332) 842191
www.nationaltrust.org.uk/main/w-
kedlestonhall
A fine example of a neo-classical mansion built between 1759-65 by the architecht Robert Adam and set in over 800 acres of parkland and landscaped pleasure grounds. Administered by The National Trust.

Lamport Hall and Gardens
Northamptonshire NN6 9HD
(01604) 686272
www.lamporthall.co.uk
Northamptonshire
Grade 1 listed building that was home to the Isham family and their collections for over four centuries.

Normanby Hall Museum and Country Park
Scunthorpe, Lincolnshire DN15 9HU
(01724) 720588
www.northlincs.gov.uk/normanby
Set in 300 acres of gardens, parkland, deer park, woods, ornamental and wild birds, well-stocked gift shop.

Nottingham Castle
Nottingham NG1 6EL
(0115) 915 3700
www.nottinghamcity.gov.uk/
museums
Situated on a high rock, Nottingham Castle commands spectacular views over the city and once rivalled the great castles of Windsor and the Tower of London.

Papplewick Hall & Gardens
Nottinghamshire NG15 8FE
(0115) 963 3491
www.papplewickhall.co.uk
A fine Adam house, built in 1787 and Grade I listed building with a park and woodland garden.

Prebendal Manor Medieval Centre
Nassington, Northamptonshire PE8 6QG
(01780) 782575
http://www.prebendal-manor.co.uk
Visit a unique medieval manor and enjoy the largest recreated medieval gardens in Europe.

Rockingham Castle
Market Harborough, Northamptonshire LE16 8TH
(01536) 770240
www.rockinghamcastle.com
Rockingham Castle stands on the edge of an escarpment giving dramatic views over five counties and the Welland Valley below.

Sudbury Hall
Ashbourne, Derbyshire DE6 5HT
(01283) 585305
www.nationaltrust.org.uk/
sudburyhall/
Explore the grand 17th Century hall with its richly decorated interior and see life below stairs.

Sulgrave Manor
Northamptonshire OX17 2SD
(01295) 760205
www.sulgravemanor.org.uk
A Tudor manor house and garden, the ancestral home of George Washington's family with authentic furniture shown by friendly guides.

Tattershall Castle

Lincolnshire LN4 4LR
(01526) 342543
www.nationaltrust.org.uk/tattershall
Tattershall Castle was built in the 15th Century to impress and dominate by Ralph Cromwell, one of the most powerful men in England. The castle is a dramatic red brick tower.

NATURE & WILDLIFE

Ayscoughfee Hall Museum and Gardens

Spalding, Lincolnshire PE11 2RA
(01775) 764555
www.ayscoughfee.org
Ayscoughfee Hall Museum is housed in a beautiful wool merchant's house built in 1451 on the banks of the River Welland.

Castle Ashby Gardens

Northamptonshire NN7 1LQ
(01604) 695200
www.castleashbygardens.co.uk
A haven of tranquility and beauty in the heart of Northamptonshire. Take your time to explore these beautiful gardens and enjoy the fascinating attractions from the rare breed farmyard to the historic orangery.

Conkers Discovery Centre

Ashby-de-la-Zouch, Leicestershire DE12 6GA
(01283) 216633
www.visitconkers.com/thingstodo/discoverycentre
Enjoy the great outdoors and explore over 120 acres of the award winning parkland.

Hardys Animal Farm

Ingoldmells, Lincolnshire PE25 1LZ
(01754) 872267
www.hardysanimalfarm.co.uk
An enjoyable way to learn about the countryside and how a farm works. There are animals for the children to enjoy as well as learning about the history and traditions of the countryside.

Renishaw Hall and Gardens

Dronfield, Derbyshire S21 3WB
(01246) 432310
www.renishaw-hall.co.uk
The Gardens are Italian in design and were laid out over 100 years ago by Sir George Sitwell. The garden is divided into 'rooms' with yew hedges, flanked with classical statues.

Salcey Forest

Hartwell, Northamptonshire NN17 3BB
(01780) 444920
www.forestry.gov.uk/salceyforest
Get a birds eye view of this wonderful woodland on the tremendous Tree Top Way.

Sherwood Forest Farm Park

Nottinghamshire NG21 9HL
(01623) 823558
www.sherwoodforestfarmpark.co.uk
Meet over 30 different rare farm breeds, plus other unusual species!

Sherwood Forest Country Park

Nottinghamshire NG21 9HN
(01623) 823202
www.nottinghamshire.gov.uk/sherwoodforestcp
Sherwood Forest Country Park covers 450 acres and incorporates some truly ancient areas of native woodland.

Twycross Zoo

Hinckley, Leicestershire CV9 3PX
(01827) 880250
www.twycrosszoo.com
Meet Twyford's famous orangutans, gorillas and chimpanzees plus many other mammals, birds and reptiles.

Events 2012

Leicester Comedy Festival
Leicester
www.comedy-festival.co.uk
February

Lincoln Music and Drama Festival
Lincoln
www.lincolnmdfest.org.uk
March

Churches Festival
Various Locations
www.churchesfestival.com
May

Derbyshire Food and Drink Fair
Derby
www.derbyshirefoodfestival.co.uk
May

Dot to Dot Festival
Nottingham
www.dottodotfestival.co.uk
May

Lincolnshire Wolds Walking Festival
Louth
www.woldswalkingfestival.co.uk
May - June

Newark Jazz Festival
Newark
www.newarkjazz.co.uk
May

The Lincolnshire Show
Lincoln
www.lincolnshireshowground.co.uk/lincolnshire_show
June

British Grand Prix
Silverstone
www.silverstone.co.uk/events
July

Buxton Festival
Buxton
www.buxtonfestival.co.uk
July

Chesterfield Medieval Market
Chesterfield
www.visitchesterfield.info
July

RAF Waddington Air Show
Waddington
www.waddingtonairshow.co.uk
July

The Gilbert and Sullivan Festival
Buxton
www.gsfestivals.org
July - August

Wellingborough Carnival and Party in the Park
Wellingborough
www.wellingborough-carnival.co.uk
July

Bakewell Acoustic Music Festival
Bakewell
www.bamf.co.uk
August

Summer Sundae
Leicester
www.summersundae.com
August

Land Rover Burghley Horse Trials
Peterborough
www.burghley-horse.co.uk
September

Diwali Light Switch On
Leicester
www.leicester.gov.uk/diwali
October

Tourist Information Centres

When you arrive at your destination, visit an Official Partner Tourist Information Centre for quality assured help with accommodation and information about local attractions and events, or email your request before you go. To find a Tourist Information Centre by region look at http://www.enjoyengland.com under Destination Finder.

ASHBOURNE	13 Market Place	01335 343666	ashbourneinfo@derbyshiredales.gov.uk
ASHBY-DE-LA-ZOUCH	North Street	01530 411767	ashby.tic@nwleicestershire.gov.uk
BAKEWELL	Old Market Hall	01629 813227	bakewell@peakdistrict-npa.gov.uk
BUXTON	The Crescent	01298 25106	tourism@highpeak.gov.uk
CASTLETON	Buxton Road	01433 620679	castleton@peakdistrict.gov.uk
CHESTERFIELD	Rykneld Square	01246 345777	tourism@chesterfield.gov.uk
DERBY	Assembly Rooms	01332 255802	tourism@derby.gov.uk
LEICESTER	7/9 Every Street	0844 888 5181	info@goleicestershire.com
LINCOLN CASTLE HILL	9 Castle Hill	01522 873213	tourism@lincoln.gov.uk
MATLOCK	Crown Square	01629 583388	matlockinfo@derbyshiredales.gov.uk
NEWARK	The Gilstrap Centre	01636 655765	gilstrap@nsdc.info
NORTHAMPTON	Sessions House, County Hall	01604 838800	tic@northamptonshire.gov.uk
NOTTINGHAM CITY	1-4 Smithy Row	08444 775 678	tourist.information@nottinghamcity.gov.uk
OLLERTON	Sherwood Heath	01623 824545	sherwoodheath@nsdc.info
SILVERSTONE	Silverstone Circuit	0844 3728330	enquiries@silverstone.co.uk
SWADLINCOTE	Sharpe's Pottery Museum	01283 222848	Jo@sharpespotterymuseum.org.uk

Regional Contacts and Information

The publications listed are available from the following organisations:

East Midlands Tourism
Web: www.discovereastmidlands.com
Discover East Midlands

Experience Nottinghamshire
Tel: 0844 477 5678
Web: www.visitnotts.com
Nottinghamshire Essential Guide, Where to Stay
Guide, City Breaks, The City Guide,
Robin Hood Breaks

Peak District and Derbyshire
Web: www.visitpeakdistrict.com
Peak District and Derbyshire
Visitor Guide
Well Dressing
Camping and Caravanning Guide
Walking Festivals Guide and Visitor Guide

Discover Rutland
Tel: (01572) 720924
Web: www.discover-rutland.co.uk
Discover Rutland, Eat drink Rutland, Attractions,
Uppingham, Oakham, Oakham Heritage Trail

Lincolnshire
Tel: (01522) 545458
Web: www.visitlincolnshire.com
Visit Lincolnshire – Destination Guide, Great Days
Out, Good Taste
Keep up with the flow

Explore Northamptonshire
Tel: (01604) 609393
Web: www.explorenorthamptonshire.co.uk
Northamptonshire Visitor Guide,
Northamptonshire presents Britain on show
County Map

Leicestershire
Tel: 0844 888 5181
Web: www.goleicestershire.com
Leicestershire City Guide
Stay, Play, Explore
Great Days Out in Leicestershire

Where to Stay

Entries appear alphabetically by town name in each county. A key to symbols appears on page 6. Maps start on page 298. Further listings of VisitEngland assessed accommodation appear on the CD at the back of this guide.

ALSOP-EN-LE-DALE, Derbyshire Map ref 4B2 SAT NAV DE6 1QU

enjoyEngland.com ★★★★ HOLIDAY, TOURING & CAMPING PARK

(81)	£15.50–£25.70
(81)	£15.50–£25.70
(30)	£16.00–£23.00
	£38.00–£48.00
	£260.00–£395.00

111 touring pitches

SPECIAL PROMOTIONS
Stay Sunday - Thursday & get 5 nights for the price of 4.

Rivendale Caravan & Leisure Park

Rivendale Caravan & Leisure Park, Buxton Road, Nr Alsop en le dale, Ashbourne DE6 1QU
t (01335) 310311 **f** (01335) 310100 **e** enquiries@rivendalecaravanpark.co.uk
w rivendalecaravanpark.co.uk ONLINE BOOKING LAST MINUTE OFFERS

Surrounded by spectacular Peak District scenery, convenient for Alton Towers, Chatsworth, Dove Dale and Carsington Water. Ideal for cyclists and ramblers with a network of footpaths and trails accessible directly from site. Choice of all-grass, hardstanding or 50/50 pitches. Yurts, Camping Pods, Electric Bikes & fire pits for hire.

open Open all year EXCEPT 3rd Jan - 28th Jan
payment credit/debit cards, cash, cheques

directions From A515, Rivendale is situated 6.5 miles north of Ashbourne, directly off the A515 Buxton road on the right-hand side, travelling north.

General Leisure

Looking for something else?

You can also buy a copy of our popular 'B&B' guide including guest accommodation, B&B's, guest houses, farmhouses, inns, and campus and hostel accommodation in England 2012.
Now available in good bookshops and online at **visitbritainshop.com** **£8.99**

AMBERGATE, Derbyshire Map ref 4B2

SAT NAV DE56 2JH

The Firs Caravan Club Site
Crich Lane, Belper DE56 2JH
t (01773) 852913 **e** enquiries@caravanclub.co.uk
w caravanclub.co.uk

🚐 (79) £15.90–£35.51
🚐 (79) £15.90–£35.51
79 touring pitches

Set in the heart of the Derbyshire countryside. Peaceful and well presented, there are breathtaking views to Derwent Valley Mills World Heritage Site. **directions** M1 jct 28, A38 (Ripley). 5.75 miles A610 (Ambergate). 3 miles A6 (Belper). 0.5 miles A609, B6013. Into Crich Lane. Site on left. **open** April to November **payment** credit/debit cards, cash, cheques

General 🗑️ 📶 🐕 📻 🔥 ☀️ 🚐 🕐 🚻 ♿ Leisure ▶ 🏊

ASHBOURNE, Derbyshire Map ref 4B2

SAT NAV DE6 3JL

Blackwall Plantation Caravan Club Site
Kirk Ireton, Ashbourne DE6 3JL
t (01335) 370903 **e** enquiries@caravanclub.co.uk
w caravanclub.co.uk

🚐 (130) £13.50–£25.40
🚐 (130) £13.50–£25.40
130 touring pitches

Set in a pine plantation, beautifully landscaped within walking distance of Carsington Reservoir. Good walking and cycling area. Explore the Peak District National Park. Alton Towers 15 miles. **directions** A517 from Ashbourne. In 4.5 miles, turn left at signpost to Carsington Water/Atlow/Hognaston. Right at crossroads, towards Carsington Water. Site on right after 1 mile. **open** March to November **payment** credit/debit cards, cash, cheques

General 🗑️ 🐕 📻 ☀️ 🚐 🕐 🚻 ♿ Leisure ⛰️

BAKEWELL, Derbyshire Map ref 4B2

SAT NAV DE45 1PN

Chatsworth Park Caravan Club Site
Baslow, Bakewell, Derbyshire DE45 1PN
t (01246) 582226 **f** (01246) 583762 **e** enquiries@caravanclub.co.uk
w caravanclub.co.uk

🚐 (120) £17.40–£42.00
🚐 (120) £17.40–£42.00
120 touring pitches

Breathtaking setting in walled garden on the Estate. Farmyard and adventure playground. Visit the house with its beautifully proportioned rooms, paintings and formal gardens. **directions** From Bakewell on A619. In 3.75 miles on the outskirts of Baslow turn right at roundabout (signposted Sheffield). Site entrance on right in 150 yds. **payment** credit/debit cards, cash, cheques

General 🗑️ 📶 🐕 📻 🔥 ☀️ 🚐 🕐 🚻 ♿

BUXTON, Derbyshire Map ref 4B2

SAT NAV SK17 9TQ

Beech Croft Farm Caravan & Camping Park
Blackwell-in-the-Peak, Nr Buxton, Derbyshire SK17 9TQ
t (01298) 85330 **e** mail@beechcroftfarm.net
w beechcroftfarm.net

🚐 (30) £16.00–£20.00
🚐 (30) £16.00–£20.00
⛺ (50) £12.50–£14.60
30 touring pitches

In the heart of the Peak District, small family run site, alongside their small sheep farm. Southerly facing. On the Pennine Bridleway with Monsal Trail & Limestone Way close by. **directions** Midway between Buxton & Bakewell being 6 miles to each town. Signposted & easily accessible from the A6. **open** All year **payment** credit/debit cards, cash, cheques

General 🗑️ 📶 🐕 🧺 📻 ☀️ ♿ 🚐 🕐 🚻

BUXTON, Derbyshire Map ref 4B2

SAT NAV SK17 6UJ

Grin Low Caravan Club Site

Grin Low Road, Ladmanlow, Buxton, Derbyshire SK17 6UJ
t (01298) 77735 **e** enquiries@caravanclub.co.uk
w caravanclub.co.uk

THE
CARAVAN
CLUB

🚐 (117) £14.30–£32.79
🚐 (117) £14.00–£32.79
117 touring pitches

Site surrounded by the Peak District National Park - ideal for walkers and cyclists. Nearby Buxton, with its Pavilion Gardens and Opera House makes a great day or evening out. **directions** From Buxton left off A53 to Leek road. 1.5 miles Grin Low signposted, in 300 yds left into approach road; site entrance 0.25 miles. **open** March to November **payment** credit/debit cards, cash, cheques

General 🖥🎦📠📷☼🔌🕒🐕🏕 Leisure ⛰

BUXTON, Derbyshire Map ref 4B2

SAT NAV SK17 0DT

Newhaven Caravan and Camping Park

Newhaven, Buxton SK17 0DT
t (01298) 84300 **f** (01332) 726027 **e** newhavencaravanpark@btconnect.com
w newhavencaravanpark.co.uk

🚐 (73) £11.25–£19.75
🚐 (14) £11.25–£19.75
⛺ (30) £11.25–£17.75
95 touring pitches

Halfway between Ashbourne and Buxton in the Peak District National Park. Well-established park with modern facilities, close to the Tissington and High Peak trails, historic houses and Derbyshire Dales. **directions** Half way between Ashbourne and Buxton on the A515 at junction with A5012. **open** March to October **payment** credit/debit cards, cash, cheques

General 🖥🐕🔧📷☼🔌🕒🐕 Leisure ⚓🎣⛰

DERBY, Derbyshire Map ref 4B2

SAT NAV DE72 3EP

Elvaston Castle Caravan Club Site

Borrowash Road, Elvaston, Derby, Derbyshire DE72 3EP
t (01332) 573735 **e** enquiries@caravanclub.co.uk
w caravanclub.co.uk

THE
CARAVAN
CLUB

🚐 (47) £10.70–£28.00
🚐 (47) £10.70–£28.00
47 touring pitches

Site within 280 acre country park where squirrels and rabbits roam freely and colourful azaleas and rhododendrons abound in season. Many walks to choose from. **directions** Leave A50, turn right onto B5010. Continue left on B5010, in about 1 mile turn left into country park. Site on left. **open** April to November **payment** credit/debit cards, cash, cheques

General 🐕📠📷🔌🕒 Leisure ▶⚓

RIPLEY, Derbyshire Map ref 4B2

SAT NAV DE55 4ES

Golden Valley Caravan & Camping

Golden Valley, Coach Road, Alfreton DE55 4ES
t (01773) 513881 **e** enquiries@goldenvalleycaravanpark.co.uk
w goldenvalleycaravanpark.co.uk ONLINE MAP GUEST REVIEWS

🚐 (45) £22.50–£30.00
🚐 (10) £22.00–£27.50
⛺ (100) £15.00–£27.50

Secluded woodland hideaway. All-weather children's play facilities. caravan and tent pitches. Jacuzzi, gymnasium, pool table, bar, cafe and takeaway. Fishing. Nr Butterley Railway. Fort Adventure facility. Gold Conservation Award. **directions** M1 jct 26 onto A610. Follow signs to Alfreton. Turn right at lights at Codnor. Then right onto Alfreton Road. Follow for 1 mile. **open** All year **payment** credit/debit cards, cash, cheques

General 🔥🖥🐕🔧📠📷☼🔌🚰🔌🕒🐕📠✕ Leisure ▶∪🚴⚓🎣🍽🎵⚓⛰

STAVELEY, Derbyshire Map ref 4B2 — SAT NAV S43 3WL

(86) £15.90–£35.51
(86) £15.90–£35.51
86 touring pitches

Poolsbrook Country Park Caravan Club Site

Staveley, Derbyshire S43 3WL
t (01246) 470659 **e** enquiries@caravanclub.co.uk
w caravanclub.co.uk

This site incorporates a number of sustainable resource and energy features and is set within 165 acres. Cafe and children's adventure play area. Ideal for fishing, walking and cycling. **directions** M1 jct 30 onto A616, then A619 (Chesterfield). 2.5 miles left into Fan Road. Follow signs to Poolsbrook Country Park Only. Site on right. **open** April to November **payment** credit/debit cards, cash, cheques

General **Leisure**

SWADLINCOTE, Derbyshire Map ref 4B3 — SAT NAV DE12 8JD

(30) £12.00–£20.00
(15) £12.00–£20.00
(60) £10.00–£24.00
30 touring pitches

Beehive Woodland Lakes

Rosliston, Swadlincote, Derbyshire DE12 8HZ
t (01283) 763981 **e** info@beehivefarm-woodlandlakes.co.uk
w beehivefarm-woodlandlakes.co.uk ONLINE MAP

Premier fishing venue, onsite tearoom, set within 65 acres of woodland. Local attractions include, Conkers, Alton Towers, National Memorial Arboretum, Drayton Manor & Coors museum. Pre-book only. **directions** For SAT NAV users enter DE12 8JD, Look for Beehive brown signs. Always avoid narrow bridge at Walton On Trent. **open** All year except Xmas and New Year **payment** credit/debit cards, cash, cheques

General **Leisure**

ANDERBY, Lincolnshire Map ref 4D2 — SAT NAV PE24 5YB

(130) £12.00–£24.00
(10) £12.00–£24.00
(50) £10.00–£24.00
140 touring pitches

Manor Farm Caravan Park

Sea Road, Anderby, Skegness PE24 5YB
t (01507) 490372 **e** skegnessinfo@e-lindsey.gov.uk
w manorfarmcaravanpark.co.uk ONLINE MAP GUEST REVIEWS ONLINE BOOKING LAST MINUTE OFFERS

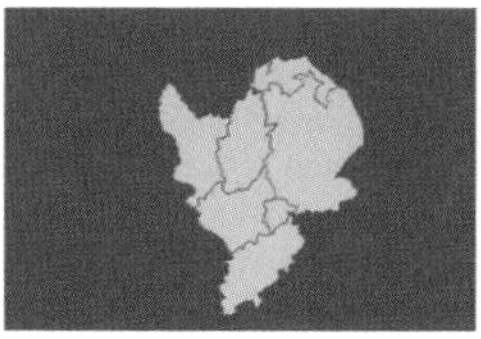

A peaceful and relaxed atmosphere await those who choose our park as their base to enjoy the East Coast and Surrounding Countryside. **directions** Turn right off A52 Skegness to Mablethorpe into Anderby 1½ miles on left. **open** 1st March to 30th November **payment** credit/debit cards, cash, cheques

General **Leisure**

BOSTON, Lincolnshire Map ref 3A1 — SAT NAV PE20 3QU

£16.00
£16.00
£8.00–£16.00
(4) £230.00–£270.00
87 touring pitches

Orchard Park

Frampton Lane, Hubberts Bridge, Boston PE20 3QU
t (01205) 290328 **f** (01205) 290247 **e** info@orchardpark.co.uk
w orchardpark.co.uk ONLINE MAP

Level, grassy, peaceful park with bus service into local towns. Bar and cafe on site. Village pub five minutes walk. Coarse fishing on site. Adults only. **directions** On B1192 between A52 (Boston-Grantham) and A1121 (Boston-Sleaford). **open** All year **payment** cash, cheques

General **Leisure**

BURGH-LE-MARSH, Lincolnshire Map ref 4D2

SAT NAV PE24 5LN

enjoyEngland.com
★★★★
TOURING &
CAMPING PARK

Sycamore Lakes Park

Skegness Road, Burgh le Marsh PE24 5LN
t (01754) 811411 f (01754) 811411 e info@sycamorelakes.co.uk
w **sycamorelakes.co.uk** ONLINE MAP

(54)	£16.50–£18.50
(54)	£16.50–£18.50
A (54)	£15.00–£16.50
(4)	£435.00–£495.00
(5)	£355.00–£415.00

54 touring pitches

SPECIAL PROMOTIONS
Out of season short breaks
in cottages or cabins are
£80–90 per night, for up to
five people.

Set in landscaped grounds with four fishing lakes (well stocked with carp, tench, rudd, roach and perch). Spacious, level pitches (hard standing and grass) with hook-ups. Dog walks. Superb amenity block. Lakeside cafeteria, Sunday lunches. Tackle shop. Lakeside holiday cottages and cabins. Sycamore lakes premier static caravan park, sales office.

open March to November
payment cash, cheques

directions Situated on the A158 between Burgh-le-Marsh and Skegness at Sycamore Lakes roundabout.

General 🏧 🛏 🌃 🔥 ☼ 🖥 🚲 🔌 🚽 🎮 ✕ Leisure ► ∪ ⨏ ⚠

LINCOLN, Lincolnshire Map ref 4C2

SAT NAV LN6 0EY

enjoyEngland.com
★★★★
TOURING PARK

Hartsholme Country Park

Skellingthorpe Road, Lincoln LN6 0EY
t (01522) 873578 e hartsholmecp@lincoln.gov.uk
w **lincoln.gov.uk/hartsholmecampsite** ONLINE MAP

	£14.20–£19.30
	£14.20–£19.30
A (10)	£7.50–£19.30

26 touring pitches

Our 4 star VisitEngland rated site offers flat, level grassy pitches set in mature wooded parkland. Easy access to city centre and local attractions. **directions** Main entrance is on the B1378 (Skellingthorpe Road). It is signposted from the A46 (Lincoln Bypass) and from the B1003 (Tritton Road). **open** 1st March to 31st October **payment** credit/debit cards, cash, cheques

General 🛏 🌃 🔥 ☼ 🔌 🚽 ✕ Leisure ⨏ ⚠

Looking for something else?

You can also buy a copy of our popular guide 'Hotels' including country house and town house hotels, metro and budget hotels, serviced apartments and restaurants with rooms in England 2012.

Now available in good bookshops and online at
visitbritainshop.com

£7.99

LINCOLN, Lincolnshire Map ref 4C2 | SAT NAV LN4 4LR

Tattershall Lakes Country Park

Sleaford Road, Tattershall, Lincolnshire LN4 4LR
t (01526) 348800 **f** (01526) 345424 **e** tattershall.holidays@away-resorts.com
w **tattershall-lakes.com** ONLINE MAP ONLINE BOOKING LAST MINUTE OFFERS

(132)	£4.00–£30.00
(32)	£4.00–£42.00
(125)	£2.00–£24.00
(14)	£219.00–£999.00
(20)	£183.00–£889.00
300 touring pitches	

SPECIAL PROMOTIONS
We have special offers available from time to time, please check our website for details.

A beautiful park set amongst stunning parkland, lakes and woodland. With lakes totalling over 180 acres, there's lots to do! Enjoy water skiing, Jet Skiing, fishing or any of our other water sports. There's an 18 hole golf course, a fantastic pool & spa complex complete with lake-view hot tub.

payment credit/debit cards, cash, cheques

directions It couldn't be easier, simply find the A153 and head to Tattershall. That's it!

General ⬧ 🗑 ⚘ ☎ 🛒 ☂ ☀ 🔌 ☕ 🍴 💳 ✗ Leisure ▶ 🚴 ♪ ⚓ 🍺 🎵 ⚫ ⛰

OLD LEAKE, Lincolnshire Map ref 3A1 | SAT NAV PE22 9RF

Long Acres (Adult Only) Caravan & Camping Site

Station Road, Old Leake, Boston PE22 9RF
t (01205) 871555 **f** (01205) 871555 **e** lacp@btconnect.com
w **longacres-caravanpark.co.uk** ONLINE MAP GUEST REVIEWS

(40)	£15.00–£18.00
(40)	£15.00–£18.00
(15)	£15.00–£18.00
40 touring pitches	

Escape to our 'Adult Only' Touring Park for peace and tranquility. Superb facilities with a warm and friendly atmosphere. All individual hardstanding/grass pitches with electrics. The Fens offer a fantastic starting point for exploring Lincolnshires aviation, history and heritage, arts and culture, waterways, cycling, walking and wildlife.

open March to October
payment credit/debit cards, cash, cheques, euros

directions From the A16 at Sibsey, take the B1184 (Station Road), turn left at T junction, approx 1.5 miles turn right into Station Road.

General ⚘ ☎ ☂ ☀ 🛏 🛒 ☕ 💳 Leisure ♪

SKEGNESS, Lincolnshire Map ref 4D2

SAT NAV PE25 1NJ

Butlins Skegness

Ingoldmells, Skegness, Lincolnshire PE25 1NJ
t 0845 070 4736 **e** butlins.holiday@bourne-leisure.co.uk
w **butlins.com/resorts/skegness/**
ONLINE MAP ONLINE BOOKING LAST MINUTE OFFERS

SPECIAL PROMOTIONS
See butlins.com for our
latest offers and prices.

Superb live entertainment and a fantastic range of facilities and activities; sub tropical waterworld, funfair, all weather sports areas, children's play areas and clubs, bars and restaurants. Set on the Lincolnshire coastline, our Skegness Resort is the place to go if you're a beach lover!

There's a theme park nearby for teens, a farm the little ones will love and the gorgeous beach and countryside for everyone to enjoy. With lots of great live shows and activities, beautifully landscaped gardens, we will put a smile on everyone's face.

While each of our resorts offers everything you'd expect from an exciting family break, Skegness boasts a luxury spa, fantastic outdoor family pools and the longest, sandiest beach!

Staying in charming New England style accommodation you'll feel right at home. Make the most of the county famous for its agriculture, why not take the kids to visit a real working farm, or even meet the seals at the seal sanctuary.

open All year
payment credit/debit cards, cheques

directions Simply follow the A52 Skegness to Mablethorpe, the Chapel St Leonards and Ingoldmells Road. We're about three miles from Skegness.

General   Leisure

SKEGNESS, Lincolnshire Map ref 4D2

SAT NAV PE25 1JF

Skegness Water Leisure Park
Walls Lane, Skegness PE25 1JF
t (01754) 899400 f (01754) 897867 e enquiries@skegnesswaterleisurepark.co.uk
w **skegnesswaterleisurepark.co.uk**

🚐 £16.50–£24.00
🚐 £16.50–£24.50
⛺ £16.50–£22.50
250 touring pitches

Family-orientated caravan and camping site 'where the coast meets the countryside'. Ten-minute walk to award-winning beaches with scenic, rural views. Close to Butlins and Fantasy Island. **directions** A52 north from Skegness 2.5 miles. Turn left at Cheers pub into Walls Lane. Site entrance is 400 yards on the left hand side. **open** March to November **payment** credit/debit cards, cash, cheques

General 🖥 ❤ 🗑 ⛽ 🔆 💤 🚻 ♿ ✕ Leisure ∪ ⚓ 🍴 ♪ ⛰

FINESHADE, Northamptonshire Map ref 3A1

SAT NAV NN17 3BB

Top Lodge Caravan Club Site
Fineshade, Stamford, Lincolnshire NN17 3BB
t (01780) 444617 e enquiries@caravanclub.co.uk
w **caravanclub.co.uk**

THE
CARAVAN
CLUB

🚐 (85) £11.40–£28.00
🚐 (85) £11.40–£28.00
85 touring pitches

Tranquil, open meadowland site surrounded by woodland, birds and deer. Visit Brarnsdale Gardens at Oakham. Own sanitation required. **directions** Turn right off A43 at junction A47 Corby (signposted Fineshade). Top Lodge within 0.5 mile. **open** March to November **payment** credit/debit cards, cash, cheques

General ❤ 🗑 ⛽ 🚻 ♿ Leisure ▶ ⚓

NOTTINGHAM, Nottinghamshire Map ref 4C2

SAT NAV NG12 2LU

National Water Sports Centre Caravan & Camping Park
Adbolton Lane, Holme Pierrepont, Nottingham NG12 2LU
t (0115) 982 1212 e nwsccampsite@nottscc.gov.uk
w **nwscnotts.com** ONLINE MAP GUEST REVIEWS LAST MINUTE OFFERS

🚐 (52) £10.50–£14.00
🚐 (52) £14.00–£16.00
⛺ (360) £8.00–£29.00
52 touring pitches

SPECIAL PROMOTIONS
Electric hook-up available for £4.00 per night. Special Easter & Halloween weekend events available to book.

Set in a 270 acre country park the National Water Sports Centre is just 3 miles from Nottingham City Centre. The Campsite has 40 hard standing pitches along with grassed areas. Activities on site include white water rafting, water skiing, windsurfing and canoeing; with great walks and good cycling routes.

open All year
payment credit/debit cards, cash, cheques

directions 3 Miles From City Centre on A52. (Please See Website).

General 📹 🖥 ❤ 🗑 ⛽ 🔆 🛏 🚻 ♿ ✕ Leisure ▶ ∪ ⚓ 🍴 ⛰

TEVERSAL, Nottinghamshire Map ref 4C2

SAT NAV NG17 3JJ

Teversal Camping and Caravanning Club Site

Silverhill Lane, Teversal, Nottinghamshire NG17 3JJ
t (01623) 551838 f 0870 705 8416 e teversal@thefriendlyclub.co.uk
w **campingandcaravanningclub.co.uk/teversal** ONLINE MAP GUEST REVIEWS

Camping and
Caravanning
Club
The Friendly Club

£23.00–£26.00
£23.00–£26.00
£23.00–£26.00

126 touring pitches

Set in six acres of glorious countryside, our award-winning Club Site at Teversal gives you the chance to explore both Nottinghamshire and neighbouring Derbyshire. Safari Tents from £40 per night. **directions** OS Map Reference: 120 - SK472615 Sutton in Ashford 3 miles, Bus Stop 300m from site. Market towns of Chesterfield and Mansfield are close by. **open** All year **payment** credit/debit cards, cash, cheques

General 🗒 🛜 🐕 🚻 🎨 🌞 🔌 🕒 🚽 💻 Leisure ⛷ 🏔

WORKSOP, Nottinghamshire Map ref 4C2

SAT NAV S80 3AE

Clumber Park Caravan Club Site

Limetree Avenue, Clumber Park, Worksop, Nottinghamshire S80 3AE
t (01909) 484758 f (01909) 479611 e enquiries@caravanclub.co.uk
w **caravanclub.co.uk**

CARAVAN
CLUB

(180) £16.00–£38.90
(180) £16.00–£38.90

180 touring pitches

Set in the heart of Sherwood Forest 20 acre site is within 4,000 acres of parkland. Redeveloped to a high standard in 2002. Visit Nottingham Castle. **directions** At junction of the A1 and A57, take the A614 signposted Nottingham for 0.5 miles. Turn right into Clumber Park site. The site is signposted. **open** All year **payment** credit/debit cards, cash, cheques

General 🗒 🛜 🎨 🌞 🔌 🕒 🚽 💻 Leisure ▶ 🏌

Looking for something else?

You can also buy a copy of our popular 'B&B' guide including guest accommodation, B&B's, guest houses, farmhouses, inns, and campus and hostel accommodation in England 2012.

Now available in good bookshops and online at
visitbritainshop.com   **£8.99**

Walkers and cyclists welcome

Look out for quality-assessed accommodation displaying the Walkers Welcome and Cyclists Welcome signs.

Participants in these schemes actively encourage and support walking and cycling. In addition to special meal arrangements and helpful information, they'll provide a water supply to wash off the mud, an area for drying wet clothing and footwear, maps and books to look up cycling and walking routes and even an emergency puncture-repair kit! Bikes can also be locked up securely undercover.

The standards for these schemes have been developed in partnership with the tourist boards in Northern Ireland, Scotland and Wales, so wherever you're travelling in the UK you'll receive the same welcome.

Heart of England

Herefordshire, Shropshire, Staffordshire, Warwickshire, West Midlands, Worcestershire

174 **Where to Go**   **177** **Events**   **180** **Where to Stay**

The birthplace of William Shakespeare, the Industrial Revolution, and Cadbury's chocolate – it doesn't get better or more English than the Heart of England.

The six counties of the Heart of England: Herefordshire, Shropshire, Staffordshire, Warwickshire, West Midlands and Worcestershire, each have their own unique heritage, attractions and accent. Take some time to explore this region and you'll soon discover what really makes England tick.

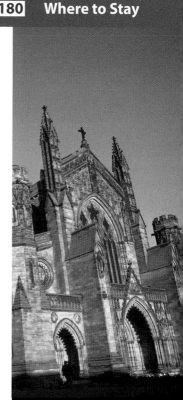

History and Heritage

Stratford is full of historic buildings associated with its most famous son, including Shakespeare's birthplace and final resting place. Considering it's where the Industrial Revolution started, Ironbridge Gorge is full of natural beauty as well as history. There's also the imposing Warwick Castle and the world famous Wedgwood potteries to explore.

Arts and Culture

Culture vultures should get busy by taking in a play at the Royal Shakespeare Company Theatre or a classical performance by the Birmingham Symphony Orchestra at the incredible Symphony Hall. Compton Verney is a must for art-lovers with collections from around the world and fascinating Chinese bronzes.

Food and Drink

Culinary astronomers should look to Birmingham and Ludlow for Michelin-starred restaurants. But as far as flavour-sensations go it doesn't get better than a Balti at one of Birmingham's many curry houses. Be sure to sample local specialities wherever you go such as Black Country 'faggots' and Staffordshire oatcakes before washing it all down with a pint of Bass.

Sports

Where better to visit in the year England hosts the Olympics but Much Wenlock, the home of the modern Olympic Games. It was here in 1850 that Dr Penny Brookes introduced the first Wenlock Olympian Games which went on to inspire Baron De Coubertin to create the Olympics we know today. The town still holds its own annual Olympiad in July.

Music and Nightlife

Get your summer festival season sorted with V Festival and The Big Chill. If camping and late night revelling aren't for you, then Birmingham's Symphony Hall offers everything from folk to classical in a stunning and more salubrious setting. Birmingham also has a thriving clubbing scene with the legendary Q Club and Gatecrasher guaranteed to get those hands in the air.

Shopping

If you're a fashionista on the hunt for the latest trends or just someone that likes to shop until they drop then Birmingham's Bullring ticks all the right boxes. And with the goods on offer in Selfridges as cutting edge and funky as the building itself, then there is no better place to be a consumer.

Family Fun

Want to travel from 0 – 60 mph in two seconds or experience a face-melting 4 Gs during a vertical drop? Of course you do. Then Alton Towers and Drayton Manor are for you.

Although you'll travel a whole lot slower, you'll have no less fun at the West Midland Safari Park. With over 600 animals including rare white lions, you're guaranteed close encounters galore on the self-drive safari – just be very careful hand feeding the rhinos.

Handy Hints

Chocoholics – don't miss 'bean to bar' at Cadbury World.

Cheers - Combine drinking, history and walking by trundling the Cider Trail, starting at the Cider Museum.

Back in time – Visit the Black Country Living Museum

Cathedrals and choral music – Head to the Three Choirs Festival which has been running since the 18th century.

Evolution - Explore the origins of Charles Darwin in Shrewsbury, where the naturalist was born.

OUT & ABOUT IN THE HEART OF ENGLAND

Day 1 - Arts and Rides

- Visit Compton Verney and its art gallery housed in a Grade I listed Georgian mansion
- Take a heritage train ride Chasewater Railway
- Take a half-hour cruises on the River Avon in a traditional passenger boat

Day 2 - Countryside and Fun Museums

- Visit Hatton Farm Village - an incredible countryside experience for the whole family
- Ironbridge Gorge Museums, ten family friendly museums, is a fun interactive 'Victorian' town and World Heritage Site
- Take a guided ghost walk around Stratford

Day 3 - Fashion, Music and Treasure

- Pick up a Vivienne Westwood design in Harvey Nichols in Birmingham
- Imagine a totally electrifying, full day out at one of England's most iconic castles, Warwick Castle
- Walk the 200 acres of cool pine forests & open heath land of Kingsford Forest Park

Day 4 - Castle, Fresh Air and Science

- Go and relive the turbulent history of Goodrich Castle
- Walk the paths of Bodenham Arboretum which is beautifully landscaped and set within a working farm
- Listen, learn and laugh at Thinktank, Birmingham's science museum

Day 5 - All Shapes and Sizes

- Watch 4D Cinema at Drayton Manor Theme Park
- Tackle the 18 hole, par 71, Ansty Golf Course
- See Wenlock Priory, with its stunning clipped topiary

Day 6 - Bag a Bargain, Go to the Dogs

- Take a tour inside Anne Hathaway's world-famous thatched cottage
- Wander the 170 stalls under the famous circular roof of Coventry market
- Win big at Hall Green Greyhound Stadium in Birmingham

Day 7 - Locks and Getting Lost

- Worcester's Pump House Environment centre has free admission, activities and displays around the environment
- Visit the flight of 21 locks at Hatton on the Grand Union Canal near Warwick
- Get lost in a maze, in view of the Malvern Hills at Broadfields A-Maize-ing Maze

Where to Go

 Attractions with this sign participate in the **Places of Interest Quality Assurance Scheme**.

 Attractions with this sign participate in the **Visitor Attraction Quality Assurance Scheme**.

Both schemes recognise high standards in all aspects of the visitor experience (see page 6)

ENTERTAINMENT & CULTURE

Barber Institute of Fine Arts
Edgbaston, West Midlands B15 2TS
(0121) 414 7333
www.barber.org.uk
British and European paintings, drawings and sculpture from the 13thC-mid 20thC.

Black Country Living Museum
Dudley, West Midlands DY1 4SQ
(0121) 557 9643
www.bclm.co.uk
A warm welcome awaits you at Britain's friendliest open-air museum. Wander around original shops and houses, ride on fair attractions, take a look down the underground coalmine.

Cadbury World
Bournville, West Midlands B30 2LU
0845 450 3599
www.cadburyworld.co.uk
Story of Cadbury's chocolate includes chocolate-making demonstration and attractions for all ages, with free samples, free parking, shop and restaurant. Phone to check availability and reserve admission.

Compton Verney
Stratford-upon-Avon CV35 9HZ
(01926) 645500
www.comptonverney.org.uk
Award-winning art gallery housed in a grade I listed Robert Adam mansion.

Etruria Industrial Museum
Staffordshire ST4 7AF
(01782) 233144
www.stoke.gov.uk/museum
Discover how they put the 'bone' in bone china at the last working steam-powered potters mill in Britain. Includes a Bone and Flint Mill and family-friendly interactive exhibition.

Hereford Museum and Art Gallery
Herefordshire HR4 9AU
(01432) 260692
www.herefordshire.gov.uk/leisure/museums_galleries/2869.asp
In the museum, aspects of Herefordshire history and life - in the Gallery, regularly changing exhibitions of paintings, photography and crafts.

Ledbury Heritage Centre
Herefordshire, HR8 1DN
(01432) 260692
www.herefordshire.gov.uk/leisure/museums_galleries/2861.asp
The story of Ledbury's past displayed in a timber-framed building in the picturesque lane leading to the church.

Royal Air Force Museum Cosford
Shifnal, Shropshire TF11 8UP
(01902) 376200
www.rafmuseum.org
FREE Admission. The award winning museum houses one of the largest aviation collections in the United Kingdom.

Rugby Art Gallery and Museum
Warwickshire CV21 3BZ
(01788) 533201
www.ragm.org.uk
Contemporary art & craft exhibitions; museum showcasing the Tripontium Collection of Roman artefacts & Rugby's Social History; the Rugby Collection of 20th century & contemporary British art (annually); fun activities for children/families.

Thinktank-Birmingham Science Museum
West Midlands B4 7XG
(0121) 202 2222
www.thinktank.ac
Thinktank is Birmingham's science museum where the emphasis is firmly on hands on exhibits and interactive fun.

Wolverhampton Art Gallery
West Midlands WV1 1DU
(01902) 552055
www.wolverhamptonart.org.uk
Explore 300 years of art in this newly refurbished city centre gallery.

Worcester City Art Gallery & Museum
Worcestershire WR1 1DT
(01905) 25371
www.worcestercitymuseums.org.uk
The art gallery & museum runs a programme of exhibitions/events for all the family. Explore the fascinating displays, exhibitions, cafe, shop and Worcestershire Soldier Galleries.

FAMILY FUN

Aerial Extreme Trentham
Staffordshire ST4 8AX
0845 652 1736
www.aerialextreme.co.uk/index.php/
courses/trentham-estate
*Our tree based adventure ropes course,
set within the tranquil grounds of
Trentham Estate is a truly spectacular
journey.*

Enginuity
Telford, Shropshire TF8 7DG
(01952) 433424
www.ironbridge.org.uk
*At Enginuity you can turn the wheels
of your imagination, test your horse
power and discover how good ideas
are turned in to real things.*

HERITAGE

Coventry Cathedral - St Michael's
West Midlands CV1 5AB
(024) 7652 1257
www.coventrycathedral.org.uk
*Glorious 20th century Cathedral, with
stunning 1950's art & architecture,
rising above the stark ruins of the
medieval Cathedral destroyed by
German air raids in 1940.*

Darby Houses (Ironbridge)
Telford, Shropshire TF8 7EW
(01952) 433424
www.ironbridge.org.uk
*In the Darby houses, Dale House and
Rosehill House, you can delve in to the
everyday life of Quaker families.*

Eastnor Castle
Ledbury, Herefordshire HR8 1RL
(01531) 633160
www.eastnorcastle.com
*Fairytale Georgian Castle
dramatically situated in the Malvern
Hills.*

Goodrich Castle
**Ross-on-Wye, Herefordshire
HR9 6HY**
(01600) 890538
www.english-heritage.org.uk/
goodrich
*Come and relive the turbulent history
of Goodrich Castle with our free audio
and then climb to the battlements for
breathtaking views over the Wye Valley.*

Hanbury Hall
**Droitwich Spa, Worcestershire
WR9 7EA**
(01527) 821214
www.nationaltrust.org.uk/hanburyhall
*Early 18th Century house, garden &
park owned by the Vernon family for
nearly 300 years.*

Hereford Cathedral
Herefordshire HR1 2NG
(01432) 374202
www.herefordcathedral.org
*Hereford Cathedral contains some of
the finest examples of architecture
from Norman times to the present day.*

Iron Bridge and Toll House
Telford, Shropshire TF8 7DG
(01952) 433424
www.ironbridge.org.uk
*You can peer through its railings and
conjure a vision of sailing vessels
heading downstream towards Bristol
and the markets of the world.*

Kenilworth Castle and Elizabethan Garden
Warwickshire CV8 1NE
(01926) 852078
www.english-heritage.org.uk/
kenilworth
*One of the most spectacular castle
ruins in England.*

Lichfield Cathedral
Staffordshire WS13 7LD
(01543) 306100
www.lichfield-cathedral.org
*A medieval Cathedral with 3 spires in
the heart of an historic City set in its
own serene Close.*

Much Wenlock Priory
Shropshire TF13 6HS
(01952) 727466
www.english-heritage.org.uk/
wenlockpriory
*Wenlock Priory, with it's stunning
clipped topiary, has a pastoral setting
on the edge of lovely Much Wenlock.*

National Memorial Arboretum
**Lichfield, Staffordshire
DE13 7AR**
(01283) 792333
www.thenma.org.uk
*150 acres of trees and memorials,
planted as a living tribute to those
who have served, died or suffered in
the service of their Country.*

Packwood House
Solihull, Warwickshire B94 6AT
0844 800 1895
www.nationaltrust.org.uk/main/w-
packwoodhouse
*Much restored tudor house, park and
garden with notable topiary.*

Ragley Hall
**Stratford-upon-Avon,
Warwickshire B49 5NJ**
(01789) 762090
www.ragleyhall.com
*Ragley Hall is set in 27 acres of
beautiful formal gardens.*

Severn Valley Railway
**Bewdley, Worcestershire
DY12 1BG**
(01299) 403816
www.svr.co.uk
*Steam-hauled trains running along
the beautiful Severn Valley from
Kidderminster - Bridgnorth.*

Stokesay Castle
**Craven Arms, Shropshire
SY7 9AH**
(01588) 672544
www.english-heritage.org.uk/
stokesaycastle
*Stokesay Castle, near Craven Arms,
nestles in peaceful South Shropshire
countryside near the Welsh Border. It
is one of more than a dozen English
Heritage properties in the county.*

Tamworth Castle
Staffordshire B79 7NA
(01827) 709629
www.tamworthcastle.co.uk
*The number one Heritage attraction
located in the town. Explore over 900
years of history in the magnificent
Motte and Bailey Castle.*

The Almonry Museum and Heritage Centre
**Evesham, Worcestershire
WR11 4BG**
(01386) 446944
www.almonryevesham.org
*The 14th century house has 12 rooms
of exhibits from 2000 years of Evesham
history and pleasant gardens to the
rear.*

Warwick Castle
Warwickshire CV34 4QU
0871 265 2000
www.warwick-castle.co.uk
*Imagine a totally electrifying, full day
out at Britain's ultimate castle.*

Wedgwood Visitor Centre
**Stoke-on-Trent, Staffordshire
ST12 9ER**
(01782) 282986
www.wedgwoodvisitorcentre.com
*Enjoy the past, buy the present
and treasure the experience. The
Wedgwood Visitor Centre offers a
unique chance to immerse yourself
in the heritage of Britain's greatest
ceramics company.*

Worcester Cathedral
Worcestershire WR1 2LA
(01905) 732900
www.worcestercathedral.co.uk
*Worcester Cathedral is one of
England's most magnificent and
inspiring buildings, a place of prayer
and worship for fourteen centuries.*

Wroxeter Roman City
Shrewsbury, Shropshire
SY5 6PH   (01743) 761330
www.english-heritage.org.uk/
wroxeter
Wroxeter Roman City, or Viroconium,
to give it its Roman title, is thought to
have been one of the largest Roman
cities in the UK with over 200 acres of
land, 2 miles of walls and a population
of approximately 5,000.

NATURE & WILDLIFE

Birmingham Botanical Gardens and Glasshouses
Edgbaston, West Midlands
B15 3TR
(0121) 454 1860
www.birminghambotanicalgardens.
org.uk
Fifteen acres of ornamental gardens
and glasshouses.

Cannock Chase
Staffordshire WS15 2UQ
(01543) 877666
www.visitcannockchase.co.uk
Central England's woodland jewel,
packed with things to see and do.

Dudley Zoological Gardens
West Midlands DY1 4QB
(01384) 215313
www.dudleyzoo.org.uk
From lions and tigers to snakes and
spiders there's something for all ages.
Animal feeding, encounters, face
painting, land train and fair rides.

Heart Park
Fillongley, Warwickshire
CV7 8DX
(01676) 540333
www.heartpark.co.uk
"We believe that the heart of our Park
is the beach and lake. But for those of
you who'd like to try out a few 'different'
activities - we've got a great assortment
for you to try."

Hergest Croft Gardens
Kington, Herefordshire HR5 3EG
(01544) 230160
www.hergest.co.uk
The gardens extend over 50 acres,
with more than 4000 rare shrubs
and trees. With over 60 champion
trees and shrubs it is one of the finest
collections in the British Isles.

Park Hall - The Countryside Experience
Oswestry, Shropshire SY11 4AS
(01691) 671123
www.parkhallfarm.co.uk
With 40,000 square feet of indoor
attractions, regular hands-on animal
activities, lots of outdoor play and
driving activities there is never a dull
moment.

Ryton Pools Country Parks
Coventry, Warwickshire
CV8 3BH
(024) 7630 5592
www.warwickshire.gov.uk/parks
The 100 acres of Ryton Pools Country
Park are just waiting to be explored.
The many different habitats are
home to a wide range of birds and
other wildlife.

West Midland Safari and Leisure Park
Bewdley, Worcestershire
DY12 1LF
(01299) 402114
www.wmsp.co.uk
Fantastic family entertainment for the
summer season this year.

Events 2012

Darwin Festival
Shrewsbury
www.darwinshrewsbury.org
February

Oswestry Festival of the Word
Oswestry
www.oswestrylitfest.co.uk
March

Blues Festival
Bromsgrove
www.bromsgrovefestival.co.uk
April - May

Upton and Severn Riverside Folk Festival
Upton-upon-Severn
www.uptonfolk.org
April - May

The Guardian Hay Festival
Hay-on-Wye
www.hayfestival.com
May - June

Jazz Festival
Upton-upon-Severn
www.uptonjazz.co.uk
June

RAF Cosford Air Show
Shifnal
www.cosfordairshow.co.uk
June

The Three Counties Show
Malvern
www.threecounties.co.uk
June

Beer on the Wye VII
Hereford
www.herefordcamra.org.uk
July

Festival at the Edge
Wem
www.festivalattheedge.org
July

Upton Blues Festival
Upton-upon-Severn
www.uptonbluesfestival.org.uk
July

Heart Food
Worcester
www.heartfood.co.uk/worcester-
food-and-drink-festival
August

Shrewsbury Flower Show
Shrewsbury
www.shrewsburyflowershow.org.uk
August

Worcester Festival
Worcester
www.worcesterfestival.co.uk
August

Coventry Festival of Motoring
Coventry
www.transport-museum.com
September

Ludlow Food Festival
Ludlow
www.foodfestival.co.uk
September

Bewdley Arts Festival
Bewdley
www.bewdleyfestival.org.uk
October

Tenbury Wells Mistletoe Festival
Tenbury Wells
www.tenbury-mistletoe-festival.
co.uk
December

Tourist Information Centres

When you arrive at your destination, visit an Official Partner Tourist Information Centre for quality assured help with accommodation and information about local attractions and events, or email your request before you go. To find a Tourist Information Centre by region look at http://www.enjoyengland.com under Destination Finder.

BEWDLEY	Load Street	01299 404740	bewdleytic@wyreforestdc.gov.uk
BIRMINGHAM Rotunda	The Rotunda	0844 888 3883	visit@marketingbirmingham.com
BRIDGNORTH	The Library	01746 763257	bridgnorth.tourism@shropshire.gov.uk
CHURCH STRETTON	Church Street	01694 723133	churchstretton.scf@shropshire.gov.uk
COVENTRY CATHEDRAL	Coventry Cathedral, 1 Hill Top	024 7622 5616	tic@cvone.co.uk
HEREFORD	1 King Street	01432 268430	tic-hereford@herefordshire.gov.uk
IRONBRIDGE	Ironbridge Gorge Museum Trust	01952 884391	tic@ironbridge.org.uk
LEEK	Stockwell Street	01538 483741	tourism.services@staffsmoorlands.gov.uk
LICHFIELD	Lichfield Garrick	01543 412112	info@visitlichfield.com
LUDLOW	Castle Street	01584 875053	ludlow.tourism@shropshire.gov.uk
MALVERN	21 Church Street	01684 892289	malvern.tic@malvernhills.gov.uk
OSWESTRY (MILE END)	Mile End	01691 662488	oswestrytourism@shropshire.gov.uk
ROSS-ON-WYE	Swan House	01989 562768	tic-ross@herefordshire.gov.uk
RUGBY	Rugby Visitor Centre	01788 533217	visitor.centre@rugby.gov.uk
SHREWSBURY	Rowley's House	01743 281200	visitorinfo@shrewsbury.gov.uk
SOLIHULL	Central Library	0121 704 6130	artscomplex@solihull.gov.uk
STAFFORD	Stafford Gatehouse Theatre	01785 619619	tic@staffordbc.gov.uk
STOKE-ON-TRENT	Victoria Hall, Bagnall Street	01782 236000	stoke.tic@stoke.gov.uk
STRATFORD-UPON-AVON	62 Henley Street	01789 264293	tic@discover-stratford.com
TAMWORTH	Tamworth Information Centre	01827 709581	tic@tamworth.gov.uk
WARWICK	The Court House	01926 492212	touristinfo@warwick-uk.co.uk
WORCESTER	The Guildhall	01905 726311	touristinfo@visitworcester.com

Regional Contacts and Information

Marketing Birmingham
Tel: (0121) 202 5115
Web: www.visitbirmingham.com

Visit Coventy & Warwickshire
Tel: (024) 7622 5616
Web: www.visitcoventryandwarwickshire.co.uk

Visit Herefordshire
Tel: (01432) 260621
Web: www.visitherefordshire.co.uk

Shakespeare Country
Tel: 0870 160 7930
Web: www.shakespeare-country.co.uk

Shropshire Tourism
Tel: (01743) 261919
Web: www.shropshiretourism.co.uk

Destination Staffordshire
Tel: 0870 500 4444
Web: www.enjoystaffordshire.com

Stoke-on-Trent
Tel: (01782) 236000
Web: www.visitstoke.co.uk

Destination Worcestershire
Tel: (01905) 728787
Web: www.visitworcestershire.org

Where to Stay

Entries appear alphabetically by town name in each county. A key to symbols appears on page 6. Maps start on page 298. Further listings of VisitEngland assessed accommodation appear on the CD at the back of this guide.

BROMYARD, Herefordshire Map ref 2B1

SAT NAV WR6 5TE

Bromyard Downs Caravan Club Site
Brockhampton, Bringsty, Bromyard, Herefordshire WR6 5TE
t (01885) 482607 e enquiries@caravanclub.co.uk
w **caravanclub.co.uk**

THE
CARAVAN
CLUB

🚐 (40)   £10.00–£18.00
🚃 (40)   £10.00–£18.00
40 touring pitches

Secluded woodland site set in beautiful countryside between the cathedral cities of Hereford and Worcester, with many lovely walks nearby. **directions** Site on left of A44 (Worcester-Bromyard) about 0.25 miles past Brockhampton (National Trust) entrance. **open** April to October **payment** credit/debit cards, cash, cheques

General 🛏 🐕 🚐 ⊖

EARDISLAND, Herefordshire Map ref 2A1

SAT NAV HR6 9BG

Arrow Bank Holiday Park
Nun House Farm, Eardisland, Leominster HR6 9BG
t (01544) 388312 f (01544) 388312 e enquiries@arrowbankholidaypark.co.uk
w **arrowbankholidaypark.co.uk**

🚐 (36)   £18.00–£20.00
🚃   £18.00–£20.00
▲ (9)   £15.00–£20.00
🏠 (1)   £320.00–£445.00
45 touring pitches

Based in rural Herefordshire amid the peace and tranquility, is Arrow Bank Holiday Park. Come and relax in this quiet, adult only park, surrounded by beautiful trees. **directions** From Leominster, follow A44 West, after Morrisons bear right to Eardisland. Park entrance on right just after village sign. **payment** credit/debit cards, cash, cheques

General 🗑 🕪 🛏 🛒 📷 ☼ ♨ 🚐 🏠 🚾 Leisure 🎣

Looking for something else?

You can also buy a copy of our popular guide 'Self Catering' including self-catering holiday homes, approved caravan holiday homes, boat accommodation and holiday cottage agencies in England 2012. Now available in good bookshops and online at **visitbritainshop.com £8.99**

SYMONDS YAT WEST, Herefordshire Map ref 2A1

SAT NAV HR9 6BY

★★★★
HOLIDAY &
TOURING PARK

Sterrett's Caravan Park
Symonds Yat West, nr Ross-on-Wye, Symonds Yat HR9 6BY
t (01594) 832888 / (01594) 833162
w **ukparks.co.uk/sterretts**

🚐 (8)	£10.00–£14.00
🚐 (8)	£10.00–£14.00
▲ (8)	£10.00–£20.00
🏠 (3)	£195.00–£330.00
8 touring pitches	

Grass or hard standing pitches for touring vans, tents welcome. Luxury caravans for hire close to river Wye and ideal for touring the Wye Valley and Forest of Dean. **directions** Mid way A40 Ross on Wye to Monmouth at Whitchurch. Follow signs to Symonds Yat West. **open** 1st Feb to 30th Nov **payment** cash, cheques

General 🖥 ⊀ 🐾 ☼ 🐶 🎇 🚐   Leisure ▶ ∪ ♿ ⚓ ⛰

KINNERLEY, Shropshire Map ref 4A3

SAT NAV SY10 8DY

★★★★★
TOURING PARK

Oswestry Camping and Caravanning Club Site
Cranberry Moss, Kinnerley, Oswestry, Shropshire SY10 8DY
t (01743) 741118 e oswestry.site@thefriendlyclub.co.uk
w **campingandcaravanningclub.co.uk/oswestry** ONLINE MAP GUEST REVIEWS

The Camping and Caravanning Club
The Friendly Club

🚐	£23.00–£26.00
🚐	£23.00–£26.00
▲	£23.00–£26.00
65 touring pitches	

Where Shropshire meets Wales. The sandstone crags of Nesscliffe Country Park overlook our lovely Club Site in the rolling pastureland of Shropshire with its ancient woodlands and commons. **directions** Turn off the A5 at the roundabout (signed B4396 Knockin). Site is about 350 yards from A5, on the left of B4396. **open** All year

General 🖥 ⊕ ⊀ ⚡ 🛢 🐾 ☼ 🐶 ⊕ 🎇

PRESTHOPE, Shropshire Map ref 4A3

SAT NAV TF13 6DQ

★★★
TOURING PARK

Presthope Caravan Club Site
Stretton Road, Much Wenlock, Shropshire TF13 6DQ
t (01746) 785234 e enquiries@caravanclub.co.uk
w **caravanclub.co.uk**

THE
CARAVAN
CLUB

🚐 (71)	£10.00–£18.00
🚐 (71)	£10.00–£18.00
71 touring pitches	

An interesting site with abundant wildlife on site. National Trust properties nearby. Shrewsbury, Telford and Bridgnorth are all well worth visiting. **directions** From A458 (signposted Shrewsbury) in 0.25 miles turn left onto B4371. Site on left. **open** April to September **payment** credit/debit cards, cash, cheques

General ⊀ 🐶 ⊕   Leisure ⚓

BLACKSHAW MOOR, Staffordshire Map ref 4B2

SAT NAV ST13 8TW

★★★★★
TOURING PARK

Blackshaw Moor Caravan Club Site
Blackshaw Moor Caravan Club Site, Blackshaw Moor, Leek, Staffordshire
ST13 8TW t (01538) 300203
w **caravanclub.co.uk**

THE
CARAVAN
CLUB

🚐 (89)	£13.50–£32.79
🚐 (89)	£13.50–£32.79
89 touring pitches	

Attractive, level and terraced site with spacious pitches. On the quieter, southern edge of the Peak District with some of the best views and walks in the region. **directions** From Buxton on A53 site on left 200 yards past Blackshaw Mooor Sign. From Leek on A53 site on right within 3 miles. **open** March to January **payment** credit/debit cards, cash, cheques

General 🖥 ⊕ ⊀ 🛢 🐾 ⚡ ⊕ 🐶 🎇   Leisure ▶

RUGELEY, Staffordshire Map ref 4B3

SAT NAV WS15 2TX

Silver Trees Holiday Park - Static Vans

Stafford Brook Road, Penkridge Bank, Rugeley, Cannock Chase, Staffordshire WS15 2TX
t (01889) 582185 **f** (01889) 582373 **e** info@silvertreesholidaypark.co.uk
w silvertreesholidaypark.co.uk ONLINE MAP GUEST REVIEWS

(9) £249.00–£549.00

Rose Award holiday homes on quiet woodland park, suitable for couples and families enjoying wildlife, walks, cycling on Cannock Chase. Area of Outstanding Natural Beauty. View deer from your caravan! **directions** From A51 or A34 follow brown tourist signs for Silver Trees Holiday Park, the park is located between Rugeley and Penkridge on Cannock Chase. **open** March to January **payment** credit/debit cards, cash, cheques

General ▨ ⏻ ⌂ ☼ Leisure ∪ ⚲ ♠ ⚓

UTTOXETER, Staffordshire Map ref 4B2

SAT NAV ST14 8BD

Uttoxeter Racecourse Caravan Club Site

Uttoxeter Racecourse, Wood Lane, Uttoxeter ST14 8BD
t (01889) 564172 **e** enquiries@caravanclub.co.uk
w caravanclub.co.uk

(76) £11.40–£28.00
(76) £11.40–£28.00
76 touring pitches

Popular destination near to Alton Towers. Golf adj, access to bar, picnic and play areas on racecourse. **directions** Turn off A50 at roundabout onto A518. Site entrance on left. **open** March to November **payment** credit/debit cards, cash, cheques

General ▨ ⛺ ⏻ ⌂ ⊙ ⊙ 🖥 Leisure ▶

ASTON CANTLOW, Warwickshire Map ref 2B1

SAT NAV B95 6JP

Island Meadow Caravan Park

The Mill House, Aston Cantlow, Stratford-upon-Avon B95 6JP
t (01789) 488273 **e** holiday@islandmeadowcaravanpark.co.uk
w islandmeadowcaravanpark.co.uk ONLINE MAP GUEST REVIEWS

(24) £20.00
(24) £20.00
(10) £15.00–£20.00
(5) £365.00–£470.00
24 touring pitches

A small secluded park in rural Warwickshire, close to the historic and picturesque village of Aston Cantlow, and just six miles from Stratford. Ideal for visiting Warwick and the Cotswolds. **directions** Aston Cantlow village lies within the triangle formed by Stratford-upon-Avon, Henley-in-Arden and Alcester. The park is South west of the village. **open** March to October **payment** credit/debit cards, cash, cheques, euros

General ▨ ⛺ ⚡ ⏻ ⌂ ☼ 🚿 ⊙ ⊙ ☎ 🖥 Leisure ✈

STRATFORD-UPON-AVON, Warwickshire Map ref 2B1

SAT NAV CV37 9SR

Dodwell Park

Evesham Road (B439), Dodwell, Stratford-upon-Avon CV37 9SR
t (01789) 204957 **e** enquiries@dodwellpark.co.uk
w dodwellpark.co.uk ONLINE MAP

(50) £16.50–£21.00
(50) £16.50–£21.00
(50) £15.50–£20.00
50 touring pitches

Small, family-run touring park 2 miles SW of Stratford-upon-Avon. Country walks to River Avon and Luddington village. Ideal for visiting Warwick Castle, Shakespeare properties and Cotswolds. Brochure on request. **directions** Leaving Stratford-Upon-Avon take the B439 signposted 'B349 Bidford' (also signposted Racecourse) for 2 miles, we are on left (after going over a large hill). **open** All year **payment** credit/debit cards, cash, cheques

General ⛺ ⚡ ⏻ ⌂ ☼ 🚿 ⊙ ⊙ ☎ Leisure ⚲ ✈

WARWICK, Warwickshire Map ref 2B1

SAT NAV CV34 6HN

Warwick Racecourse Caravan Club Site
Hampton Street, Warwick CV34 6HN
t (01926) 495448 e enquiries@caravanclub.co.uk
w **caravanclub.co.uk**

(55) £13.50–£32.79
(55) £13.50–£32.79
55 touring pitches

Set on grass and tarmac in the racecourse enclosure. 6 minutes from the centre of Warwick. **directions** M40 jct 15 at roundabout A429 (Warwick). 1m left at Racecourse sign Shakespeares Avenue. 300 yds right onto A4189. Site on left across race track. **open** March to January **payment** credit/debit cards, cash

General ⬜ 🐾 📞 🚻 Leisure ► 🏊

BIRMINGHAM, West Midlands Map ref 4B3

SAT NAV B47 6JX

Chapel Lane Caravan Park
Chapel Lane, Wythall, Birmingham, West Midlands B47 6JX
t (01564) 826483 e enquiries@caravanclub.co.uk
w **caravanclub.co.uk**

(108) £15.90–£35.51
(108) £15.90–£35.51
108 touring pitches

Wythall is a quiet, rural area yet convenient for Birmingham (9 miles) and the NEC (13 miles). Visit Cadbury's World or explore the surrounding countryside and local canals. **directions** J3 off M42 then A435 to Birmingham. After 1 mile at roundabout, 1st exit, Middle Lane. Turn right at church then immediately right into site. **open** All year **payment** credit/debit cards, cash, cheques

General ⬜ 📶 🏕 🐾 ☀ 🔌 📞 🚻 🚽 📶 Leisure ► 🏊

EVESHAM, Worcestershire Map ref 2B1

SAT NAV WR11 7PR

Ranch Caravan Park
Honeybourne, Evesham WR11 7PR
t (01386) 830744 f (01386) 833503 e enquiries@ranch.co.uk
w **ranch.co.uk** ONLINE MAP

(100) £23.00–£28.00
(20) £23.00–£28.00
(4) £310.00–£475.00
120 touring pitches

An established family-run holiday park located in Honeybourne, 6 miles from Evesham. Level pitches in a landscaped setting. Well situated for visiting the Cotswolds and Shakespeare Country. **directions** From A46 Evesham bypass take B4035 to Badsey and Bretforton. Caravan park signposted from Bretforton. **open** March to November **payment** credit/debit cards, cash, cheques

General ⬜ 🐕 🛒 🏕 🐾 ☀ 🔌 🍴 📞 🚻 🚽 📶 ✖ Leisure ∪ ⚡ 🍽 🎣 ⛰

Looking for something else?

You can also buy a copy of our popular guide 'Hotels' including country house and town house hotels, metro and budget hotels, serviced apartments and restaurants with rooms in England 2012.

Now available in good bookshops and online at
visitbritainshop.com

£7.99

Yorkshire

The largest county in the UK, Yorkshire also claims to be the greenest, hosting the North York Moors, the Yorkshire Dales and the Pennines within its borders.

Add cities like York, Leeds, Hull and Sheffield; contemporary, thriving hubs with interesting histories and it's not just the size of Yorkshire that starts to amaze. No wonder then that the locals call it "God's Country".

History and Heritage

Yorkshire's heritage encompasses magnificent ruins, grand estates, traces of marauding Vikings, as well as mills and mining, legacy of the Industrial Revolution. Yorkshire's stunning gardens and museums give you a hands-on way to interact with this impressive heritage. Between the cathedrals and castles, railways and mines and fossilized remains on the coast, Yorkshire's history and heritage is easily accessible and endlessly rewarding.

Sports

Yorkshire is famed for producing some of England's fiercest and finest sports people. The county is cricket crazy with the famed Headingly Cricket Ground in Leeds the place to head for world-class international and first class cricket. In addition rugby league, union and football is passionately followed. Add thrilling racehorse meets and some of England's best golf courses and whether you want to watch sport, or get involved, there's a place to do it in Yorkshire.

Arts and Culture

For a seasonal spectacle, watch the Northern Ballet perform the Nutcracker at Leeds Grand Theatre. With touring exhibitions celebrating greats like David Hockney, York Gallery brings together the best of the past and present. Lovers of less traditional art should also keep their eyes open for Art in Unusual Places, a project that transforms urban spaces into exhibition sites for visual art and installations. Haworth in Yorkshire is the home of the Brontë Parsonage and Museum where the Brontë sisters spent so much of their lives penning their classic novels.

Food and drink

Prepare to be inspired by the range of local specialties just waiting to be sampled in the restaurants, cafes, tearooms and pubs of Yorkshire. And although the county holds six Michelin stars, sometimes it's just as rewarding to take a few ingredients home after a visit to one of the many farm shops and delicatessens.

Music and Nightlife

Yorkshire's musical pedigree is legendary, from Joe Cocker and The Human League to Pulp and the Arctic Monkeys this a place that likes to party. Be it massive rock venues like the 02 in Leeds to the small Black Swan Folk Club in York; the region offers everything from indie to jazz, pop to bhangra and R&B to soul.

Shopping

Yorkshire has a healthy array of shopping opportunities, from small specialist shops to vast modern malls, from vibrant cities to rural market towns. Hot spots include York's Shambles, The Light Leeds, Devonshire Quarter in Sheffield and the town of Hebden Bridge, recently voted as having the least-cloned High Street in the country.

Family Fun

Keeping the family in a whole heap of fun in Yorkshire is all too easy. For the outdoor types there are fabulous mountain bike centres, wildlife parks, the adrenalin rush of high ropes and miles and miles of coast for messing about on the beach. If the weather turns why not fuse fun with education and choose from the quality hands-on science, mining, Viking and dinosaur museums that dot the county. Then there's The Deep, one of the world's most spectacular aquariums.

Handy Hints

The Turner Trails - includes audio trails and self-guided walking trails giving you the opportunity to truly discover the many scenes that inspired the painter JMW Turner.

Yorkshire Pass - is a smart card that allows entry to a wider choice of 75 leading attractions across the county. Go to www.yorkshirepass.com for more details.

Michelin Stars - The Yorke Arms at Pateley Bridge, The Box Tyree in Ilkley, The Burlington at the Devonshire Arms Hotel near Bolton Abbey, and The Pipe and Glass Inn at South Dalton.

Downhill - Take on the Dalby Forest downhill mountain bike trail, which hosted the 2009 World Cup.

OUT & ABOUT IN YORKSHIRE

Day 1 - York Arts and Culture

- Hit the UK's only museum dedicated to quilting and textile arts in St Anthony's Hall
- Try the York Art Gallery, which combines a proud history of displaying fine paintings and ceramics
- Walk down the Shambles, York's oldest and best-preserved medieval street

Day 2 - Beverley and Hull

- Head to Beverley Minster, one of Britain's finest examples of medieval gothic architecture
- Journey back, Hull's Museum Quarter, situated in the heart of the historic Old Town
- Have dinner at The Boar's Nest, a classic English restaurant in Hull, East Yorkshire

Day 3 - Scarborough Coast

- Travel to Scarborough Castle which conceals over 3000 years of turbulent history
- Visit nearby Scarborough Sea Life and Marine Sanctuary
- Take a backstage tour of the Stephen Joseph Theatre in Scarborough

Day 4 - Bradford

- Take a voyage of discovery at the National Media Museum
- Lunch at Mumtaz, high class dining, steeped in the art of Kashmiri cooking
- Head to Oakwell Hall, this Elizabethan manor house has delighted visitors for centuries

Day 5 - Yorkshire Dales

- Try Forbidden Corner, a unique labyrinth of tunnels and chambers created in a 4-acre garden
- Visit How Stean Gorge, often called 'Yorkshire's Little Switzerland'
- Take a wander along the winding Pateley Bridge High Street

Day 6 - Leeds

- Shop at Harvey Nichols Leeds, in the Victorian Quarter, the first branch outside London
- Check The Corn Exchange, one of Britain's finest Victorian buildings
- Catch a show at the West Yorkshire Playhouse

Day 7 - Spa Time

- Explore Harrogate's spa history at the Royal Pump Room Museum
- Indulge yourself at the Turkish Baths and Health Spa, built in 1897
- Go to Fountains Abbey & Studley Royal, the largest monastic ruins in the country

Where to Go

Attractions with this sign participate in the **Places of Interest Quality Assurance Scheme**.

Attractions with this sign participate in the **Visitor Attraction Quality Assurance Scheme**.

Both schemes recognise high standards in all aspects of the visitor experience (see page 6)

ENTERTAINMENT & CULTURE

Clifton Park Museum
Rotherham, South Yorkshire S65 2AA
(01709) 336633
www.rotherham.gov.uk/graphics/Learning/Museums/OSCliftonParkMuseum.htm
Local pottery, antiquities, natural and social history. Restored period kitchen. Major collection of Rockingham porcelain.

East Riding Rural Life Museum
Beverley, Yorkshire HU16 5TF
(01482) 392777
www.eastriding.gov.uk
Working early 19th-century four-sailed windmill, plus Museum of East Riding Rural Life.

Eureka! The National Children's Museum
Halifax, West Yorkshire HX1 2NE
(01422) 330069
www.eureka.org.uk
Eureka! The National Children's Museum is a magical place where children play to learn and grown-ups learn to play.

Ferens Art Gallery
Hull, East Riding of Yorkshire HU1 3RA
(01482) 613902
www.hullcc.gov.uk/museums
Combines internationally renowned permanent collections with a thriving programme of temporary exhibitions.

National Coal Mining Museum for England
Wakefield, West Yorkshire WF4 4RH
(01924) 848806
www.ncm.org.uk/
The National Coal Mining Museum offers an exciting and enjoyable insight into the working lives of miners through the ages.

National Media Museum
Bradford, West Yorkshire BD1 1NQ
0870 701 0200
www.nationalmediamuseum.org.uk
The museum is open Tuesday to Sunday (along with Bank and school holiday Mondays) from 10:00am until 6.00pm. Admission to the National Media Museum is FREE (charges apply for cinemas/IMAX).

National Railway Museum
York, North Yorkshire YO26 4XJ
0844 815 3139
www.nrm.org.uk
Awesome trains, interactive fun – and the world's largest railway museum is free.

Royal Armouries Museum
Leeds, West Yorkshire LS10 1LT
0870 034 4344
www.royalarmouries.org
Over 8,000 objects displayed in five galleries - War, Tournament, Oriental, Self Defence and Hunting. Among the treasures are Henry VIII's tournament armour and the world record breaking elephant armour. Regular jousting and horse shows.

Sheffield: Millennium Gallery
South Yorkshire S1 2PP
(0114) 278 2600
www.museums-sheffield.org.uk
The Millennium Gallery is one of modern Sheffield's landmark public spaces. Whether you're in town or just passing through, the Gallery always has something new to offer.

Treasure House and Art Gallery
Beverley, East Riding of Yorkshire HU17 8HE
(01482) 392790
www.eastriding.gov.uk/treasurehouse
Enthusiasts for East Riding history can access archive, library, art gallery and museum material. Exhibitions.

Xscape Castleford
Castleford, West Yorkshire WF10 4TA
(01977) 5230 2324
www.xscape.co.uk
The ultimate family entertainment awaits! Dine, bowl, snow, skate, climb, movies, shop, dance ice.

Yorkshire Air Museum
York, North Yorkshire YO41 4AU
(01904) 608595
www.yorkshireairmuseum.co.uk
The Yorkshire Air Museum is based on a unique WWII Bomber Command Station with fascinating exhibits and attractive Memorial Gardens that have won 3 consecutive Yorkshire in Bloom awards.

FAMILY FUN

Flamingo Land Theme Park and Zoo
Malton, North Yorkshire YO17 6UX
0871 911 8000
www.flamingoland.co.uk
One-price family funpark with over 100 attractions, 5 shows and Europe's largest privately-owned zoo.

Magna Science Adventure Centre
Rotherham, South Yorkshire S60 1DX
(01709) 720002
www.visitmagna.co.uk
Magna is the UK's 1st Science Adventure Centre set in the vast Templeborough steelworks in Rotherham. Fun is unavoidable here with giant interactives.

HERITAGE

Beverley Guildhall
East Riding of Yorkshire HU17 9XX
(01482) 392783
www.eastriding.gov.uk
Beverley Guildhall is a Grade 1 listed building, originally late medieval, remodelled in 17th and 18th C.

Brodsworth Hall and Gardens
Doncaster, South Yorkshire DN5 7XJ
(01302) 722598
www.english-heritage.org.uk/daysout/properties/brodsworth-hall-and-gardens
One of England's most complete surviving Victorian houses. Inside many of the original fixtures & fittings are still in place, although faded with time. Outside the 15 acres of woodland & gardens have been restored to their 1860's heyday.

Castle Howard
Malton, North Yorkshire YO60 7DA
(01653) 648444
www.castlehoward.co.uk
Magnificent 18th Century historic house and Stable Courtyard within 1,000 acres of breathtaking gardens.

Harewood House
Leeds West Yorkshire LS17 9LG
(0113) 218 1010
www.harewood.org
Harewood House, Bird Garden, Grounds and Adventure Playground - The Ideal day out for all the family.

JORVIK Viking Centre
York, North Yorkshire YO1 9WT
(01904) 615505
www.jorvik-viking-centre.co.uk
Travel back 1000 years on board your time machine through the backyards and houses to the bustling streets of Jorvik.

Lotherton Hall & Gardens
Leeds, West Yorkshire LS25 3EB
(0113) 264 5535
www.leeds.gov.uk/lothertonhall
Lotherton is an Edwardian country house set in beautiful grounds with a bird garden, red deer park and formal gardens.

Skipsea Castle
Hornsea, East Riding of Yorkshire
0870 333 1181
www.english-heritage.org.uk/daysout/properties/skipsea-castle/
The remaining earthworks of a motte-and-bailey castle dating from the Norman era.

Wilberforce House
Hull, East Riding of Yorkshire HU11NQ
(01482) 613902
www.hullcc.gov.uk/museums
Slavery exhibits, period rooms and furniture, Hull silver, costume, Wilberforce and abolition.

Yorkshire Sculpture Park
West Bretton, West Yorkshire WF4 4LG
(01924) 832631
www.ysp.co.uk
YSP is an extraordinary place that sets out to challenge, inspire, inform and delight.

NATURE & WILDLIFE

RSPB Bempton Cliffs Reserve
Bridlington, East Riding of Yorkshire YO15 1JF
(01262) 851179
www.rspb.org.uk/reserves/guide/b/bemptoncliffs/index.aspx
Nature trail and spectacular cliff top walks.

RSPB Old Moor Nature Reserve
Barnsley, South Yorkshire S73 0YF
(01226) 751593
www.rspb.org.uk/reserves/guide/d/dearne-oldmoor/index.aspx
Whether you're feeling energetic or just fancy some time out visit Old Moor to get closer to the wildlife.

Sheffield Botanical Gardens
South Yorkshire S10 2LN
(0114) 267 1115
www.sbg.org.uk
Extensive gardens with over 5,500 species of plants, Grade II Listed garden pavillion.

The Deep
Hull, East Riding of Yorkshire HU1 4DP
(01482) 381000
www.thedeep.co.uk
Full with over 3500 fish and more than 40 sharks, it tells the story of the world's oceans using live animals and the latest hands on interactives.

The Walled Garden at Scampston
Malton, North Yorkshire YO17 8NG
(01944) 759111
www.scampston.co.uk
An exciting 4 acre contemporary garden, created by Piet Oudolf, with striking perennial meadow planting as well as traditional spring/autumn borders.

Wentworth Castle Gardens
Barnsley, South Yorkshire S75 3ET
(01226) 776040
www.wentworthcastle.org
This magnificent 600 acre Parkland estate features over 26 listed monuments as well as a 60-acre Garden.

Yorkshire Wildlife Park
Doncaster, South Yorkshire DN3 3NH
(01302) 535057
www.yorkshirewildlifepark.co.uk
A fabulous fun day and animal experience. Walk through 'Lemar Woods' and meet these mischievous primates, or come face to face with the wallabies in Wallaby Walk.

OUTDOOR ACIVITIES

York Boat Guided River Trips
North Yorkshire YO1 7DP
(01904) 628324
www.yorkboat.co.uk/buytickets-online.html
Sit back, relax and enjoy a drink from the bar as the sights of York city and country sail by onboard a 1 hour Guided River Trip with entertaining live commentary.

Events 2012

iesel Gala Weekend
aworth
ww.kwvr.co.uk
ay

CultureShock Festival
Harrogate
www.cultureshockfestival.co.uk
June

Ilkley Summer Festival
Ilkley
www.summerfestival.ilkley.org
August

Malton Food Lovers Festival
Malton
www.maltonfoodfestival.co.uk
ay

Filey Town Festival
Filey
www.fileytownfestival.co.uk
June - July

Leeds Festival
Wetherby
www.leedsfestival.com
25th-26th August

May Day Craft Fair
radford
ww.htgevents.com
ay

Grassington Festival
Grassington
www.grassington-festival.org.uk
June - July

Ripon International Festival
Ripon
www.riponinternationalfestival.com
September

waledale Festival
arious Locations
ww.swaledale-festival.org.uk
ay - June

Pontefract Liquorice Festival
Wakefield
www.experiencewakefield.co.uk
July

Scarborough Jazz Festival
Scarborough
www.scarboroughjazzfestival.co.uk
September

everly Festival
everly
ww.beverleyfestival.com
une

Scarborough Seafest
Scarborough
www.seafest.org.uk
July

St. Ledger Festival
Doncaster
www.doncaster-racecourse.co.uk
September

radford Mela
radford
ww.bradfordmela.org.uk
une

York Early Music Festival
York
www.ncem.co.uk
July

Whitby Alt Festival
Whitby
www.darkdaisypromotions.co.uk
October

Tourist Information Centres

When you arrive at your destination, visit an Official Partner Tourist Information Centre for quality assured help with accommodation and information about local attractions and events, or email your request before you go. To find a Tourist Information Centre by region look at http://www.enjoyengland.com under Destination Finder.

AYSGARTH FALLS	Aysgarth Falls National Park Centre	01969 662910	aysgarth@ytbtic.co.uk
BRIDLINGTON	25 Prince Street	01262 673474	info@vhey.co.uk
BEVERLEY	34 Butcher Row	01482 391672	beverley.tic@eastriding.gov.uk
BRADFORD	City Hall	01274 433678	bradford.vic@bradford.gov.uk
BRIGG	The Buttercross	01652 657053	brigg.tic@northlincs.gov.uk
CLEETHORPES	Cleethorpes Library	01472 323111	cleetic@nelincs.gov.uk
DANBY	The Moors Centre, Danby Lodge	01439 772737	moorscentre@northyorkmoors-npa.gov.uk
DONCASTER	Blue Building	01302 734309	tourist.information@doncaster.gov.uk
FILEY	Filey TIC	01723 383637	fileytic@scarborough.gov.uk
GRASSINGTON	National Park Centre	01756 751690	grassington@ytbtic.co.uk
HALIFAX	Piece Hall	01422 368725	halifax@ytbtic.co.uk
HARROGATE	Royal Baths	01423 537300	tic@harrogate.gov.uk
HAWES	Dales Countryside Museum	01969 666210	hawes@ytbtic.co.uk
HAWORTH	2/4 West Lane	01535 642329	haworth.vic@bradford.gov.uk
HEBDEN BRIDGE	Visitor and Canal Centre	01422 843831	hebdenbridge@ytbtic.co.uk
HELMSLEY	The Visitor Centre, Helmsley Castle	01439 770173	helmsley.tic@english-heritage.org.uk
HOLMFIRTH	49-51 Huddersfield Road	01484 222444	holmfirth.tic@kirklees.gov.uk
HORNSEA	120 Newbegin	01964 536404	hornsea.tic@eastriding.gov.uk
HUDDERSFIELD	3 Albion Street	01484 223200	huddersfield.tic@kirklees.gov.uk
HULL	1 Paragon Street	01482 223559	tourist.information@hullcc.gov.uk
HUMBER BRIDGE	North Bank Viewing Area	01482 640852	humberbridge.tic@vhey.co.uk
ILKLEY	Town Hall	01943 602319	ilkley.vic@bradford.gov.uk
KNARESBOROUGH	9 Castle Courtyard	0845 389 0177	kntic@harrogate.gov.uk
LEEDS	Leeds Visitor Centre	0113 242 5242	tourinfo@leeds.gov.uk
LEEMING BAR	The Yorkshire Maid	01677 424262	leemingbar@ytbtic.co.uk
LEYBURN	4 Central Chambers	01969 623069	leyburn@ytbtic.co.uk

MALHAM	National Park Centre	01969 652380	malham@ytbtic.co.uk
MALTON	Malton Museum	01653 600048	maltontic@btconnect.com
OTLEY	Otley Library & Tourist Information	01943 462485	otleytic@leedslearning.net
PATELEY BRIDGE	18 High Street	0845 389 0177	pbtic@harrogate.gov.uk
PICKERING	Ropery House	01751 473791	pickering@ytbtic.co.uk
REETH	Hudson House, The Green	01748 884059	reeth@ytbtic.co.uk
RICHMOND	Friary Gardens	01748 828742	richmondtic@richmondshire.gov.uk
RIPON	Minster Road	01765 604625	ripontic@harrogate.gov.uk
ROTHERHAM	40 Bridgegate	01709 835904	tic@rotherham.gov.uk
SCARBOROUGH	Brunswick Shopping Centre	01723 383636	tourismbureau@scarborough.gov.uk
SCARBOROUGH	Harbourside TIC	01723 383636	harboursidetic@scarborough.gov.uk
SELBY	Visitor Information Centre	01757 212181	selby@ytbtic.co.uk
SETTLE	Town Hall	01729 825192	settle@ytbtic.co.uk
SHEFFIELD	Visitor Information Point	0114 2211900	visitor@yorkshiresouth.com
SKIPTON	35 Coach Street	01756 792809	skipton@ytbtic.co.uk
SUTTON BANK	Sutton Bank Visitor Centre	01845 597426	suttonbank@ytbtic.co.uk
THIRSK	Thirsk Tourist Information Centre	01845 522755	thirsktic@hambleton.gov.uk
TODMORDEN	15 Burnley Road	01706 818181	todmorden@ytbtic.co.uk
WAKEFIELD	9 The Bull Ring	0845 601 8353	tic@wakefield.gov.uk
WETHERBY	Wetherby Library & Tourist Info. Centre	01937 582151	wetherbytic@leedslearning.net
WHITBY	Langborne Road	01723 383637	whitbytic@scarborough.gov.uk
WITHERNSEA	Withernsea Lighthouse Museum	01964 615683	withernsea.tic@eastriding.gov.uk
YORK	1 Museum Street	01904 550099	info@visityork.org

Regional Contacts and Information

For more information on accommodation, attractions, activities, events and holidays in Yorkshire, contact the regional tourism organisation. Their website has a wealth of information and produces many free publications to help you get the most out of your visit.

The following publications are available from the Yorkshire Tourist Board by logging on to www.yorkshire.com or calling 0844 888 5123

This is Y Magazine

Where to Stay

Entries appear alphabetically by town name in each county. A key to symbols appears on page 6. Maps start on page 298. Further listings of VisitEngland assessed accommodation appear on the CD at the back of this guide.

ALLERSTON, Yorkshire Map ref 5D3   SAT NAV YO18 7PQ

★★★★★
TOURING &
CAMPING PARK

🚐 £16.00–£27.00
🚏 £16.00–£27.00
⛺ £13.00–£17.00
120 touring pitches

Vale of Pickering Caravan Park

Vale of Pickering Caravan Park, Allerston, Pickering YO18 7PQ
t (01723) 859280 **f** (01723) 850060 **e** tony@valeofpickering.co.uk
w valeofpickering.co.uk

Family-owned park in Allerston. High standard of service and superb facilities. Peacefully located in open countryside offering panoramic views. A well-stocked licensed shop. **directions** Helmsley to Scarborough A170. Turn right down village of Allerston on the B1415 to Malton. Continue out of Village for approx 700 yds. **open** Closed 3 January to 5 March **payment** credit/debit cards, cash, cheques

General 🔋 🛉 🎄 📶 🌐 ☼ 🔲 ♨ 📞 ➕ 🚱 🚐   **Leisure** ► ∪ ♪ ⚠

BARDSEY, Yorkshire Map ref 4B1   SAT NAV LS17 9DY

★★★★★
HOLIDAY PARK

ROSE AWARD
CARAVAN HOLIDAY PARK

🚐 (4) £12.00–£14.00
🚏 (4) £12.00–£14.00
⛺ (30) £6.00–£12.00
🏚 (10) £160.00–£460.00
4 touring pitches

Haighfield Caravan Park

5 Blackmoor Lane, Bardsey, Leeds LS17 9DY
t (01937) 574658 **f** (01937) 574242 **e** haighfieldcp@aol.com
w haighfieldcaravanpark.co.uk ONLINE MAP GUEST REVIEWS LAST MINUTE OFFERS

Pristine. Only 20 minutes from Leeds, Harrogate & 3 miles from Wetherby market town & Emmerdale set. Perfect for touring Yorkshire. 2011 Holiday Homes. Tranquil setting open 12 months. **directions** Situated off A58 (Leeds to Wetherby road) turn into Bardsey at Church lane, past Bardsey church and Bingley Arms. Park top of hill on left. **open** All year **payment** credit/debit cards, cash, cheques, euros

General 🔌 🔋 ⚲ 🛉 📶 📠 ☼ 📞 ➕   **Leisure** ► ∪ ♪

Looking for something else?

You can also buy a copy of our popular guide 'Hotels' including country house and town house hotels, metro and budget hotels, serviced apartments and restaurants with rooms in England 2012. Now available in good bookshops and online at **visitbritainshop.com**   **£7.99**

BOLTON ABBEY, Yorkshire Map ref 4B1

SAT NAV BD23 6AN

Strid Wood Caravan Club Site
Bolton Abbey, North Yorkshire BD23 6AN
t (01756) 710433 e enquiries@caravanclub.co.uk
w **caravanclub.co.uk**

THE CARAVAN CLUB

🚐 (57)   £15.30–£35.51
🚐 (57)   £15.30–£35.51
57 touring pitches

One of the prettiest sites on our network and part of the Bolton Abbey Estate. Open glades surrounded by woodland and the glorious Yorkshire Dales. **directions** A59 onto B6160, after 3 miles turn right into Strid car park. Please note that approach from north on B6160 is unsuitable for caravans. **open** March to January **payment** credit/debit cards, cash, cheques

General 🔲 🎣 🐕 🛖 🅿 🔁 🔌 🚾 **Leisure** ⚓

CONSTABLE BURTON, Yorkshire Map ref 5C3

SAT NAV DL8 5LJ

Constable Burton Hall Caravan Park
Constable Burton, Leyburn, North Yorkshire DL8 5LJ
t (01677) 450428 e caravanpark@constableburton.com
w **cbcaravanpark.co.uk** ONLINE MAP GUEST REVIEWS ONLINE BOOKING LAST MINUTE OFFERS

🚐 (35)   £18.00–£23.00
🚐 (5)   £18.00–£23.00
120 touring pitches

Situated in the beautiful mature parkland and set behind the walls to the old deer park extending across picturesque farmland this site gives a real sense of peace and tranquility. **directions** Conveniently located within easy reach of the A1 on the A684 between Bedale and Leyburn the gateway to the Yorkshire dales National parks. **payment** credit/debit cards, cash, cheques

General ♿ 🔲 🐕 🛖 ☼ 🔁 🔌 🔌 **Leisure** ▶ ∪ ⚓

FILEY, Yorkshire Map ref 5D3

SAT NAV YO14 0PU

Orchard Farm Holiday Village
Stonegate, Hunmanby, Filey YO14 0PU
t (01723) 891582 f (01723) 891582 e info@orchardfarmholidayvillage.co.uk
w **orchardfarmholidayvillage.co.uk**

🚐   £14.00–£22.00
🚐   £14.00–£22.00
⛺ (25)   £14.00–£22.00
60 touring pitches

Family park in edge-of-village location with easy access to resorts of Filey, Scarborough and Bridlington. Amenities include children's play area, fishing lake and entertainment during peak season. **directions** From A165 from Scarborough take 1st right to Hunmanby under railway bridge 1st right. **open** March to October **payment** cash, cheques

General 🔲 🐕 🔌 🛖 ☼ 🚲 🔁 🔌 🔌 **Leisure** ▶ ∪ ⚓ ❄ 🍽 🎵 🎯 🎢

Looking for something else?

You can also buy a copy of our popular 'B&B' guide including guest accommodation, B&B's, guest houses, farmhouses, inns, and campus and hostel accommodation in England 2012.

Now available in good bookshops and online at

visitbritainshop.com   **£8.99**

For **key to symbols** see page 6

FLAMBOROUGH, Yorkshire Map ref 5D3

SAT NAV YO15 1AU

Thornwick and Sea Farm Holiday Centre

North Marine Road, Flamborough YO15 1AU
t (01262) 850369 **f** (01262) 851550 **e** enquiries@thornwickbay.co.uk
w **thornwickbay.co.uk** ONLINE BOOKING

🚐 (100) £19.00–£29.00
🚐 (10) £19.00–£29.00
⚑ (40) £17.00–£29.00
🏠 (20) £165.00–£555.00
🏠 (60) £230.00–£520.00
150 touring pitches

SPECIAL PROMOTIONS
Mini breaks - Monday to
Friday or Friday to Monday
- call for details.

Set close to the spectacular cliffs, coves and beaches of Flamborough Head, we are the ideal
family destination. On park, we have a pool, fishing lake, gym and spa, amusements, cafe, shop
and three bars. We have a varied entertainment programme for both adults and children. It's fun
at Flamborough!

open 1st March to 31st October
payment credit/debit cards, cash, cheques

directions M62 jct 16, follow the B1255 from
Bridlington to Flamborough, the park is approx
1 mile further towards North Landing.

General 🏷🎇🐕🛠️📶🅟☀️♿🔌🅭🚿 Leisure ▶🚴🏊🎣🎱🍺🎵🎯⛰️

GILLING WEST, Yorkshire Map ref 5C3

SAT NAV DL10 5LJ

Hargill House Caravan Club Site

Gilling West, Richmond, North Yorkshire DL10 5LJ
t (01748) 822734 **e** enquiries@caravanclub.co.uk
w **caravanclub.co.uk**

THE
CARAVAN
CLUB

🚐 (66) £12.50–£30.80
🚐 (66) £12.50–£30.80
66 touring pitches

Gently sloping site in the old town of Richmond. Breathtaking
views over the Yorkshire Dales National Park. J M W Turner painted
some of his most famous watercolours here. **directions** Leave the
A1 at Scotch Corner onto A66. 1.5 miles left at the crossroads. Site
entrance 100 yds on left. For alternative routes visit
caravanclub.co.uk. **open** March to November **payment** credit/debit
cards, cash, cheques

General 🔌🎇📶🅟☀️🔌🅭🚿🚐 Leisure ▶🎣

HARMBY, Yorkshire Map ref 5C3

SAT NAV DL8 5NU

Lower Wensleydale Caravan Club Site

Harmby, Leyburn, North Yorkshire DL8 5NU
t (01969) 623366 **e** enquiries@caravanclub.co.uk
w **caravanclub.co.uk**

THE
CARAVAN
CLUB

🚐 (92) £11.80–£30.80
🚐 (92) £11.80–£30.80
92 touring pitches

This site in the hollow of a disused quarry, over run with wild
flowers, offers charming pitching areas. Interesting attractions
nearby and wonderful walking country. **directions** From east on
A684, turn right 0.75 miles past railway bridge; turn immediately
left and follow signs to site entrance. **open** April to November
payment credit/debit cards, cash, cheques

General 🔌🎇📶🔌🅭🚿🚐 Leisure 🎣

HARROGATE, Yorkshire Map ref 4B1

SAT NAV HG3 2LT

High Moor Farm Park
Skipton Road, Felliscliffe, Harrogate HG3 2LT
t (01423) 563637 **f** (01423) 529449 **e** highmoorfarmpark@btconnect.com
w highmoorfarmpark.co.uk ONLINE MAP

🚐 (200) £21.00–£24.00
🚐 (57) £21.00–£24.00
200 touring pitches

Secluded site surrounded by trees on the edge of the Yorkshire Dales. **directions** On A59 4 miles west of Harrogate. **open** April to October **payment** credit/debit cards, cash, cheques

General 🔲 🐕 🗲 🏛 🐾 ☼ 🔲 🔲 🕛 🔩 ✗ **Leisure** ► ∪ 🖊 ≷ 🍽 🔴 ⋀

HARROGATE, Yorkshire Map ref 4B1

SAT NAV HG3 1JH

Rudding Holiday Park
Follifoot, Harrogate, North Yorkshire HG3 1JH
t (01423) 870439 **f** (01423) 870859 **e** holiday-park@ruddingpark.com
w ruddingpark.co.uk ONLINE MAP LAST MINUTE OFFERS

🚐 £19.00–£37.00
🚐 £19.00–£37.00
🛆 £19.00–£37.00
141 touring pitches

Award-winning campsite in 300 acres of beautiful parkland just south of Harrogate. Offering Deer House Pub, swimming pool, two golf courses, driving range and shop. Self-catering timber lodges also available. **directions** Situated only 3 miles south of Harrogate, Rudding Park lies just off the A658 linking the A61 from Leeds to the A59 York Road. **payment** credit/debit cards, cash, cheques, euros

General 🔥 🔲 ❀ 🐕 🗲 🏛 🐾 ☼ 🔲 🔲 🕛 🔩 🔲 ✗ **Leisure** ► ∪ 🖊 ≷ 🍽 🎵 🔴 ⋀

HAWORTH, Yorkshire Map ref 4B1

SAT NAV BD22 9SS

Upwood Holiday Park
Black Moor Road, Oxenhope, Haworth BD22 9SS
t (01535) 644242 **e** info@upwoodpark.co.uk
w upwoodpark.co.uk ONLINE MAP GUEST REVIEWS LAST MINUTE OFFERS

🚐 (60) £9.50–£24.50
🚐 (2) £9.50
🛆 (15) £9.50
🏠 (1) £99.00–£395.00
🚙 (3) £150.00–£99.00
75 touring pitches

SPECIAL PROMOTIONS
Camping Pods available
2009. Mega pods available
2011.

A family-owned park pleasantly situated close to the Yorkshire Dales National Park - an ideal base from which to explore the area by car or on foot. Large, modern toilet facilities, comfortable lounge bar serving snacks, games room with pool and arcade games, small shop for essential items.

open 1st March to 4th January
payment credit/debit cards, cash, cheques, euros

directions Please contact us for directions.

General 🔥 🔲 ❀ 🐕 🗲 🏛 🐾 ☼ 🔲 🔲 🔲 🕛 🔩 ✗ **Leisure** ► ∪ 🚲 🖊 🍽 🎵 🔴 ⋀

HEBDEN BRIDGE, Yorkshire Map ref 4B1

SAT NAV HX7 5RU

★★★★★
TOURING PARK

Lower Clough Foot Caravan Club Site
Cragg Vale, Hebden Bridge, West Yorkshire HX7 5RU
t (01422) 882531 e enquiries@caravanclub.co.uk
w **caravanclub.co.uk**

THE
CARAVAN
CLUB

🚐 (45) £11.40–£28.00
🚐 (45) £11.40–£28.00
45 touring pitches

Pretty site, set in a grassy enclave, well screened by mature trees
and bordered by a stream. Good for walkers. Enjoy Victorian style
shops in nearby Hebden Bridge. **directions** Turn off A646 onto
B6138. Site on right in 1 mile. **open** April to November **payment**
credit/debit cards, cash, cheques

General 🐾 🔌 🚿 Leisure ▶ ⚓

HELMSLEY, Yorkshire Map ref 5C3

SAT NAV YO62 5YQ

★★★★★
HOLIDAY, TOURING
& CAMPING PARK

Golden Square Caravan Park
Oswaldkirk, Helmsley, York YO62 5YQ
t (01439) 788269 f (01439) 788236 e reception@goldensquarecaravanpark.com
w **goldensquarecaravanpark.com** ONLINE MAP ONLINE BOOKING LAST MINUTE OFFERS

🚐 £16.00–£23.00
🚐 £16.00–£23.00
▲ £14.00–£23.00
129 touring pitches

Secluded family park magnificent views in the North York Moors.
Heated shower block, bathrooms, shop, indoor/outdoor play area.
Pitches: Tents, touring, seasonal, storage compound. Holiday Home
for sale. **directions** From South leave A1 junction 49 onto A168 to
Thirsk A170 and A19 to York. Follow Caravan Route to Coxwold
Ampleforth 1 mile signposted Helmsley. **payment** credit/debit
cards, cash, cheques, euros

General 🗄 🐾 🚿 💷 🎣 🔌 🚿 🚿 🚿 Leisure ▶ ∪ 🚲 ⚓ 🔦 ⚠

HELMSLEY, Yorkshire Map ref 5C3

SAT NAV YO62 7RY

★★★★★
TOURING &
CAMPING PARK

Wombleton Caravan Park
Moorfield Lane, Wombleton, Helmsley YO62 7RY
t (01751) 431684 e info@wombletoncaravanpark.co.uk
w **wombletoncaravanpark.co.uk** ONLINE MAP GUEST REVIEWS ONLINE BOOKING

🚐 (100) £17.00–£21.00
🚐 (8) £17.00–£21.00
▲ (10) £8.00–£21.00
118 touring pitches

A quiet park halfway between Helmsley and Kirkbymoorside, a flat
level site with electric hook-ups, modern shower block/disabled
facilities and a small shop. Touring and seasonal pitches, tents
welcome. **directions** off the A170 through Wombleton village drive
through the village turn left at the war memorial on the left down
the lane towards the airfield. **open** March to October **payment**
credit/debit cards, cash, cheques

General 🗄 🐾 🚿 💷 🎣 ☼ 🔌 🚿 🚿 Leisure ∪

HOLMFIRTH, Yorkshire Map ref 4B1

SAT NAV HD9 7TD

★★★★
TOURING &
CAMPING PARK

Holme Valley Camping and Caravan Park
Thongsbridge, Holmfirth, West Yorkshire HD9 7TD
t (01484) 665819 f (01484) 663870 e enquiries@homevalleycamping.com
w **holmevalleycamping.com**

🚐 (62) £15.00–£17.00
🚐 (62) £13.50–£15.50
▲ (62) £6.00–£12.50
62 touring pitches

Picturesque, setting in 'Summer Wine' country. Grass, concrete,
gravel pitches. 16-amp hook-ups. Well-stocked food shop. Off-
licence. Fishing in small lake and river. Kiddie's play area. Five
minutes' walk from village. **directions** The entrance to our lane is 1
mile north of Holmfirth, off A6024. Passing bottle banks, continue
to valley bottom. (No vehicular access from A616.) **open** All year
payment credit/debit cards, cash, cheques, euros

General 🗄 📶 🐾 🚿 💷 🎣 ☼ 🔌 🚿 🚿 Leisure ∪ ⚓ ⚠

198

ILKLEY, Yorkshire Map ref 4B1

SAT NAV BD17 6BG

Faweather Grange

Faweather Grange, Sconce Lane, High Eldwick BD16 3BL
t (01943) 878777 **e** enquires@faweathergrange.com
w **faweathergrange.com**
ONLINE MAP GUEST REVIEWS ONLINE BOOKING LAST MINUTE OFFERS

🛏 (11)   £170.00–£1750.00

SPECIAL PROMOTIONS
Romantic 1 Night Breaks
from £170, 1 night Bentley
Bollinger Breaks from £360,
Pamper Breaks for Girls,
Gourmet Breaks. 2011
Excellence Award (Silver
Winner)

Award Winning 5 star Lodge park that combines wonderful location close to Ilkley with the opportunity to create your own unique holiday experience.

From our Website you can select an unusual and bespoke variety of experiences that make a stay at Faweather Grange unforgettable.

Select Pamper Weekends with your friends, Romantic Extras for your partner or wow factor experiences like our Bentley to a Michelin Restaurant or to the Heliport to fly over the Yorkshire Dales. Get Active with Guided Horse and Mountain Bike Rides from the lodges or simply relax and enjoy the wonderful woodland and moorland views from your private outdoor Hot Tub.

open All year
payment credit/debit cards, cash, cheques

directions 5 Miles from Ilkley. See website for Details Sat Nav use BD17 6BG

General 🔥 🐾 ☀️   Leisure ► ∪ 🚲 ✈ 🏛

KNARESBOROUGH, Yorkshire Map ref 4B1

SAT NAV HG5 9HH

Knaresborough Caravan Club Site

New Road, Scotton, Knaresborough, North Yorkshire HG5 9HH
t (01423) 860196 e enquiries@caravanclub.co.uk
w **caravanclub.co.uk**

THE
CARAVAN
CLUB

🚐 (74)   £15.90–£35.51
🚏 (74)   £15.90–£35.51
74 touring pitches

This site offers a gateway to the Yorkshire Dales and the many attractions of the North of England. Knaresborough is an historic market town with ancient walkways and castle ruins. **directions** Right off A59 onto B6165. After approximately 1.5 miles turn right into New Road. Site is on right-hand side after 50 yds. **open** March to January **payment** credit/debit cards, cash, cheques

General 🖥 👤 🐕 🏚 ☀ 🔲 ⊘ 🕒 🚻 🆒 Leisure ▶ 🚣 ⛰

PICKERING, Yorkshire Map ref 5D3

SAT NAV YO18 8ES

Spiers House Caravan and Camping Site

Cropton, Pickering, North Yorkshire YO18 8ES
t (01751) 417591 e spiershouse.site@forestholidays.co.uk
w **forestholidays.co.uk** ONLINE MAP GUEST REVIEWS

🚐   £13.50–£28.50
🚏   £13.50–£28.50
▲   £13.50–£28.50
160 touring pitches

Surrounded by the conifers of Cropton Forest within the North York Moors National Park, there are marked footpaths and cycle routes through the forest. **directions** A170-Pickering and Kirkbymoorside, turn off Wrelton, Cropton and Rosedale Abbey (going north), Rosedale Abbey, and one and a half miles after Cropton, right turn. **open** All year **payment** credit/debit cards, cash

🌼

General 🖥 🐕 ⚒ 🏚 🕰 ⊘ 🕒 🚻 Leisure ⛰

PICKERING, Yorkshire Map ref 5D3

SAT NAV YO18 8PG

Wayside Holiday Park

Wrelton, Pickering YO18 8PG
t (01751) 472608 e Wrelton@Waysideholidaypark.co.uk
w **Waysideholidaypark.co.uk** ONLINE MAP GUEST REVIEWS

🚐 (40)   £20.00
🚏 (3)   £20.00
4 touring pitches

Sheltered, quiet, south-facing holiday-park consisting of Holiday Homes, Seasonal tourers, and Touring pitches. Delightfully located with lovely country views. A walker's paradise. Whitby, Scarborough York nr. Holiday Homes for sale. **directions** Two and a half miles west of Pickering at Wrelton off A170 - Follow signs. **open** 1st April to 31 October **payment** credit/debit cards, cash, cheques

General ⚡ 🖥 👤 🐕 🏚 ☀ 🔲 🚲 ⊘ 🕒 🚻 Leisure ▶ ∪ ♿ 🚣 ⛰

Looking for something else?

You can also buy a copy of our popular guide 'Hotels' including country house and town house hotels, metro and budget hotels, serviced apartments and restaurants with rooms in England 2012.

Now available in good bookshops and online at
visitbritainshop.com

£7.99

RIGGS HEAD, Yorkshire Map ref 5D3

SAT NAV YO12 5TG

Pinewood Holiday Park
Racecourse Road, Scarborough YO12 5TG
t (01723) 367278 e info@pinewood-holiday-park.co.uk
w pinewood-holiday-park.co.uk LAST MINUTE OFFERS

(5)	£7.00–£14.00
(5)	£7.00–£14.00
(14)	£7.00–£14.00
(20)	£35.00–£80.00

5 touring pitches

SPECIAL PROMOTIONS
Birthday and Anniversary packages availble. Details of specils offers and events can be found on the website.

A small, quiet, family run site, situated in a suberb location within walking distance of Scarborough. 3 seperate areas; an adult only touring area, a camping field, and a Wild west themed campground with Indian Tipis and Western Wagons. A fun, unique and memorable holiday destination.

open All year
payment credit/debit cards, cash

directions See website for directions.

General ⛺ 🐕 ☼ 🔌 💧 🅿️ Leisure 🏊

ROOS, Yorkshire Map ref 4D1

SAT NAV HU12 0JQ

ROSE AWARD CARAVAN HOLIDAY PARK

Sand-le-Mere Caravan & Leisure Park
Southfield Lane, Tunstall HU12 0JF
t (01964) 670403 e info@sand-le-mere.co.uk
w sand-le-mere.co.uk

	£12.00–£18.00
(59)	£12.00–£18.00
(6)	£235.00–£941.00
(50)	£80.00–£585.00

59 touring pitches

A great place to visit, an even better place to stay, with its superb coastal setting, natural park and mere, plus first-class facilities. directions From Hull to Hedon take the B1362 at Withernsea, B1242 to Roos. Look for brown signs marked SLM. open 1 February to 1 January payment credit/debit cards, cash, cheques

General 🚿 📺 🐕 ⛺ 📞 🔌 ☼ 🅿️ 🅿️ ✖ Leisure ▶ ∪ 🚴 🏊 🎣 ♟ 🎵 🎯 ⛰

SCARBOROUGH, Yorkshire Map ref 5D3

SAT NAV YO11 3NN

Cayton Village Caravan Park Ltd
Mill Lane, Cayton Bay, Scarborough YO11 3NN
t (01723) 583171 e info@caytontouring.co.uk
w caytontouring.co.uk LAST MINUTE OFFERS

(179)	£13.50–£34.00
(92)	£13.50–£34.00
(39)	£13.50–£28.00

310 touring pitches

Playground, shop, bus service from park entrance. Seasonal Pitches, Winter Storage, Caravan Sales. Super Sites, Hard Standing, Grass. Beach 0.5m, Scarborough 3m. Adjoining village with fish shop & pubs. directions From A64 take B1261 to Filey. In Cayton turn left into Mill Lane. From A165 turn inland at Cayton Bay Roundabout onto Mill Lane. open 1st March to 31st October. payment credit/debit cards, cash, cheques

General 📺 🐕 ⛺ 📞 🔌 ☼ 🅿️ 🅿️ Leisure ▶ ∪ 🏊 ⛰

SCARBOROUGH, Yorkshire Map ref 5D3 — SAT NAV YO14 9PS

★★★★ HOLIDAY PARK — ROSE AWARD CARAVAN HOLIDAY PARK

(50)	£15.00–£25.00
(50)	£15.00–£25.00
(100)	£15.00–£25.00
(40)	£220.00–£530.00

50 touring pitches

Crows Nest Caravan Park

Crows Nest Caravan Park, Gristhorpe, Filey YO14 9PS
t (01723) 582206 **e** enquiries@crowsnestcaravanpark.com
w **crowsnestcaravanpark.com** ONLINE MAP ONLINE BOOKING LAST MINUTE OFFERS

Situated on the glorious Yorkshire coast between Scarborough and Filey. This family owned, Rose Award winning park is a perfect base. The facilities are of a very high standard, including heated-indoor swimming pool, children's play area and supermarket. Holidays and short breaks for families and couples. Tents and tourers welcome.

open March to October
payment credit/debit cards, cash, cheques

directions Just off A165 between Scarborough (5 miles) and Filey (2 miles). Turn off at roundabout with Jet petrol station. Well signposted.

General **Leisure**

SCARBOROUGH, Yorkshire Map ref 5D3 — SAT NAV YO11 3NU

★★★★★ HOLIDAY, TOURING & CAMPING PARK

(220)	£15.00–£21.00
(30)	£15.00–£21.00
(50)	£13.00–£21.00
(20)	£360.00–£660.00

300 touring pitches

SPECIAL PROMOTIONS
Early Booking Offer and other Offers available. Please refer to website.

Flower of May Holiday Parks Ltd

Flower of May Holiday Parks Ltd, Lebberston Cliff, Scarborough YO11 3NU
t (01723) 584311 **f** (01723) 585716 **e** info@flowerofmay.com
w **flowerofmay.com** ONLINE MAP LAST MINUTE OFFERS

Excellent family-run park. Luxury indoor pool, adventure playground, bar complex, mini-market, fish & chip shop and cafe and 9 hole golf course. Ideal for coast and country. Prices per pitch, per night, four people with car. Luxury hire caravans. Seasonal serviced pitches.

open Easter to October
payment credit/debit cards, cash

directions From A64 take the A165 Scarborough/Filey coast road. Well signposted at Lebberston.

General **Leisure**

SCARBOROUGH, Yorkshire Map ref 5D3

SAT NAV YO13 9BE

Jasmine Park

Cross Lane, Snainton, Scarborough YO13 9BE
t (01723) 859240 **e** enquiries@jasminepark.co.uk
w jasminepark.co.uk ONLINE MAP ONLINE BOOKING LAST MINUTE OFFERS

⊞ (74)	£18.00–£30.00
⊞ (74)	£18.00–£30.00
⛺ (20)	£18.00–£30.00
⊞ (4)	£220.00–£445.00
94 touring pitches	

Family-owned, tranquil park in picturesque countryside setting between Scarborough (8 miles) and Pickering. Superbly maintained facilities including our fantastic new Childrens Play Area. Yorkshire Coast Caravan Park of the Year 2010. Tents and tourers welcome. Seasonal pitches and storage available. Luxury caravans for hire.

open March to October
payment credit/debit cards, cash, cheques

directions Turn south off the A170 in Snainton opposite the junior school at traffic lights. Signposted.

General 🔧 🗄 ⌖ 🐕 ⚡ 📶 ⛱ ☼ 🚲 🔌 🕒 📞 💳 Leisure ► ∪ 🚴 ♨ ⛰

SCARBOROUGH, Yorkshire Map ref 5D3

SAT NAV YO11 3PE

Lebberston Touring Park

Lebberston, Scarborough YO11 3PE
t (01723) 585723 **e** info@lebberstontouring.co.uk
w lebberstontouring.co.uk ONLINE MAP GUEST REVIEWS

⊞	£15.00–£27.00
⊞	£15.00–£27.00
125 touring pitches	

Our multi-award winning park, set on a south facing slope in beautiful countryside, is a peaceful, relaxing haven for your holiday escape. Providing a pristine and tranquil setting for your holiday is our major priority. Your enjoyment is paramount in everything we do while working harmoniously with the natural environment.

open 1st March to 31st October
payment credit/debit cards, cash, cheques

directions A64, approaching Scarborough, take right turn for the B1261 at the 'MacDonalds' roundabout. Proceed in the direction of Filey, follow the signs for Lebberston.

General 🗄 ⌖ 🐕 ⚡ 📶 ⛱ ☼ 🖥 🚲 🔌 🕒 📞 💳 Leisure ► ∪ ♨

SLINGSBY, Yorkshire Map ref 5C3 SAT NAV YO62 4AP

Robin Hood Caravan Park
Slingsby, York YO62 4AP
t (01653) 628391 f (01653) 628392 e info@robinhoodcaravanpark.co.uk
w **robinhoodcaravanpark.co.uk** ONLINE MAP ONLINE BOOKING LAST MINUTE OFFERS

⊠ (38)	£16.00–£28.00
⊟ (38)	£16.00–£28.00
Å (38)	£15.00–£25.00
⊞ (16)	£185.00–£510.00
38 touring pitches	

A privately owned park set in the heart of picturesque Ryedale. Peaceful and tranquil, a perfect base for families and couples wishing to explore the stunning countryside of North Yorkshire. Within easy reach of York, Castle Howard, Flamingoland and the coastal resorts of Scarborough, Whitby and Filey.

open March to October
payment credit/debit cards, cash, cheques

directions Situated on the edge of Slingsby with access off the B1257 Malton to Helmsley road.

General ⊡ ⓨ ★ ⚡ ⦿ ⏣ ☼ ▣ 🛆 ⦿ ⏰ ♀ Leisure ∪ ✦ ⋔

SNEATON, Yorkshire Map ref 5D3 SAT NAV YO22 5JE

Low Moor Caravan Club Site
Sneaton, Whitby, North Yorkshire YO22 5JE
t (01947) 810505 e enquiries@caravanclub.co.uk
w **caravanclub.co.uk**

THE
CARAVAN
CLUB

⊠ (92)	£10.70–£28.00
⊟ (92)	£10.70–£28.00
92 touring pitches	

Set in the North Yorkshire Moors National Park, an ideal site for dog owners. Scenic drives through forests and across moors. **directions** Turn left off A171 (Scarborough-Whitby). In 13.5 miles turn onto B1416. In 1.75 miles turn left through red gates. Site on right. **open** April to November **payment** credit/debit cards, cash, cheques

General ★ ⦿ ⏰ ⦿

SOUTH OTTERINGTON, Yorkshire Map ref 5C3 SAT NAV DL7 9JB

Otterington Park
Station Farm, South Otterington, Northallerton DL7 9JB
t (01609) 780656 e info@otteringtonpark.com
w **otteringtonpark.com** ONLINE MAP

⊠ (66)	£18.00–£25.00
⊟ (66)	£18.00–£25.00
66 touring pitches	

Situated in the Vale of York, Otterington is an ideal base for visiting the Moors and Dales of Yorkshire, historic cities, market towns, leisure centres, tourist attractions and stately homes. **directions** Between Northallerton and Thirsk. Situated just off the C10 which links the A168 at Thornton-le-Moor and the A167 at South Otterington. **open** 1st March to 31st October **payment** credit/debit cards, cash, cheques

General ⚲ ⊡ ⓨ ★ ⦿ ⏣ ☼ ▣ 🛆 ⦿ ⏰ ♀ Leisure ∪ ✦ ⋔

STIRTON, Yorkshire Map ref 4B1

SAT NAV BD23 3LQ

£16.00–£25.00
£16.00–£25.00
13 touring pitches

Tarn House Caravan Park
Stirton, Nr Skipton, Yorkshire BD23 3LQ
t (01756) 795309 e reception@tarnhouse.net
w **partingtons.com** ONLINE BOOKING

Family-run caravan park situated in a rural location in the beautiful Yorkshire Dales. Bar on park, fantastic views. All touring pitches are now hard standing. New elsan point.

open 1 March to 31 October
payment credit/debit cards, cash, cheques
directions 1.25 miles north west of Skipton.

General ⚷ ▯ ⊨ ⬙ ⋔ ☼ ⊡ ⬚ ⬛ ⬙ ⬘ ⬛ ⊞ ✕ Leisure ▶ ∪ ⚲ ⬙ ⚲ ⍟ ♫

THIRSK, Yorkshire Map ref 5C3

SAT NAV YO7 1QL

(60)   £10.70–£28.00
(60)   £10.70–£28.00
60 touring pitches

Thirsk Racecourse Caravan Club Site
Thirsk, North Yorkshire YO7 1QL
t (01845) 525266 e enquiries@caravanclub.co.uk
w **caravanclub.co.uk**

THE CARAVAN CLUB

Pitches are within sight of the racecourse main stand, looking over the famous turf, surrounded by Herriot Country and the Dales. **directions** Site on left of A61 (Thirsk-South Kilvington). **open** March to October **payment** credit/debit cards, cash, cheques

General ▯ ⊨ ⬙ ⬙ ⬛ ⬘ Leisure ▶

THORNE, Yorkshire Map ref 4C1

SAT NAV DN8 5TD

(10)   £12.00
       £12.00
       £12.00
10 touring pitches

Elder House Touring Park
Sandtoft Road, Crow Tree Bank, Thorne Levels, Doncaster DN8 5TD
t (01405) 813173 e gffoliver@googlemail.com

Elder House Touring Park offers landscaped gardens in lovely surroundings and ample space for exercising dogs. Modern toilet block with showers and shaving points, also a disabled toilet and shower. **directions** M18 J5 M180 leave for A18 towards Scunthorpe at the Black Bull turn right into Crow Tree Bank 500 yds turn left down farm drive. **open** All year except Xmas and New Year **payment** cash, cheques

General ⊨ ⬙ ☼ ⬛ ⬙ ⬛ ⊞ Leisure ▶ ∪ ⚲ ⍟ ⚲ ⍈

WHITBY, Yorkshire Map ref 5D3

SAT NAV YO22 4QH

Flask Inn Holiday Home Park

Blacksmiths Hill, Robin Hood's Bay, Whitby, North Yorkshire YO22 4QH
t (01947) 880592 f (01947) 880592 e info@flaskinn.com
w **flaskinn.com** ONLINE MAP GUEST REVIEWS

(10)   £290.00–£520.00

SPECIAL PROMOTIONS
Book 4 weeks and recieve a free 3 night break in March, April, May or October. (Excluding Bank Holidays).

Small, family-run 5 star site for over 30 years, in the North York Moors. All our holiday homes have central heating and double glazing throughout. Also all have a double bedroom en suite, Freeview TV, DVD, full kitchen with fridge/freezer, and microwave. All holiday homes have outside decking and seating.

open March to November
payment credit/debit cards, cash, cheques

directions Situated in the North Yorkshire Moors on the A171, 7 miles to Whitby, 12 miles to Scarborough and 4 miles to Robin Hood's Bay.

General 🔥 🖥 ♨ 🎱 📷 ☼ 🕀 ✕ Leisure ∪ ⚓ ♩ 🏆 ⚱

WHITBY, Yorkshire Map ref 5D3

SAT NAV YO22 4UF

Middlewood Farm Holiday Park

Middlewood Lane, Fylingthorpe, Whitby YO22 4UF
t (01947) 880414 f (01947) 880871 e info@middlewoodfarm.com
w **middlewoodfarm.com** ONLINE MAP GUEST REVIEWS LAST MINUTE OFFERS

🚐 (21)	£15.00–£25.00
🚏 (21)	£15.00–£25.00
⛺ (100)	£12.00–£25.00
(30)	£170.00–£599.00

21 touring pitches

SPECIAL PROMOTIONS
Short Breaks available early & late season, from £120.00 (3 night minimum) TOURERS & TENTS: 1st March to 31st October.

Peaceful, 5 star award-winning family park. A walker's paradise with magnificent, panoramic coastal and moorland views! Level, sheltered, hardstandings, luxury heated facilities, private wash-cubicles, bath, children's Play Area. 10 minutes walk to pub/shops/beach and Robin Hood's Bay. Superb caravans for hire. A friendly welcome awaits!

open Holiday Hire: Open 12 months. Tourers & Tents: March 1st to October 31st
payment credit/debit cards, cash

directions Follow A171 Scarborough/Whitby road, signposted from Fylingthorpe/Robin Hood's Bay junction. In Fylingthorpe turn onto Middlewood Lane. Park is 500 yds. Follow brown tourist signs.

General 🖥 🐕 🌲 ☼ 🔌 🕀 🚻 🚐 Leisure ▶ ∪ ⚓ ♩ ⚱

WHITBY (3 MILES), Yorkshire Map ref 5D3   SAT NAV YO22 4JX

Whitby Holiday Park
Saltwick Bay, Whitby, North Yorkshire YO22 4JX
t (01947) 602664 f (01947) 820356 e info@whitbyholidaypark.co.uk
w **whitbypark.co.uk**

(18)	£16.00–£33.50
(18)	£16.00–£33.50
(18)	£140.00–£628.87
119 touring pitches	

Family friendly spectacular cliff top location with views to Whitby Abbey. Beautiful sandy beaches great for seaside fun walking and fossil hunting. Pretty peaceful villages and Whitbys bustling attractions nearby. **directions** Approach Whitby directing you to Whitby Abbey. Follow green lane, t-junction, turn right, look out for brown signs (tourist) with caravan symbol. **open** 1st March - 14th January **payment** credit/debit cards, cash, cheques

General   Leisure

YORK, Yorkshire Map ref 4C1   SAT NAV YO61 1RY

Alders Caravan Park
Home Farm, Monk Green, Alne nr Easingwold, York YO61 1RY
t (01347) 838722 f (01347) 838722 e enquiries@homefarmalne.co.uk
w **alderscaravanpark.co.uk** ONLINE MAP

	£17.00–£19.00
	£17.00–£19.00
	£17.00–£19.00
(2)	£28.00–£30.00
87 touring pitches	

A working farm in historic parkland where visitors may enjoy peace and tranquillity. York (on bus route), moors, dales and coast nearby. Tastefully landscaped, adjoins village cricket ground. Woodland walk. **directions** From A19 exit at Alne sign, in 1.5 miles turn left at T-junction, 0.5 miles park on left in village centre. **open** March to October **payment** credit/debit cards, cash, cheques

General   Leisure

YORK, Yorkshire Map ref 4C1   SAT NAV YO32 9TH

Beechwood Grange Caravan Club Site
Malton Road, York, North Yorkshire YO32 9TH
t (01904) 424637
w **caravanclub.co.uk**

THE
CARAVAN
CLUB

(115)	£15.30–£35.51
(115)	£15.30–£35.51
115 touring pitches	

This site is an ideal base from which to explore the fascinating city of York. Plenty of space for children to play on site and many local attractions nearby. **directions** A64 at roundabout turn left onto A1237. At roundabout turn right (3rd exit) into road signposted local traffic only. Site at end of drive. **open** March to January **payment** credit/debit cards, cash, cheques

General   Leisure

Looking for something else?

You can also buy a copy of our popular guide 'Self Catering' including self-catering holiday homes, approved caravan holiday homes, boat accommodation and holiday cottage agencies in England 2012.

Now available in good bookshops and online at
visitbritainshop.com   **£8.99**

YORK, Yorkshire Map ref 4C1   SAT NAV YO61 1ET

Goosewood Holiday Park
Sutton on the Forest, York, Easingwold YO61 1ET
t (01347) 810829 f (01347) 811498 e enquiries@goosewood.co.uk
w **flowerofmay.com** ONLINE BOOKING LAST MINUTE OFFERS

⬤ (90)	£15.00–£21.00
⬤ (10)	£15.00–£21.00
⬤ (22)	£330.00–£681.00
⬤ (28)	£330.00–£797.00
100 touring pitches	

SPECIAL PROMOTIONS
Three night weekends, ring for details. Early booking offers. Two person booking offers.

A quiet peaceful park with fishing lake, children's adventure play area and play barn. A perfect place to relax and amble through wooded walks. Ideal for visiting historic City of York and surrounding beauty spots of Yorkshire. A warm welcome!

open March to 2nd January
payment credit/debit cards, cash

directions North of York. Follow route to Strensall.

General 🅰🅱🅲🅳🅴🅵🅶🅷🅸🅹🅺🅻🅼 Leisure 🏊 🏔

YORK, Yorkshire Map ref 4C1   SAT NAV YO23 1JQ

Rowntree Park Caravan Club Site
Terry Avenue, York, North Yorkshire YO23 1JQ
t (01904) 658997 e enquiries@caravanclub.co.uk
w **caravanclub.co.uk**

CARAVAN CLUB

⬤ (102)	£16.60–£38.90
⬤ (102)	£16.60–£38.90
102 touring pitches	

On the banks of the river Ouse in the heart of York, this popular site is just a few minutes walk from the city centre. **directions** A64 onto A19 signposted York centre. 2 miles keep left over bridge. Left at International Caravan Club site. Right onto Terry Avenue. Site on right. **open** All year **payment** credit/debit cards, cash, cheques

General 🅱🅲🅳🅴🅵🅶🅷🅸🅹🅺🅻 Leisure ▶ 🏊

YORK, Yorkshire Map ref 4C1   SAT NAV YO32 9UB

York Caravan Park YCP
Stockton Lane, York YO32 9UB
t (01904) 424222 e mail@yorkcaravanpark.com
w **yorkcaravanpark.com** ONLINE MAP GUEST REVIEWS LAST MINUTE OFFERS

⬤ (40)	£19.00–£24.00
⬤ (40)	£19.00–£24.00
⬤ (40)	£17.00–£24.00
40 touring pitches	

5 Star Adult only caravan & campsite. 2 miles from York city centre, on main bus route. Fully serviced pitches (electric, water, TV & drains). Fishing on site. Quiet location. **directions** Join A1036 from Northeastern side of York. Turn left onto Hopgrove lane, then right onto Stockton Lane. We are 1/2 mile on right. **open** 15 March to 6 November **payment** credit/debit cards, cash, cheques, euros

General 🅰🅱🅲🅳🅴🅵🅶🅷🅸🅹🅺 Leisure ▶ ∪ 🚲 🏊

YORK, Yorkshire Map ref 4C1 | SAT NAV YO32 9ST

★★★★
TOURING &
CAMPING PARK

York Touring Caravan Site
Towthorpe Moor Lane, Towthorpe, York YO32 9ST
t (01904) 499275 f (01904) 499271 e info@yorkcaravansite.co.uk
w **yorkcaravansite.co.uk** ONLINE MAP GUEST REVIEWS

🚐 (20)   £16.00–£22.00
🚏 (20)   £16.00–£22.00
🅰 (10)   £16.00–£22.00
40 touring pitches

Small family-run secluded park in countryside setting, 5 miles from York centre. Spacious pitches, luxury free showers and toilets. On-site driving range and 9-hole golf course. **directions** Travelling on the A64 towards Scarborough/Malton take the turn-off to the left signposted Strensall/Haxby. We are 1 mile down that road on the left. **open** All year **payment** credit/debit cards, cash, cheques

General 🖥 📶 🐕 🏔 ☼ 📞 🚻   Leisure ▶ 🏊

Bonus CD inside
containing over 20,000 more
quality-assessed properties

enjoyEngland.com™
The official website for breaks and days out in England

BED &
BREAKFAST 2012
England's quality-assessed guest accommodation
GUIDE

OFFICIAL TOURIST BOARD GUIDE

Looking for something else?

You can also buy a copy of our popular 'B&B' guide including guest accommodation, B&B's, guest houses, farmhouses, inns, and campus and hostel accommodation in England 2012.

Now available in good bookshops and online at
visitbritainshop.com   **£8.99**

North West

Cheshire, Cumbria, Lancashire,
Manchester, Merseyside

They tend to take pride in their region, those from Cheshire, Cumbria, Lancashire Manchester and Merseyside that form the North West. Looking at the many attractions on offer, it is easy to see why. Here you'll find the proud rival cities Manchester and Liverpool, as well as historic Chester and fun-packed Blackpool.

Bordering the region to the north, the beautiful wilderness of the Lake District, while Blackburn, Bolton, Oldham, Wigan and Preston are the proud heartland of the country's football culture.

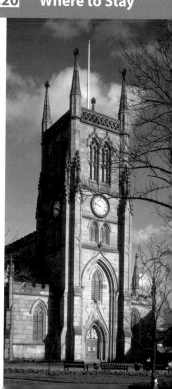

History and Heritage

Forget the TV soaps, and instead get busy with Chester's original locals; the Romans. This market town is beautifully preserved, with the city walls a great way to take a trip into the past. Elsewhere, Manchester and Liverpool were both hugely important centres of trade during the Industrial Revolution, and have museums and exhibitions explaining these roles. And don't miss the towns of the Lancashire heartland, which were the engine of Empire during those years of rapid expansion.

Arts and Culture

Forget the TV soaps, and instead get busy with Chester's original locals; the Romans. This market town is today beautifully preserved, with the city walls a great way to take a trip through the past. Elsewhere, Manchester and Liverpool were both hugely important centres of trade during the Industrial Revolution, and have museums and exhibitions explaining these roles. And don't miss the towns of the Lancashire heartland, which were the engine of Empire during those years of rapid expansion.

Food and Drink

'Don't just stick to the big cities' could be a general rule of thumb when exploring this part of the world, and it is doubly so when it comes to the food up here, with some of the nooks and crannies hiding some real gems. Chester Grosvenor restaurant is Michelin-starred, while Northcote Manor is also locally-renowned. The Longridge, in Preston, is another that would probably enjoy national renown if it wasn't in Preston - and that is just the way the regulars like it.

Sports

Sports lovers have hit the jackpot. From world famous clubs names (Manchester United, Liverpool) or the teams at the slightly more workaday end of the footballing spectrum (Bolton Wanderers, Wigan Athletic, Preston North End), the North West has just about the highest concentration of football clubs on the planet. The North West is also the home of rugby league; brilliant horse racing (the Grand National is held at Liverpool's Aintree each spring) and Old Trafford in Manchester, one of the country's best cricketing stadiums.

Music and Nightlife

It has to be about those two urban powerhouses, Manchester and Liverpool. As you might expect from cities with such a powerful musical legacy, live music is especially popular, whether you're visiting Manchester's Roadhouse to find the next Elbow, or hitting the Liverpool Philharmonic for a bigger show.

Shopping

Chester has long-been famed for its pretty shopping galleries (known as Rows), home to independent shops and chains alike. It is a favourite of WAGs and celebrities, and is a potent shopping mix. Elsewhere, Liverpool and Manchester are probably the main places to head, with Manchester's Northern Quarter and King Street boutiques two sides of the same coin. Liverpool ONE, Metquarter and Bold Street the places to head.

Family Fun

Generations of North West kids have a soft spot for Chester Zoo, Blackpool Pleasure Beach and Camelot Theme Park. The Blue Planet Aquarium at Ellesmere Port is the UK's largest, while Knowsley Safari Park is also a perennial favourite. Kids with a yen for knowledge will love Jodrell Bank and the new Spaceport in Wallasey as well.

Handy Hints

Celebrations - Coincide your visit to Manchester with Gay Pride (August) – a week long event that celebrated its 21st birthday in 2011.

Anyone for Footie? - Football fans should try and attend some one of the fearsome local derbies, although you're more likely to get tickets for Bolton v Blackburn than Liverpool v Everton.

Onwards and Upwards - At only 978 metres above sea level, England's highest peak, Scafell Pike, is an easy day's walk from Wasdale Head. Finish off with a pint in the historic Wasdale Head Inn.

By the sea - With more than 1,000 km of coastline, it's no wonder the Northwest is a prime location for sun seekers and sightseers.

OUT & ABOUT IN THE NORTH WEST

Day 1 - Sefton Coast

- Between Southport and Crosby you'll find miles of deserted sand dunes and ten separate nature reserves. It is one of the Red Squirrel's last remaining homes, so keep your eyes peeled
- Another Place by artist Antony Gormley, is on view on Crosby beach consisting of 100 cast-iron, life-size figures spread out along three kilometres of the foreshore, stretching almost one kilometre out to sea

Day 2 - Blackpool

- Grab a stick of rock and some candy floss and enjoy a classic English seaside town in all its glory
- Enjoy the sights and sounds of the Blackpool Tower
- If you are looking for arts, culture and heritage then you are spoilt for choice

Day 3 - Lake District

- Impossible to fit it all in to a day but start with Ambleside and Keswick; busy, pretty little tourist towns and gateways to the most beautiful countryside in Britain
- Follow in the footsteps of Beatrix Potter on the National Trust country walk at Hill Top

Day 4 - Lancashire Heartland

- Make your own homage to Orwell by visiting Wigan and the newly reconstructed Trencherfield Mill
- Whatever part of the county you are exploring, take your binoculars and prepare to be rewarded for your patience by a real wildlife show

Day 5 - Manchester

- Spend the morning exploring the city's exciting Northern Quarter, Manchester's answer to Soho
- Take a tour of one of the city's iconic football stadiums in the afternoon
- Check out the Curry Mile, a half-mile long stretch of curry restaurants, sari shops, and jewellery stores in Rusholme.

Day 6 - Liverpool

- Indulge your inner Beatle by taking a Magical Mystery Tour around the city's Fab Four trail
- There's no better way to experience Liverpool City Region than from the deck of the world iconic Mersey Ferry
- Tate Liverpool, featuring work by everyone from Tracey Emin to Picasso, the must visit city art gallery.

Day 7 - Chester

- Take a unique step back in time and walk the walls of Chester - an unmissable piece of history
- 'Splash the cash' at some of the city's exclusive boutiques
- Take a walk on the wild side and visit the UK's number one zoo with over 7000 animals

Where to Go

 Attractions with this sign participate in the **Places of Interest Quality Assurance Scheme**.

 Attractions with this sign participate in the **Visitor Attraction Quality Assurance Scheme**.

Both schemes recognise high standards in all aspects of the visitor experience (see page 6)

ENTERTAINMENT & CULTURE

Beatles Story
Liverpool, Merseyside L3 4AD
(0151) 709 1963
www.beatlesstory.com
Located within Liverpool's historic Albert Dock, the Beatles Story is a unique visitor attraction that transports you on an enlightening and atmospheric journey into the life, times, culture and music of the Beatles.

Imperial War Museum North
Greater Manchester M17 1TZ
(0161) 836 4000
www.iwm.org.uk/north
Located at The Quays and offers dynamic display techniques to reflect on how people's lives are shaped by war. Free Admission.

Liverpool Football Club
Merseyside L4 0TH
(0151) 260 6677
www.liverpoolfc.tv
Meet an LFC Legend; get your photograph with one of our many trophies or indulge yourself in one of our award winning Experience Days.

Lowry
Salford, Greater Manchester M50 3AZ
08432 086000
www.thelowry.com
Salford's answer to the Sydney Opera House and the Guggenheim rolled into one. See LS Lowry's works and other outstanding exhibitions or take in a performance.

Manchester Art Gallery
Greater Manchester M2 3JL
(0161) 235 8888
www.manchestergalleries.org
Houses one of the country's finest art collections in spectacular Victorian and Contemporary surroundings. Also changing exhibitions and a programme of events and a host of free family friendly resources.

Manchester Museum
Greater Manchester M13 9PL
(0161) 275 2648
www.manchester.ac.uk/museum
Found on Oxford Road, on The University of Manchester campus (in a very impressive gothic-style building), highlights include Stan the T.rex, mummies, live animals such as frogs and snakes, object handling and a varied programme of events.

Manchester United Museum & Tour Centre
Greater Manchester M16 0RA
(0161) 868 8000
www.manutd.com
The official museum and tour offers every football fan a unique insight into Manchester United Football Club and a fantastic day out.

Museum of Lakeland Life
Kendal, Cumbria LA9 5AL
(015397) 22464
www.lakelandmuseum.org.uk
This award-winning museum takes you and your family back through time to tell the story of the Lake District and its inhabitants.

National Waterways Museum
Ellesmere Port, Cheshire CH65 4FW
(0151) 335 5017
www.nwm.org.uk/ellesmere
Unlock the wonders of our waterways.

People's History Museum
Greater Manchester M3 3ER
(0161) 838 9190
www.phm.org.uk
The new People's History Museum is now open.

Ribchester Roman Museum
Preston, Lancashire PR3 3XS
(01254) 878261
www.ribchesterromanmuseum.org
Lancashire's only specialist Roman museum, located on the North bank of the beautiful River Ribble.

Tate Liverpool
Merseyside L3 4BB
(0151) 702 7400
www.tate.org.uk/liverpool
Tate Liverpool presents displays and international exhibitions of modern and contemporary art in beautiful light filled galleries.

The Gallery Liverpool
Merseyside L8 5RE
(0151) 709 2442
www.thegalleryliverpool.co.uk
Set in the heart of Liverpool's Independent Cultural District, the gallery occupies the entire upper floor of the industrial premises of John O'Keeffe and Son Ltd.

The World of Beatrix Potter
Bowness, Cumbria LA23 3BX
(015394) 88444
www.hop-skip-jump.com
A magical indoor attraction that brings to life all 23 Beatrix Potter's Peter Rabbit tales.

Walker Art Gallery
Liverpool, Merseyside L3 8EL
(0151) 478 4199
www.walkerartgallery.org.uk
Home to outstanding works by Rubens, Rembrandt, Poussin, Gainsborough and Hogarth, the Walker Art Gallery is one of the finest art galleries in Europe.

Whitworth Art Gallery
Manchester M15 6ER
(0161) 275 7450
www.whitworth.manchester.ac.uk
The Whitworth Art Gallery is home to an internationally-famous collection of British watercolours, textiles and wallpapers.

World Museum Liverpool
Merseyside L3 8EN
(0151) 478 4393
www.liverpoolmuseums.org.uk/wml
One of Britain's finest museums, with extensive collections from the Amazonian Rain Forest to the mysteries of outer space.

FAMILY FUN

Catalyst Science Discovery Centre
Widnes, Cheshire WA8 0DF
(0151) 420 1121
www.catalyst.org.uk
Interactive science centre whose aim is to make science exciting and accessible to people of all ages and abilities.

Go Ape! Hire Wire Forest Adventure - Delamere
Northwich, Cheshire CW8 2JD
0845 643 9215
www.goape.co.uk
"Take to the trees and experience an exhilarating course of rope bridges, tarzan swings and zip slides...all set high above the forest floor."

Grizedale Forest Visitor Centre
Hawkshead, Cumbria LA22 0QJ
(01229) 860010
www.forestry.gov.uk/ northwestengland
Grizedale Forest offers a range of activities for all ages through the year, from mountain biking to relaxing walks, Go-Ape to the sculpture trails.

Sandcastle Waterpark
Blackpool, Lancashire FY4 1BB
(01253) 343602
www.sandcastle-waterpark.co.uk
The UK's Largest Indoor Waterpark and with 18 slides and attractions.

Museum of Wigan Life
Greater Manchester WN1 1NU
(01942) 828128
www.wlct.org/culture/heritage/ historyshop.htm
A magnificent Grade II listed building, designed by Alfred Waterhouse in 1878 as a public library for Wigan, and is now the hub of Wigan Heritage Services.

HERITAGE

Arley Hall & Gardens
Northwich, Cheshire CW9 6NA
(01565) 777353
www.arleyhallandgardens.com
Arley Hall's gardens are a wonderful example of the idea that the best gardens are living works of art.

Chester Cathedral
Cheshire CH1 2HU
(01244) 324756
www.chestercathedral.com
A must see for Chester, a beautiful cathedral with a fascinating history.

Croxteth Hall & Country Park
Liverpool, Merseyside L12 0HB
(0151) 233 6910
www.croxteth.co.uk
Stately home with 500 acres estate including visitor farm, Victorian walled garden and seasonal events.

East Lancashire Railway
Bury, Greater Manchester BL9 0EY
(0161) 764 7790
www.east-lancs-rly.co.uk
The beautifully restored East Lancashire Railway takes you on a captivating journey to discover the region's rich transport heritage.

Holker Hall and Gardens
Grange-over-Sands, Cumbria LA11 7PL
(015395) 58328
www.holker.co.uk
Home to Lord and Lady Cavendish, Victorian wing, glorious gardens, parkland and woodlands.

Jodrell Bank Discovery Centre
Macclesfield, Cheshire SK11 9DL
(01477) 571339
www.jodrellbank.manchester.ac.uk/ visitorcentre
Come and take a trip to Mars ...

Levens Hall & Gardens
Kendal, Cumbria LA8 0PD
(015395) 60321
www.levenshall.co.uk
Elizabethan mansion and world famous topiary gardens designed by M Beaumont in 1694, fountain garden and buttery, licenced restaurant and gift shop.

Mendips & 20 Forthlin Road [Beatles]
Liverpool, Merseyside
(0151) 427 7231
www.nationaltrust.org.uk/beatles
Take a tour inside the childhood homes of John Lennon and Paul McCartney, and the places where many of the earliest Beatles songs were composed and rehearsed.

Penrith Castle
Cumbria CA11 7HX
(01912) 691200
www.english-heritage.org.uk/ daysout/properties/penrith-castle/
The mainly 15thC remains of a castle begun by Bishop Strickland of Carlisle and developed by the Nevilles and Richard III.

Ravenglass & Eskdale Railway
Cumbria CA18 1SW
(01229) 717171
www.ravenglass-railway.co.uk
Heritage steam engines haul open-top and cosy covered carriages from the Lake District coastal village of Ravenglass to the foot of England's highest mountains.

Speke Hall, Gardens & Estate
Liverpool, Merseyside L24 1XD
(0151) 427 7231
www.nationaltrust.org.uk/main/w-spekehall
One of the most famous half timbered houses in Britain, dating from the 15th century, owned by the National Trust.

NATURE & WILDLIFE

Chester Zoo
Cheshire CH2 1EU
(01244) 380280
www.chesterzoo.org
With over 7,000 animals, including some of the most exotic and endangered species on the planet.

Farmer Ted's Farm Park
Ormskirk, Lancashire L39 7HW
(0151) 526 0002
www.farmerteds.com
A safe environment for families with children 0-12 yrs, with older children also welcome.

Hare Hill Gardens
Macclesfield Cheshire SK10 4QB
(01625) 584412
www.nationaltrust.org.uk/main/w-harehill
A small but perfectly formed wooded and walled garden.

Knowsley Safari Park
Merseyside L34 4AN
(0151) 430 9009
www.knowsley.com/safari
Enjoy a 5 mile safari through 450 acres of historic parkland.

Old Holly Farm
Garstang, Lancashire PR3 1AA
(01524) 791200
www.oldhollyfarm.com
Appeals to visitors of all ages.

South Lakes Wild Animal Park
Dalton-in-Furness, Cumbria LA15 8JR
(01229) 466086
www.wildanimalpark.co.uk
The ultimate interactive animal experience. Get close to wildlife at Cumbria's top tourist attraction.

Wyre Estuary Country Park
Thornton Lancashire FY5 5LR
(01253) 857890
www.wyrebc.gov.uk/tourismplacestovisit.htm
Located in a Green Flag area and the centre catering for all ages with the ability to cater for all persons with a wide range of foods and drink.

OUTDOOR ACTIVITIES

Ullswater Steamers
Cumbria CA11 0US
(01768) 482229
The 'Steamers' create the perfect opportunity to combine a cruise with some of the most famous and spectacular walks in the lake District.

Windermere Lake Cruises, Lakeside
Newby Bridge, Cumbria LA12 8AS
(015394) 43360
www.windermere-lakecruises.co.uk
Steamers and launches sail daily between Ambleside, Bowness and Lakeside. Additional summer routes. Timetabled services.

Events 2012

John Smith's Grand National
Liverpool
www.aintree.co.uk
12th-14th April

Garstang Walking Festival
Garstang
www.wyrebc.gov.uk
May

Jennings Keswick Jazz Festival
Keswick
www.theatrebythelake.com
May

Liverpool Sound City
Liverpool
www.liverpoolsoundcity.co.uk
May

Electric Garden Progressive Rock Festival
Blackpool
www.electricgardenfestival.com
May

Blackpool Dance Festival
Blackpool
www.blackpooldancefestival.com
May - June

Great North Swim
Windermere
www.greatswim.org
June

Cheshire County Show
Knutsford
www.cheshirecountyshow.org.uk
June

Chestival
Chester
www.chestival2010.co.uk
June - July

Manchester International Festival
Manchester
www.mif.co.uk
June - July

Wirral Folk on the Coast Festival
Wirral
www.wirralfolkonthecoast.com
June

Audlem Festival of Transport
Audlem
www.audlem-aset.org
July

Chester Summer Music Festival
Chester
www.chesterfestivals.co.uk/site/music-festival
July

Catch the Wind Kite Festival
Morecambe
www.moremusic.org.uk
July

Coniston Water Festival
Coniston Water
www.conistonwaterfestival.org.uk
July

Port Sunlight Village Festival
Wirral
www.portsunlightvillage.com
July

Creamfields
Daresbury
www.creamfields.com
25th-27th August

Wirral Food and Drink Festival
Wirral
www.wirralfoodfestival.co.uk
August

Manchester Pride
Manchester
www.manchesterpride.com
August

Rebellion Festival
Blackpool
www.rebellionfestivals.com
August

Westmorland County Show
Milnthorpe
www.westmorlandshow.co.uk
September

Birkenhead Festival of Transport
Birkenhead
www.bheadtransportfest.com
September

Mintfest
Kendal
www.mintfest.org
September

Shell Chester Literature Festival
Chester
www.chesterfestivals.co.uk
OctoberNovember

Tourist Information Centres

When you arrive at your destination, visit an Official Partner Tourist Information Centre for quality assured help with accommodation and information about local attractions and events, or email your request before you go. To find a Tourist Information Centre by region look at http://www.enjoyengland.com under Destination Finder.

ALTRINCHAM	20 Stamford New Road	0161 912 5931	tourist.information@trafford.gov.uk
ACCRINGTON	Town Hall	01254 380293	information@leisureinhyndburn.co.uk
AMBLESIDE	Central Buildings	015394 32582	amblesidetic@southlakeland.gov.uk
ASHTON-UNDER-LYNE	Council Offices	0161 343 4343	tourist.information@tameside.gov.uk
BARNOLDSWICK	The Council Shop	01282 666704	tourist.info@pendle.gov.uk
BARROW-IN-FURNESS	Forum 28	01229 876505	touristinfo@barrowbc.gov.uk
BLACKBURN	50-54 Church Street	0125 568 8040	visit@blackburn.gov.uk
BLACKPOOL	1 Clifton Street	01253 478222	tic@blackpool.gov.uk
BOLTON	Central Library Foyer	01204 334321	tourist.info@bolton.gov.uk
BOWNESS	Glebe Road	015394 42895	bownesstic@lake-district.gov.uk
BURNLEY	Burnley Mechanics	01282 664421	tic@burnley.gov.uk
BURY	The Fusilier Museum	0161 253 5111	touristinformation@bury.gov.uk
CARLISLE	Old Town Hall	01228 625600	tourism@carlisle-city.gov.uk
CHESTER (TOWN HALL)	Town Hall	0845 647 7868	welcome@visitchesterandcheshire.co.uk
CLEVELEYS	Victoria Square	01253 853378	cleveleystic@wyrebc.gov.uk
CLITHEROE	Ribble Valley Borough Council	01200 425566	tourism@ribblevalley.gov.uk
CONGLETON	Town Hall	01260 271095	congletontic@cheshireeast.gov.uk
CONISTON	Ruskin Avenue	015394 41533	mail@conistontic.org
DISCOVER PENDLE CENTRE	Boundary Mill Sores	01282 856186	discoverpendle@pendle.gov.uk
ELLESMERE PORT	McArthur Glen Outlet Village	0151 356 5562	visitorinformation@cheshireoaksdesigneroutlet.com
FLEETWOOD	Old Ferry Office	01253 773953	fleetwoodtic@wyrebc.gov.uk
GARSTANG	Council Offices, Discovery Centre	01995 602125	garstangtic@wyrebc.gov.uk
JOHN LENNON AIRPORT	Arrivals Hall, South Terminal	0151 907 1058	info@visitliverpool.com
KENDAL	Town Hall	01539 797516	kendaltic@southlakeland.gov.uk
KESWICK	Moot Hall	017687 72645	keswicktic@lake-district.gov.uk
LANCASTER	The Storey Creative Industries Centre	01524 582394	lancastervic@lancaster.gov.uk
LIVERPOOL 08 PLACE	Whitechapel	0151 233 2008	08place@liverpool.gov.uk
LIVERPOOL ALBERT DOCK	Anchor Courtyard	0151 233 2008	08place@liverpool.gov.uk
LYTHAM ST ANNES	c/o Town Hall	01253 725610	touristinformation@fylde.gov.uk

MACCLESFIELD	Macclesfield	01625 378123	macclesfieldtic@cheshireeast.gov.uk
MANCHESTER	Manchester Visitor Centre	0871 222 8223	touristinformation@marketing-manchester.co.uk
MORECAMBE	Old Station Buildings	01524 582808	morecambevic@lancaster.gov.uk
NANTWICH	Civic Hall	01270 537359	nantwichtic@cheshireeast.gov.uk
NORTHWICH	Information Centre	01606 353534	infocentrenorthwich@cheshirewestandchester.gov.uk
OLDHAM	Gallery Oldham	0161 770 3064	tourist@oldham.gov.uk
PENDLE HERITAGE CENTRE	Park Hill	01282 661701	heritage.centre@pendle.gov.uk
PENRITH	Middlegate	01768 867466	pen.tic@eden.gov.uk
PRESTON	The Guildhall	01772 253731	tourism@preston.gov.uk
RHEGED	Rheged Tourist Information Centre	01768 860034	tic@rheged.com
ROCHDALE	Touchstones	01706 924928	tic@link4life.org
SADDLEWORTH	Saddleworth Museum	01457 870336	ecs.saddleworthtic@oldham.gov.uk
SALFORD	The Lowry, Pier 8	0161 848 8601	tic@salford.gov.uk
SOUTHPORT	112 Lord Street	01704 533333	info@visitsouthport.com
SOUTHWAITE	M6 Service Area	016974 73445	southwaitetic@visitscotland.com
ST HELENS	The World of Glass	01744 755150	info@sthelenstic.com
STOCKPORT	Staircase House	0161 474 4444	tourist.information@stockport.gov.uk
ULLSWATER	Main Car Park	017684 82414	ullswatertic@lake-district.gov.uk
ULVERSTON	Coronation Hall	01229 587120	ulverstontic@southlakeland.gov.uk
WARRINGTON	Horsemarket Street	01925 428585	informationcentre@warrington.gov.uk
WHITEHAVEN	Market Hall	01946 598914	tic@copelandbc.gov.uk
WIGAN	62 Wallgate	01942 825677	tic@wlct.org
WINDERMERE	Victoria Street	015394 46499	windermeretic@southlakeland.gov.uk

Regional Contacts and Information

There are various publications and guides about England's North West available from the following Tourist Boards or by logging on to www.visitenglandsnorthwest.com or calling 0845 600 6040:

Visit Chester and Cheshire

Chester Railway Station, 1st Floor, West Wing Offices, Station Road, Chester, CH1 3NT
Tel: (01244) 405600
Tel: 0845 073 1324 (accommodation booking)
Email: info@visitchesterandcheshire.co.uk
Web: www.visitchester.com or www.visitcheshire.com

Cumbria Tourism

Windermere Road, Staveley, Kendal, LA8 9PL
Tel: (015398) 22222
Email: info@cumbriatourism.org
Web: www.golakes.co.uk

The Lancashire and Blackpool Tourist Board

St. George's House, St. George's Street, Chorley, PR7 2AA
Tel: (01257) 226600 (Brochure request)
Email: info@visitlancashire.com
Web: www.visitlancashire.com

Visit Manchester – The Tourist Board For Greater Manchester

Town Hall Extension
Lloyd Street
Manchester
M60 2LA
Tel: 0871 222 8223
Email: touristinformation@visitmanchester.com
Web: www.visitmanchester.com

The Mersey Partnership – The Tourist Board for Liverpool City Region

12 Princes Parade, Liverpool, L3 1BG
Tel: (0151) 233 2008 (information enquiries)
Tel: 0844 870 0123 (accommodation booking)
Email: info@visitliverpool.com
(accommodation enquiries)
Email: liverpoolvisitorcentre@liverpool.gov.uk
(information enquiries)
Web: www.visitliverpool.com

Where to Stay

Entries appear alphabetically by town name in each county. A key to symbols appears on page 6. Maps start on page 298. Further listings of VisitEngland assessed accommodation appear on the CD at the back of this guide.

CHESTER, Cheshire Map ref 4A2 SAT NAV CH2 4HS

Chester Fairoaks Caravan Club Site
Rake Lane, Little Stanney, Chester, Cheshire CH2 4HS
t (0151) 355 1600 **e** enquiries@caravanclub.co.uk
w caravanclub.co.uk

THE
CARAVAN
CLUB

🚐 (100) £16.60–£38.90
🚎 (100) £16.60–£38.90
100 touring pitches

A tranquil site six miles from Chester with its famous zoo, historic sites and excellent shopping. Take an open-top bus or walk around the walls to absorb the colourful atmosphere. **directions** M53 take jct 10 and join A5117. Towards Queensferry, follow brown signs. Turn left in Little Stanney, signposted Chorlton. Site 0.25 miles on left. **open** All year **payment** credit/debit cards, cash, cheques

General 🗓 📶 📱 🐾 ☼ 🔌 🔁 🕐 🚻 🚐 Leisure ▶ 🏊

Looking for something else?

You can also buy a copy of our popular guide 'Hotels' including country house and town house hotels, metro and budget hotels, serviced apartments and restaurants with rooms in England 2012.

Now available in good bookshops and online at **visitbritainshop.com**   **£7.99**

FRODSHAM, Cheshire Map ref 4A2

SAT NAV WA6 6XQ

🏠 (3) £342.00–£658.00
🚐 (6) £230.00–£561.00

SPECIAL PROMOTIONS
Over 55's discount; under 5's discount, and many more. Visit www.ridge waypark.com
and click Special Offers for details.

Ridgeway Country Holiday Park

Alvanley, Frodsham WA6 6XQ
t (01928) 734981 **e** enquiries@ridgewaypark.com
w **ridgewaypark.com** ONLINE MAP GUEST REVIEWS

High quality, fully equipped caravans and lodges for hire. Nestling in a quiet valley surrounded by woodland, immediate access onto the Sandstone Trail, yet only 9 miles from Chester. Short breaks available. Dogs welcome.

open 1 March to 2 January
payment credit/debit cards, cash, cheques

directions From jct 12 M56. A56 towards Frodsham. Pass through town; left onto B5393. Left again after Foxhill Centre onto The Ridgeway. 1/2 mile on left.

General 🔥 🖥 ⊚ 🐕 🎦 ☀ **Leisure** ▸ 🚲 ✒

APPLEBY-IN-WESTMORLAND, Cumbria Map ref 5B3

SAT NAV CA16 6EJ

🚐 (221) £16.00–£33.50
🚎 (158) £16.00–£33.50
⛺ (63) £16.00–£23.00
🚐 (15) £295.00–£695.00
221 touring pitches

Wild Rose Park

Ormside, Appleby-in-Westmorland CA16 6EJ
t (017683) 51077 **f** (017683) 52551 **e** reception@wildrose.co.uk
w **wildrose.co.uk** ONLINE MAP ONLINE BOOKING LAST MINUTE OFFERS

Friendly, family park in the lovely, unspoilt Eden Valley with mountain views. Within easy reach of the Lakes and the Dales. Spotless, super loos and private wash cubicles. **directions** Please contact us for directions **open** All year **payment** credit/debit cards, cash, cheques

General 🖥 🐕 🛎 🎦 🅿 ☀ 🖥 ⚙ 🍴 🚿 🚾 ✕ **Leisure** 🚲 ✒ 🎣 🐟 ⋔

ARMATHWAITE, Cumbria Map ref 5B2

SAT NAV CA4 9SY

🚐 (63) £10.70–£28.00
🚎 (63) £10.70–£28.00
63 touring pitches

Englethwaite Hall Caravan Club Site

Armathwaite, Carlisle, Cumbria CA4 9SY
t (01228) 560202 **e** enquiries@caravanclub.co.uk
w **caravanclub.co.uk**

THE
CARAVAN
CLUB

A tranquil site, scattered with rhododendrons. The Eden Valley riverside walk has views to the Lakeland Fells from the footpaths. **directions** Exit M6/A6 onto B6263, in 1.75 miles turn right. Site on right in about 2.75 miles. **payment** credit/debit cards, cash, cheques

General 🐕 🚐 🚿 🚾 **Leisure** ✒

BOOT, Cumbria Map ref 5A3 SAT NAV CA19 1TH

Eskdale Camping and Caravanning Club Site

Boot, Holmrook, Cumbria CA19 1TH
t (01946) 723253 **e** eskdale.site@campingandcaravanningclub.co.uk
w **campingandcaravanningclub.co.uk/eskdale** ONLINE MAP GUEST REVIEWS

🚐	£23.00–£26.00
🚏	£23.00–£26.00
⛺	£23.00–£26.00

80 touring pitches

Located in a walkers' paradise described as one of the loveliest of Lakeland Valleys by Alfred Wainwright. Home to a unique Camping Barn and 10 Camping Pods. **directions** OS Map Reference: 89 - NY179011 Latitude: 54.3987 Longitude: -3.2661 Beware: Satnav may take you over Hardknott pass which is unsuitable for motorhomes vehicles towing. **open** 1st March - 14th January **payment** credit/debit cards, cash, cheques

General 🔲 📶 🐕 🏋 📮 🚿 ☀ 🎣 🚻 ♿ **Leisure** 🚴 ⛰

BOUTH, Cumbria Map ref 5A3 SAT NAV LA12 8JN

Black Beck Caravan Park

Bouth, Nr Ulverston, Cumbria LA12 8JN
t (01229) 861274 **f** (01229) 861041 **e** reception@blackbeck.net
w **blackbeck.com** ONLINE BOOKING

🚐 (43)	£15.00–£23.00
🚏 (4)	£15.00–£23.00
⛺ (1)	£619.00
🏠 (3)	£250.00–£619.00

39 touring pitches

SPECIAL PROMOTIONS
10% off 7 day tourer booking. Rebook within 28 days of holiday and receive 15% discount.

Black Beck is situated within the Lake District National Park, nestled in the beautiful Rusland Valley between the southern tips of Lake Windermere and Coniston. Surrounded by spectacular woodland scenery. Jacuzzi and sauna. Redeveloped overnight touring area with hardstanding pitches.

open 1st March to 15th November
payment credit/debit cards, cash, cheques

directions M6 jct 36. A590 towards Barrow, Newby Bridge. Pass steam railway, Next right to Bouth. Left at T-junction, 0.5 miles right after hump-backed bridge.

General ♿ 🔲 🐕 🏋 📮 🚿 ☀ 🎣 🚻 ♿ **Leisure** ∪ 🚴 🏊 ⛰

CONISTON, Cumbria Map ref 5A3 SAT NAV LA12 8DL

Crake Valley Holiday Park

Water Yeat, Blawith, Ulverston, Cumbria LA12 8DL
t (01229) 885203 **f** (01229) 885203 **e** crakevalley@coniston1.fslife.co.uk
w **crakevalley.co.uk**

⛺ (6)	£19.00
🏠 (5)	£370.00–£610.00
🏠 (10)	£225.00–£470.00

Small, top-graded holiday park. Caravans and lodges for hire in secluded setting opposite Coniston Water. Ideal base for touring the Lakes. **directions** Please contact us for directions **open** March to October **payment** cash, cheques

General 🔲 🐕 📮 🚿 ☀

CONISTON, Cumbria Map ref 5A3

SAT NAV LA21 8LA

Park Coppice Caravan Club Site
Coniston, Cumbria LA21 8LA
t (01539) 441555 **e** enquiries@caravanclub.co.uk
w caravanclub.co.uk

CARAVAN CLUB

(280) £15.30–£35.50
(280) £15.30–£35.50
280 touring pitches

Set in 63 National Trust woodland with access to Coniston Water. Take a steamboat ride on the Coniston Gondola or hire a boat. Ideal for birdwatching and walking. **directions** Follow A593, 1.5 miles south of Coniston village. Final approach from the north or south is narrow in places. **open** March to November **payment** credit/debit cards, cash, cheques

General Leisure

GILCRUX, Cumbria Map ref 5A2

SAT NAV CA7 2QX

The Beeches Caravan Park
Gilcrux, Wigton, Cockermouth CA7 2QX
t (01697) 321555 **e** holiday@thebeechescaravanpark.com
w thebeechescaravanpark.com

(12) £225.00–£315.00

The Caravan Park is a small, quiet site, in a peaceful village, close to Cockermouth Cumbria. Luxury static caravans are available for hire on a weekly or short break basis. **directions** Through the lake district on the A66, from Cockermouth take the A594 to Maryport, turn right at Dovenby for Tallentire then Gilcrux. **open** All year **payment** credit/debit cards, cash, cheques

General Leisure

GRANGE-OVER-SANDS, Cumbria Map ref 5A3

SAT NAV LA11 6HR

Greaves Farm Caravan Park
Greaves Farm Caravan Park, c/o Prospect House, Barber Green, Grange-over-Sands, Cumbria LA11 6HU
t (01539) 536329 / 536587 **w** greavesfarmcaravanpark.co.uk

(10) £16.00–£18.00
£16.00–£18.00
(10) £14.00–£18.00
(2) £275.00–£425.00
10 touring pitches

Small quiet park in rural location 2m north of Cartmel. Family owned and supervised. Convenient base for South Lakes. Two luxury holiday caravans for hire. Spacious touring and camping park. **directions** Exit 36 off M6. Follow A590 signed Barrow. 1 mile before Newby Bridge take left hand road signed Cartmel 4m. Continue 1.5m. Site signed. **open** March to October **payment** cash, cheques

General Leisure

GRANGE-OVER-SANDS, Cumbria Map ref 5A3

SAT NAV LA11 6RB

Meathop Fell Caravan Club Site
Meathop, Grange-over-Sands, Cumbria LA11 6RB
t (01539) 532912 **e** enquiries@caravanclub.co.uk
w caravanclub.co.uk

CARAVAN CLUB

(129) £16.00–£38.90
(129) £16.00–£38.90
129 touring pitches

This peaceful site is an ideal base from which to explore North Lancashire and the southern Lake District. Windermere and Coniston are great for water-based activities. **directions** M6 jct 36, A590 to Barrow. After 3.25 miles take slip road and follow A590 to Barrow. At 1st roundabout follow International Camping signs. **open** All year **payment** credit/debit cards, cash, cheques

General Leisure

HOLMROOK, Cumbria Map ref 5A3

SAT NAV CA19 1XU

RATING APPLIED FOR

🚐 (9)   £18.50–£20.50
🚃 (9)   £18.50–£20.50
⛺ (40) £14.00–£16.00
49 touring pitches

Shepherds Views Holidays
Holmrook, Nr. Ravenglass CA19 1XU
t (01946) 729907 **e** contact@shepherdsviews.co.uk
w **shepherdsviews.co.uk** ONLINE MAP GUEST REVIEWS LAST MINUTE OFFERS

A family run site close to the Wasdale Valley & within walking distance to the beach. Ideal for walking, cycling, or visiting the attractions of the Western Lake District. **directions** Situated off the A595 at Holmrook, on the B5344. Follow the B5344 to approx. 2 miles & Shepherds Views is on the right hand side. **open** 1st March until 31st October **payment** credit/debit cards, cash

General 🐕 🏕 ☼ 🖵 🛁 🔌 🚻 🕎   Leisure ▶ ∪ ⚲ ♩

KENDAL, Cumbria Map ref 5B3

SAT NAV LA8 0JZ

TOURING PARK

🚐 (141) £15.90–£35.51
🚃 (141) £15.90–£35.51
141 touring pitches

Low Park Wood Caravan Club Site
Sedgwick, Kendal, Cumbria LA8 0JZ
t (01539) 560186 **e** enquiries@caravanclub.co.uk
w **caravanclub.co.uk**

THE
CARAVAN
CLUB

This peaceful country site is a haven for birdwatchers, freshwater fisherman and wildflower enthusiasts. A dog-friendly site with extensive woodland to walk them in. **directions** M6 jct 36 onto A590 signed South Lakes. Approx 3.25 miles leave via slip road (signed Milnthorpe, Barrow) and follow caravan signs. **open** March to November **payment** credit/debit cards, cash, cheques

General 🖵 🐕 🚿 🏕 ☼ 🖳 🔌 🕐 🚻 🕎   Leisure ♦ ⚠

KENDAL, Cumbria Map ref 5B3

SAT NAV LA7 7NN

HOLIDAY, TOURING & CAMPING PARK

🚐 (26) £15.80–£22.90
🚃 (26) £15.80–£22.90
⛺ (5)   £12.00–£26.50
26 touring pitches

Waters Edge Caravan Park
Crooklands, Kendal LA7 7NN
t (01539) 567708 **e** info@watersedgecaravanpark.co.uk
w **watersedgecaravanpark.co.uk**

Friendly site in open countryside. Lake District, Morecambe, Yorkshire Dales nearby. All hardstanding pitches. Lounge, bar, pool room, patio area. Shower block with laundry. Local pub/restaurant within 300 yds. **directions** Leave M6 at jct 36, take A65 toward Kirkby Lonsdale for aprox 100 yds, then A65 toward Crooklands. Site approx 1 mile on the right. **open** 1 March to 14 November **payment** credit/debit cards, cash, cheques

General 🖵 🐕 ⚡ 🏕 ☼ 🖳 🛁 🔌 🕐 🚻   Leisure ∪ ♩ ▼ ♦

KESWICK, Cumbria Map ref 5A3

SAT NAV CA12 4TE

TOURING & CAMPING PARK

🚐   £17.00–£20.00
🚃   £17.00–£20.00
⛺ (80) £12.70–£17.20
21 touring pitches

Castlerigg Farm Camping & Caravan Site
Castlerigg, Keswick CA12 4TE
t (01768) 772479 **e** info@castleriggfarm.com
w **castleriggfarm.com** ONLINE MAP GUEST REVIEWS ONLINE BOOKING LAST MINUTE OFFERS

The rule of silence after 10.30pm is in keeping with the wonderful location of this family run site. Exceptional panoramic views of the surrounding fells and lakes. **directions** From A66 follow signs to A591 out of town towards Windermere. 1 mile near top of hill, turn right. Castlerigg Farm Camp Site on left. **open** March to November **payment** credit/debit cards, cash, cheques

General 🖵 ⚡ 🐕 ⚡ 🏕 🏕 🔌 🕐 🚻 🕎 ✕   Leisure ▶ ∪ ⚲ ♩

KESWICK, Cumbria Map ref 5A3

SAT NAV CA12 4TE

Castlerigg Hall Caravan & Camping Park
Castlerigg Hall, Keswick, Cumbria CA12 4TE
t (01768) 774499 e info@castlerigg.co.uk
w **castlerigg.co.uk** ONLINE MAP LAST MINUTE OFFERS

(58)	£20.50–£28.50
(58)	£20.50–£28.50
(120)	£19.50–£22.40
(7)	£350.00–£530.00

Our elevated position commands wonderful panoramic views of the surrounding fells. Formerly a Lakeland hill farm, Castlerigg Hall has been sympathetically developed into a quality touring park. **directions** Head out of Keswick on the A591 direction Windermere. At the top of the hill turn right at the brown tourist sign indicating Castlerigg Hall. **open** 12 March to 9 November **payment** credit/debit cards, cash, cheques

General ▯ 🏕 🐕 ⚡ ▤ ▥ ☼ ♨ 🔌 🚻 ♿ 🛒 ✕ Leisure ∪ 🚲 ⚓

KIRKBY LONSDALE, Cumbria Map ref 5B3

SAT NAV LA6 2SE

Woodclose Park
Casterton, Kirkby Lonsdale LA6 2SE
t (015242) 71597 f (015242) 72301 e info@woodclosepark.co.uk
w **woodclosepark.com** ONLINE MAP GUEST REVIEWS ONLINE BOOKING LAST MINUTE OFFERS

(17)	£12.75–£23.50
(17)	£12.75–£23.50
(18)	£13.00–£16.00
52 touring pitches	

Gold Enjoy England Winners 2011 set in the beautiful Lune valley between the Yorkshire Dales and the Lake District. Tourers, camping, self catering Wigwams and holiday homes for sale. **directions** M6 jct36, follow A65 for approx 6 miles. The park entrance can be found just past Kirkby Lonsdale on the left-hand side, up the hill. **open** 1st March to End October. Extended season for holiday home owners. **payment** credit/debit cards, cash, cheques

General ⚡ ▯ 🏕 🐕 ⚡ ▤ ▥ ☼ ♨ 🔌 🚻 ♿ 🛒 Leisure ► ∪ 🚲 ⚓ 🏔

LAMPLUGH, Cumbria Map ref 5A3

SAT NAV CA14 4SH

Dockray Meadow Caravan Club Site
Ennerdale Bridge, Cumbria CA14 4SH
t (01946) 861357 e enquiries@caravanclub.co.uk
w **caravanclub.co.uk**

THE CARAVAN CLUB

(53)	£10.70–£28.00
(53)	£10.70–£28.00
53 touring pitches	

Within easy reach of popular Keswick and Derwentwater. Revel in the glorious fell scenery during your stay. For the energetic there are plenty of walks from and around the site. **directions** From A66 turn onto A5086. In 6.5 miles turn left at signpost for Lamplugh Green. Turn right at signpost for Croasdale. Site on left. **open** April to November **payment** credit/debit cards, cash, cheques

General 🐕 🔌 ♿ 🛒 Leisure ⚓

NEWLANDS, Cumbria Map ref 5A3

SAT NAV CA12 5UG

Low Manesty Caravan Club Site
Manesty, Keswick CA12 5UG
t (01768) 777275 e enquiries@caravanclub.co.uk
w **caravanclub.co.uk**

THE CARAVAN CLUB

	£12.50–£30.80
	£12.50–£30.80
60 touring pitches	

Set in National Trust woodland, close to Derwentwater. Derwentwater is busy with boats and a marina. **directions** From B5289 turn right over bridge (1/2 mile past Borrowdale Hotel). Site on right in 1 mile. **open** April to November **payment** credit/debit cards, cash, cheques

General 🐕 🔌 ♿ 🛒 Leisure ⚓

PENRITH, Cumbria Map ref 5B2   SAT NAV CA11 0JB

Flusco Wood
Flusco, Penrith CA11 0JB
t (01768) 480020 **e** info@fluscowood.co.uk

A high-standard, quiet woodland touring caravan park with fully serviced pitches and centrally heated amenity building. Short drive to many attractions and places of interest in the Lake District. **directions** M6 jct 40, travel west on A66 towards Keswick. After about 4 miles turn right (signposted Flusco). Entrance along lane on the left. **open** Easter to November **payment** credit/debit cards, cash, cheques

🚐 (50)   £19.50–£22.00
🚐 (10)   £19.50–£22.00
60 touring pitches

General 🅰 🐕 ⚡ 🏕 🍴 ☼ 🚻 🍽 🔌 🕐 ☎   Leisure ∪ 🚲 ✦ ⛰

POOLEY BRIDGE, Cumbria Map ref 5A3   SAT NAV CA10 2NA

Waterside House Campsite
Waterside House, Howtown, Penrith, Cumbria CA10 2NA
t (01768) 486332 **f** (01768) 486332 **e** enquire@watersidefarm-campsite.co.uk
w **watersidefarm-campsite.co.uk** ONLINE MAP

Beautiful lakeside location on working farm with excellent toilet, shower and laundry facilities. Mountain bike, Canadian canoe and boat hire. Boat storage available. **directions** M6 jct 40, A66 (1 mile) then A592 (to Pooley Bridge). Right at church, right again along Howtown Road (1 mile). 2nd site on right. **open** March to October **payment** credit/debit cards, cash, cheques

🚐 (20)   £14.00–£24.00
⛺ (90)   £14.00–£24.00

General 🅰 🐕 ⚡ 🏕 🍴 ☼ 🚻 🔌 🕐 ☎   Leisure ∪ 🚲 ✦ ⛰

RAVENGLASS, Cumbria Map ref 5A3   SAT NAV CA18 1SR

Ravenglass Camping and Caravanning Club Site
Ravenglass, Cumbria CA18 1SR
t (01229) 717250 **e** Ravenglass.Site@thefriendlyclub.co.uk
w **campingandcaravanningclub.co.uk/ravenglass** ONLINE MAP GUEST REVIEWS

The Camping and Caravanning Club
The Friendly Club

Once part of the Muncaster Estate, set in six acres of mature woodland, it lies on the outskirts of the pretty Roman fishing village. 500 yards from a sandy beach. **directions** OS Map Reference: 96 - SD086965 Latitude: 54.3558 Longitude: -3.4079 Satnav may take you over Corney Fell, which is unsuitable for caravans and motorhomes. **open** 1 February- 30th November **payment** credit/debit cards, cash, cheques

🚐   £23.00–£26.00
🚐   £23.00–£26.00
⛺   £23.00–£26.00
75 touring pitches

General 🅰 ⚙ 🐕 ⚡ 🏕 🍴 ☼ 🔌 🕐 ☎   Leisure 🚲 ✦

TROUTBECK, Cumbria Map ref 5A3   SAT NAV CA11 0SX

Troutbeck Camping and Caravanning Site
Hutton Moor End, Troutbeck, Penrith, Cumbria CA11 0SX
t (01768) 779149 **e** troutbeck@thefriendlyclub.co.uk
w **campingandcaravanningclub.co.uk/troutbeck** ONLINE MAP GUEST REVIEWS

The Camping and Caravanning Club
The Friendly Club

Superb location in the Lake District. Walking country with fantastic views. In this Eden district, there are 70 main tourist attractions. Near market town of Keswick. **directions** From M6 and Penrith continue along A66 for 9.5m. Do not take A5091, sharp left at sign for Walthwaite. Railway: Penrith 9 miles away. **open** 1st March - 15th November **payment** credit/debit cards, cash, cheques

🚐   £23.00–£30.00
🚐   £23.00–£30.00
⛺   £23.00–£30.00
54 touring pitches

General 🅰 ⚙ 🐕 ⚡ 🏕 🍴 ☼ 🔌 🕐 ☎   Leisure ∪ 🚲 ⛰

TROUTBECK, Cumbria Map ref 5A3
SAT NAV CA11 0SS

Troutbeck Head Caravan Club Site
Troutbeck, Penrith CA11 0SS
t (01768) 483521 e enquiries@caravanclub.co.uk
w **caravanclub.co.uk**

CARAVAN CLUB

(151)   £16.00–£38.90
(151)   £16.00–£38.90
151 touring pitches

Set in north Lakeland countryside, near Ullswater. Ideal for nature lovers and walkers. A lake cruises on Ullswater and scenic walks between Howtown and Glenridding. **directions** Leave M6 at junction 40 onto A66. Turn left onto A5091. Site on right in about 1.25 mile. **open** March to January **payment** credit/debit cards, cash, cheques

General Leisure

ULLSWATER, Cumbria Map ref 5A3

Waterfoot Caravan Park
Pooley Bridge, Penrith, Ullswater CA11 0JF
t (017684) 86302 f (017684) 86728 e enquiries@waterfootpark.co.uk
w **waterfootpark.co.uk** ONLINE MAP GUEST REVIEWS LAST MINUTE OFFERS

(34)   £18.00–£29.00
(34)   £18.00–£29.00
34 touring pitches

Set in the grounds of a Georgian mansion overlooking Ullswater. Excellent facilities including reception, shop, licensed bar and games room. Children's play area. David Bellamy Conservation Gold Award. **directions** M6 jct40, follow signs marked Ullswater Steamers. West on A66 1 mile. Left at roundabout A592 (Ullswater). Waterfoot located on right. Not sat nav compatible. **open** 1 March to 14 November **payment** credit/debit cards, cash, cheques

General Leisure

WINDERMERE, Cumbria Map ref 5A3
SAT NAV LA23 3HB

Braithwaite Fold Caravan Club Site
Glebe Road, Bowness-on-Windermere, Windermere, Cumbria LA23 3HB
t (01539) 442177 e enquiries@caravanclub.co.uk
w **caravanclub.co.uk**

CARAVAN CLUB

(66)   £15.90–£35.51
(66)   £15.90–£35.51
66 touring pitches

Close to the shores of Windermere and within easy walking distance of the town. Windermere has an excellent sailing centre from which you can enjoy sailing, windsurfing and canoeing. **directions** From A592 follow signs for Bowness Bay, in 300 yds turn right into Glebe Road. Site on right. **open** March to November **payment** credit/debit cards, cash, cheques

General Leisure

WINDERMERE, Cumbria Map ref 5A3
SAT NAV LA23 3DL

Fallbarrow Park
Rayrigg Road, Bowness-on-Windermere, Windermere, Cumbria LA23 3DL
t (01539) 569835 f (01539) 488736 e enquiries@southlakelandparks.co.uk
w **slholidays.co.uk/Fallbarrow** ONLINE MAP LAST MINUTE OFFERS

       £18.50–£27.00
       £318.00–£1059.00
       £552.00–£1379.00
       £232.00–£771.00
38 touring pitches

Fallbarrow is located in Bowness, on the shores of Lake Windermere. Boat launch facilities, picnic area, bar and deli. Use of swimming pool at White Cross Bay at additional charge. **directions** Please contact us for directions **open** 1 March to 14 January **payment** credit/debit cards, cash, cheques

General Leisure

WINDERMERE, Cumbria Map ref 5A3

SAT NAV LA12 8NR

Hill of Oaks Park
Tower Wood, Windermere LA12 8NR
t (015395) 31578 f (015395) 30431 e enquires@hillofoaks.co.uk
w **hillofoaks.co.uk** ONLINE MAP GUEST REVIEWS ONLINE BOOKING LAST MINUTE OFFERS

 (43) £24.00–£32.00
 (43) £24.00–£32.00
43 touring pitches

Award-winning Park located on the shores of Windermere. The park has a play area and nature walks through the woodland. Five jetties, boat launching and access to watersport activities. **directions** M6 jct 36, west on A590 towards Barrow and Newby Bridge. At roundabout turn right, onto A592. Park is approx 3 mls on left-hand side. **open** 1st March to Mid November **payment** credit/debit cards, cash, cheques

General 🕹️📷🐕🧺🎣💡☀️🚗💷🔌🚻🖥️ Leisure ▶️ ⛵ 👫 🚲 ♨️ ⛰️

WINDERMERE, Cumbria Map ref 5A3

SAT NAV LA23 1PA

Limefitt Park
Patterdale Road, Windermere, Cumbria LA23 1PA
t (01539) 569835 f (01539) 432848 e enquiries@southlakelandparks.co.uk
w **slholidays.co.uk** ONLINE MAP LAST MINUTE OFFERS

🚐 £337.00–£998.00
🏠 £208.00–£693.00

Limefitt is spectacularly located in one of Lakeland's most beautiful valleys capturing the very spirit of the Lake District National Park. Limefitt is a friendly place offering peace and tranquillity. **directions** Please contact us for directions **open** 1 March to 14 January **payment** credit/debit cards, cash, cheques

General 🕹️📷👣🐕🧺🎣💡☀️✖️ Leisure 👫 🚲 ♨️ 🍷 🔍 ⛰️

WINDERMERE, Cumbria Map ref 5A3

Park Cliffe Camping & Caravan Estate
Birks Road, Windermere LA23 3PG
t (015395) 31344 f (015395) 31971 e info@parkcliffe.co.uk
w **parkcliffe.co.uk** ONLINE BOOKING

 (70) £26.00–£30.50
 (70) £26.00–£30.50
⛺ (100) £21.00–£35.00
🚐 (3) £175.00–£625.00
70 touring pitches

Set in 25 acres of picturesque, unspoilt countryside in the heart of the Lake District, Park Cliffe offers visitors a tranquil, yet accessible, retreat from the hurly-burly of modern life. **directions** M6 jct 36, follow A590 towards Barrow. At Newby Bridge take A592 towards Windermere. After 3.6 miles turn right into Birks Road. Avoid Sat Nav. **open** 1 March to 11 November **payment** credit/debit cards, cash, cheques

General 📷👣🐕🧺🎣💡☀️🚗💷🔌🚻🖥️✖️ Leisure ▶️ 👫 🍷 🔍 ⛰️

WINDERMERE, Cumbria Map ref 5A3

SAT NAV LA23 1LF

White Cross Bay Holiday Park and Marina
Ambleside Road, Windermere, Cumbria LA23 1LF
t (01539) 569835 f (01539) 488704 e enquiries@southlakelandparks.co.uk
w **slholidays.co.uk/White-Cross-Bay** ONLINE MAP LAST MINUTE OFFERS

🚐 £382.00–£1226.00
🏠 £249.00–£803.00

White Cross Bay sits directly on the shores of lake Windermere south of Ambleside, fantastic facilities swimming pool, gym and sauna. Bar and restaurant onsite. **directions** Please contact us for directions **open** 1 March to 14 Jan **payment** credit/debit cards, cash, cheques

General 🕹️📷👣🐕🧺🎣💡☀️💷✖️ Leisure ▶️ 👫 🔍 🚲 🍷 🎵 🔍 ⛰️

BLACKPOOL, Lancashire Map ref 4A1

SAT NAV FY3 0AX

★★★★
HOLIDAY PARK

Newton Hall Holiday Park

Staining Road, Staining, Blackpool, Lancashire FY3 0AX
t (01253) 882512 f (01253) 893101 e reception@newtonhall.net
w **partingtons.com** ONLINE BOOKING

(33)   £182.00–£619.00

SPECIAL PROMOTIONS
Rebook within 28 days to receive 15% discount, 3 nights minimum stay.

Family park ideally situated in open countryside, 2.5 miles from Blackpool tower. Caravans and apartments & flats for hire. New club with regular live entertainment. Indoor swimming pool. Fishing pond. Indoor bowling. New enclosed ball game area. Winner of Lancashire & Blackpool Tourism Award 2008/09 & 2010/11.

open 1st March to 15th November
payment credit/debit cards, cash, cheques

directions M55 junction 4, 3rd exit. Right at 4th traffic lights past zoo. 3rd exit at roundabout. 1 mile on right Staining Rd. Park on right.

General ⬜ 📶 ⚡ 🏠 🐾 ☼ ♿ ✕ Leisure ➤ ∪ ⌒ ？ ♟ ♫ ◆ ⚲

BLACKPOOL, Lancashire Map ref 4A1

SAT NAV FY6 8NB

★★★★
HOLIDAY &
TOURING PARK

Windy Harbour Holiday Park

Windy Harbour Road, Singleton, Poulton Le Fylde FY6 8NB
t (01253) 883064 e info@windyharbour.net
w **partingtons.com** ONLINE BOOKING

🚐   £16.00–£25.00
🚙   £16.00–£25.00
(11)   £182.00–£619.00
130 touring pitches

SPECIAL PROMOTIONS
10% discount on 7 day touring holidays, rebook holiday within 28 days to receive 15% discount.

Situated on banks of River Wyre in the beautiful Fylde countryside. Family-run park with many facilities including club with family room, newly refurbished swimming pool, extensive outdoor play area, amusement arcade and shop. Very easy access from M55 motorway. Lancashire & Blackpool Tourism Award - Highly Commended 2009/2010.

open 1st March to 15th November
payment credit/debit cards, cash, cheques

directions From M6 onto M55 take jct 3 signposted Fleetwood (A585). At traffic lights go straight ahead onto Windy Harbour Road. The park is straight ahead.

General ⬜ 📶 ⚡ 🏠 🐾 ☼ ▦ 🚗 ♿ 🚰 📺 ✕ Leisure ➤ ∪ ⌒ ？ ♟ ♫ ◆ ⚲

CLITHEROE, Lancashire Map ref 4A1

SAT NAV BB7 4JJ

HOLIDAY PARK ★★★

£261.00–£458.00

Todber Holiday Park

Burnley Road, Gisburn, Clitheroe BB7 4JJ
t (01200) 445322 **e** enquiries@southlakelandparks.co.uk
w slholidays.co.uk/todber ONLINE MAP GUEST REVIEWS LAST MINUTE OFFERS

Todber overlooks Pendle Hill and the Ribble Valley. Todber is a short drive from the Yorkshire Dales, Skipton and Lancaster. There is a bar, children's play area and football field. **directions** Please contact us for directions **open** All year **payment** credit/debit cards, cash, cheques

General ⚲ ▣ ⏚ ⼧ ⿒ ⊞ ☼ ✕ Leisure ⼁ ∪ ⚵ ♩ ⵖ ⵟ ⚭ ⟁

FLEETWOOD, Lancashire Map ref 4A1

SAT NAV FY7 8JX

HOLIDAY, TOURING & CAMPING PARK ★★★

⊞ (13)   £182.00–£619.00

SPECIAL PROMOTIONS
Rebook within 28 days to receive 15% discount, 3 night minimum stay.

Broadwater Caravan Park

Fleetwood Road, Fleetwood FY7 8JX
t (01253) 872796 **f** (01253) 877133 **e** reception@broad-water.co.uk
w partingtons.com LAST MINUTE OFFERS

Family run caravan park, ideally situated for Cleveleys, Blackpool and Fleetwood. Licensed club, childrens room, pool, spa, sauna, playground, arcade. New Astraturf area for ball games. New for 2011 Bluetooth enabled music youth shelter on Play Park which has also been refurbished.

open March - November
payment credit/debit cards, cash, cheques

directions Please contact us for directions.

General ▣ ⏚ ⼦ ⟨ ☼ ☼ ⊙ Leisure ∪ ♩ ⚘ ⵟ ♫ ⚭ ⟁

HEYSHAM, Lancashire Map ref 5A3

SAT NAV LA3 2XA

HOLIDAY PARK ★★★

£144.00–£533.00

Ocean Edge Leisure Park, Heysham

Moneyclose Lane, Heysham, Morecambe LA3 2XA
t (01539) 569835 **f** (01524) 855884 **e** enquiries@southlakelandparks.co.uk
w slholidays.co.uk/Ocean-Edge ONLINE MAP LAST MINUTE OFFERS

Ocean Edge is close to the village of Heysham on the shores of Morecambe Bay overlooking the Irish Sea. Park facilities include a beer garden, café, indoor heated swimming pool. **directions** Please contact us for directions **open** 18 February to 3 January **payment** credit/debit cards, cash, cheques

General ⚲ ▣ ⏚ ⼧ ⿒ ⟨ ⟨ ☼ ⊟ ⊙ ✕ Leisure ⼁ ∪ ⚵ ♩ ⵖ ⵟ ♫ ⚭ ⟁

LANCASTER, Lancashire Map ref 5A3   SAT NAV LA2 9HH

New Parkside Farm Caravan Park, Lancaster
Denny Beck, Caton Road, Lancaster LA2 9HH
t (01524) 770723 **e** rosannesagar@hotmail.com

🚐 (36) £14.00–£16.00
🚎 (4) £14.00–£16.00
⛺ (5) £8.00–£13.00
45 touring pitches

Peaceful, family-run park on a working farm with extensive views of the Lune Valley and Ingleborough. Excellent base for exploring the unspoilt coast and countryside of North Lancashire. **directions** Leave M6 at junction 34, A683 east towards Caton/Kirkby Lonsdale, caravan park entrance 1 mile from motorway junction on the right (signposted). **open** March to October **payment** cash, cheques

General 🐕 ⛱ ☼ 🖭 🚻 🔌 🕀 ♿ **Leisure** 🏊

LYTHAM, Lancashire Map ref 4A1   SAT NAV PR4 3HN

Little Orchard Caravan Park
Shorrocks Barn, Back Lane, Weeton, Kirkham, Preston PR4 3HN
t (01253) 836658
w littleorchardcaravanpark.com GUEST REVIEWS

🚐 £17.50
⛺ (7) £14.50
45 touring pitches

Quiet family run setting overlooks woods, open fields and fruit orchard. Close to two coarse fisheries and trout lake. 45 hardstanding all-weather pitches. Ideal for mature people and quiet families. **directions** M55 junction 3 turn north Fleetwood A55 left Greenhalgh Lane T-junction turn right caravan park on first left. **open** 14th Feb to 1st Jan **payment** cash, cheques

General 🐕 ⛱ ☼ 🚻 🔌 🕀 ♿ **Leisure** ▶ ♻ 🏊

MORECAMBE, Lancashire Map ref 5A3   SAT NAV LA3 3DF

Regent Leisure Park
Westgate, Morecambe, Lancashire LA3 3DF
t (01539) 569835 **f** (01524) 832247 **e** enquiries@southlakelandparks.co.uk
w slholidays.co.uk ONLINE MAP LAST MINUTE OFFERS

🚐 £193.00–£612.00

Regents a few minutes from Morecambe and a 40 minute drive to the Lake District and Blackpool. Facilities include cabaret lounge, children's play area, indoor heated pool. **directions** Please contact us for directions **open** 1 March to 15 January **payment** credit/debit cards, cash, cheques

General 🎣 📺 ♿ 🐕 🚲 ⛱ ☼ 🖭 🕀 ✕ **Leisure** ▶ ♻ 🏊 ♿ 🍴 🎵 🔍 ⛰

MORECAMBE, Lancashire Map ref 5A3   SAT NAV LA4 4TQ

Venture Caravan Park
Langridge Way, Westgate, Morecambe LA4 4TQ
t (01524) 412986 **f** (01524) 422029 **e** mark@venturecaravanpark.co.uk
w venturecaravanpark.co.uk

🚐 (56) £17.00–£30.00
🚎 (56) £17.00–£30.00
⛺ £14.00–£30.00
🚍 (15) £160.00–£405.00
56 touring pitches

Family-run park, 0.75 miles from the sea. Local amenities and restaurants just a walk away. Easy access to the Lake District, Yorkshire Dales and Blackpool. **directions** Please contact us for directions **open** All year **payment** credit/debit cards, cash, cheques

General 📺 🐕 🚲 ⛱ ☼ 🚻 🔌 🕀 ✕ **Leisure** ▶ ♻ 🏊 🍴 🎵 🔍 ⛰

SCARISBRICK, Lancashire Map ref 4A1 SAT NAV L40 8HB

Hurlston Hall Country Caravan Park
Hurlston Lane, Scarisbrick, Ormskirk L40 8HB
t (01704) 841064 f (01704) 841700 e enquiries@hurlstonhallcaravanpark.co.uk
w **hurlstonhall.co.uk** ONLINE MAP

🚐 (30)   £17.00–£20.00
🚐 (10)   £17.00–£20.00
20 touring pitches

Attractively landscaped in 11 acres of parkland. Close to the popular holiday resort of Southport, Access to coarse fishing lake, 18 hole golf course, leisure club, with Bistro and Bars. **directions** Hurlston Hall is situated on the A570, west of the historical market town of Ormskirk and ten minutes from the shops and attractions of Southport **payment** credit/debit cards, cash, cheques

General 🖥🛢🦮☼🚐⚡🅿🚻✕ Leisure ▶🏊♨🍽

BURY, Greater Manchester Map ref 4B1 SAT NAV BL8 1BN

Burrs Country Park Caravan Club Site
Woodhill Road, Bury, Lancashire BL8 1BN
t (0161) 761 0489 e enquiries@caravanclub.co.uk
w **caravanclub.co.uk**

THE
CARAVAN
CLUB

🚐 (85)   £15.90–£35.51
🚐 (85)   £15.90–£35.51
85 touring pitches

On a historic mill site, Burrs has much to offer, including a relaxing river and countryside walks. The country park offers activities such as climbing, abseiling and canoeing. **directions** From A676 (signposted Ramsbottom), follow signs for Burrs Country Park. **open** All year **payment** credit/debit cards, cash, cheques

General 🖥🚱🦮🦮🖥🅿⚡🅿🆗

OLDHAM, Greater Manchester Map ref 4B1 SAT NAV OL3 5UN

Moorlands Caravan Park
Ripponden Road, Denshaw, Oldham OL3 5UN
t (01457) 874348 e moorlandscp@aol.com
w **moorlandscp.co.uk** ONLINE MAP

🚐 (29)   £14.00–£30.00
🚐 (16)   £14.00–£30.00
△ (20)   £8.00–£60.00
🛏 (1)   £35.00–£40.00
16 touring pitches

Situated on the Pennine moors of Saddleworth, ideal for Walkers, Horse Riders, or just a family stay. Within half a mile of the Pennine Way and Pennine Bridal Way. **directions** Junction 22 of the M62, 2 miles in the direction of Saddleworth. **open** All year **payment** credit/debit cards, cash, cheques

General 🖥🦮🦮☼🖥🚐⚡🅿🚻🆗 Leisure ▶♨♨

Looking for something else?

You can also buy a copy of our popular guide 'Self Catering' including self-catering holiday homes, approved caravan holiday homes, boat accommodation and holiday cottage agencies in England 2012.

Now available in good bookshops and online at
visitbritainshop.com   **£8.99**

ROCHDALE, Greater Manchester Map ref 4B1

Hollingworth Lake Caravan Park

Roundhouse Farm, Hollingworth Lake, Littleborough OL15 0AT
t (01706) 378661

(30)	£10.00–£16.00
(10)	£10.00–£16.00
(10)	£8.00–£16.00

50 touring pitches

A popular, five-acre park adjacent to Hollingworth Lake, at the foot of the Pennines, within easy reach of many local attractions. Backpackers walking the Pennine Way are welcome at this family-run park. Hardstanding and grass area. Excellent train service into Manchester Victoria. 20 minutes from Littleborough/Smithybridge.

open All year
payment cash, cheques

directions From M62. Jct 21 Milnrow. Follow Hollingworth Lake Country Park signs to the Fishermans Inn/The Wine Press. Take Rakewood Road then 2nd on right.

General ⬚ 🐾 📶 ☼ 🖥 📞 ☕ 🚻 Leisure ∪ ⚓

AINSDALE, Merseyside Map ref 4A1

Willowbank Holiday Home and Touring Park

Coastal Road, Ainsdale, Southport PR8 3ST
t (01704) 571566 **e** info@willowbankcp.co.uk
w willowbankcp.co.uk ONLINE MAP GUEST REVIEWS

(87)	£13.50–£18.30
(87)	£13.50–£18.30

87 touring pitches

SPECIAL PROMOTIONS
Please note we do not let out Holiday Homes.

Willowbank Holiday Home & Touring Park offers an easily accessible location convenient for Southport with well maintained modern facilities in a quiet and relaxed atmosphere. The park is open from 1st March to 31st January for Holiday Homes, Touring Caravans, Motor Homes and Trailer Tents.

open 1st March to 31st January
payment credit/debit cards, cash

directions From M6 jct 26 for M58, from the M62 jct for M57. A5036 & A5207 leading to A565 towards Southport, RAF Woodvale, Coastal Rd.

General ⬚ 🐕 📶 ☼ 🖥 ♿ 📞 ☕ 🚻 Leisure ► ∪ 🚲 ⚓

THURSTASTON, Merseyside Map ref 4A2

SAT NAV CH61 0HN

Wirral Country Park Caravan Club Site

Station Road, Thurstaston, Wirral CH61 0HN
t (0151) 648 5228 **e** enquiries@caravanclub.co.uk
w caravanclub.co.uk

TOURING PARK

⚐ (93) £14.30–£32.79
🚐 (93) £14.30–£32.79
93 touring pitches

The Wirral is a peninsula of great beauty with unspoilt green space and wonderful sea views. The site has several flat grassy pitching areas separated by trees. **directions** A540 in the village of Thurstaston, heading north from Heswall, turn left into Station Road at the sign stating Wirral Country Park Centre. **open** March to November **payment** credit/debit cards, cash, cheques

General 🖥 ⚲ 🐕 🛍 🏠 🔄 🔌 🛁 🚻 🚐 Leisure ⚑ 🏊

Bonus CD inside

enjoyEngland.com

BED & BREAKFAST 2012
England's quality-assessed guest accommodation

OFFICIAL TOURIST BOARD GUIDE

Looking for something else?

You can also buy a copy of our popular 'B&B' guide including guest accommodation, B&B's, guest houses, farmhouses, inns, and campus and hostel accommodation in England 2012.

Now available in good bookshops and online at
visitbritainshop.com   **£8.99**

Ratings you can trust

Wherever you see a quality rating sign, you can be sure that one of VisitEngland's professional assessors has been there before you, checking the place on your behalf – and will be there again, because every place with a national rating is assessed annually.

The star ratings reflect the quality that you're looking for when booking accommodation. All properties have to meet an extensive list of minimum requirements to take part in the scheme. From there, increased levels of quality apply. For instance, you'll find acceptable quality at one star, good quality at three star and exceptional quality at five star establishments.

Quite simply, the more stars, the higher the overall level of quality you can expect to find. Establishments at higher rating levels also have to meet some additional requirements for facilities.

Many self-catering establishments have a range of accommodation units in the building or on the site, and in some cases the individual units may have different star ratings. In such cases, the entry shows the range available.

VisitEngland's unique Gold Awards are given in recognition of exceptional quality in self-catering accommodation. The assessors make recommendations for Gold Awards during the assessments. They will look at the quality provided in all areas, in particular housekeeping, hospitality, bedrooms and bathrooms, to see if it meets the highest quality for the star level achieved.

While star ratings are based on a combination of quality, range of facilities and level of service offered, Gold Awards are based solely on quality.

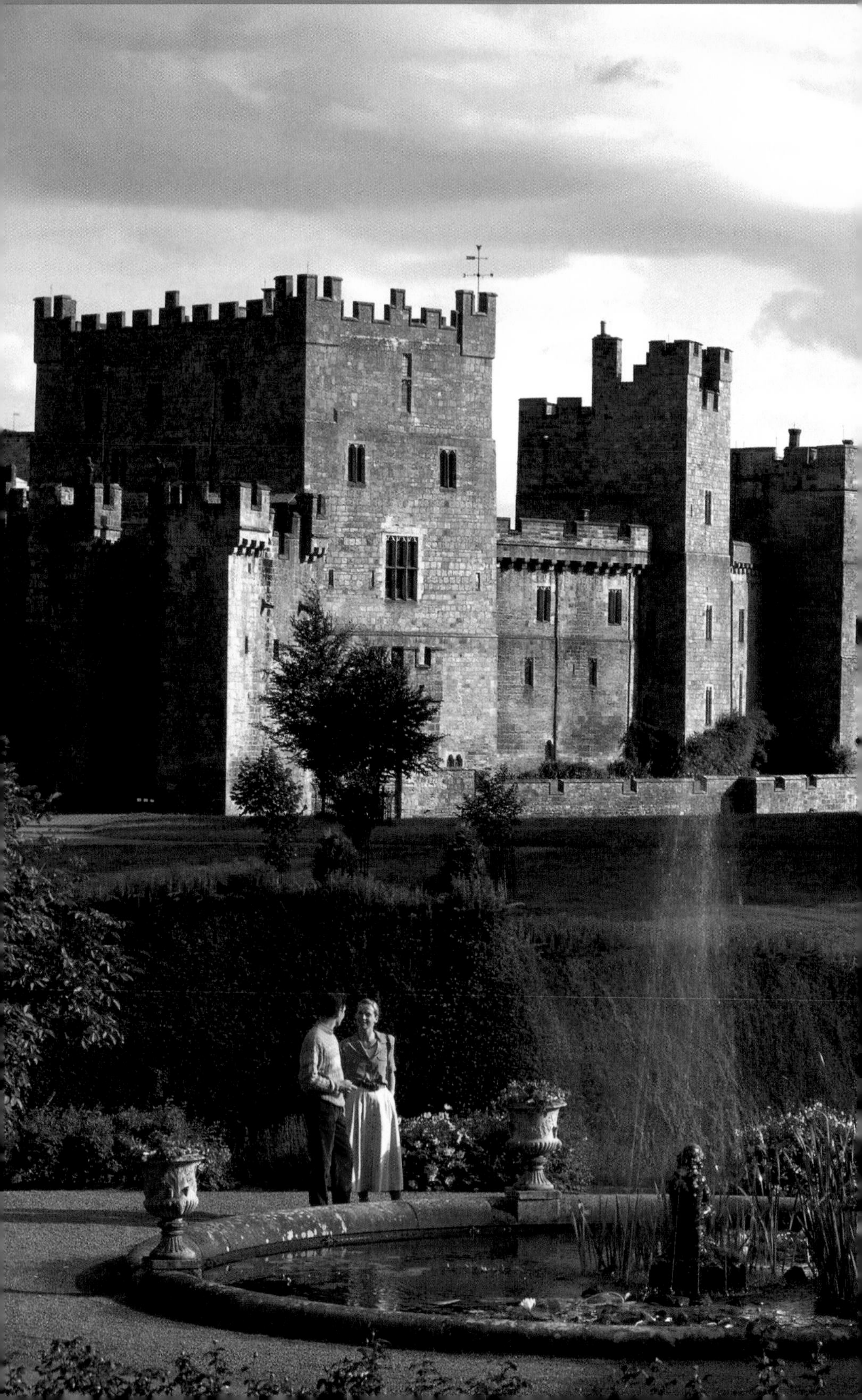

North East

County Durham, Northumberland,
Tees Valley, Tyne & Wear

It may only consist of County Durham, Northumberland, Tees Valley and Tyne & Wear but the North East certainly doesn't do things in half measures. From the breathtaking Northumberland coast with its majestic castles to the the tranquil North Pennines, this compact region is bursting with turbulent history and stunning scenery.

City slickers fear not, Durham delivers historic architecture, whereas Newcastle Gateshead buzzes with cultural cool and legendary nightlife.

History and Heritage

Budding historians should take a deep breath before heading to the North East – never has so much history been squeezed into such a compact area. There's nearly 2000 years of Roman history to explore at Hadrian's Wall, including the fascinating forts at Vindolanda; a multitude of majestic castles (including Bamburgh and Alnwick) to take in along the coast; as well as a pilgrimage to England's first Christian community at The Holy Island off Lindisfarne. Or immerse yourself in fascinating regional history at The Beamish Museum and The Great North Museum.

Arts and Culture

Anthony Gormley's The Angel of the North welcomes you to the North East's thriving cultural scene. Enjoy challenging conceptual art at the Baltic Centre in NewcastleGateshead, or fantastic exhibitions at MIMA (Middlesbrough Institute for Modern Art). See the Great Bard's work bought to life at Newcastle's Theatre Royal, the regional home to the Royal Shakespeare Company. And the iconic Sir Norman Foster-designed Sage Gateshead always comes up trumps when it comes to live music. Or dress up for an evening at Darlington's Edwardian Civic Theatre.

Shopping

With so much variety on offer, the North East is any shopper's dream. Durham City has stylish boutiques and quirky craft shops together with top-name retailers whilst Durham Market still retains its Victorian charm. Eldon Square, in the heart of Newcastle City Centre, and Gateshead's Metrocentre offer bags of choice in designer and high-street fashions. Stockton-on-Tees hosts one of the North East's largest outdoor markets. Whilst Yarm offers chic boutiques in mellow Georgian buildings, a charming and relaxing shopping experience.

Sports

Experience the thrill of Premiership football by catching a beautiful game at Newcastle or Sunderland. If the thwack of leather against willow is more your thing, then head to Durham's Cricket Ground for a one day international. Fashionistas might prefer dressing up for Ladies Day at Newcastle Racecourse or lounging on the banks of the River Wear for Durham's Regatta. The Tees Barrage white water course is a world-class sports facility with specially stabilised flat water for the novice and superb white water for the expert.

Music and Nightlife

With local lads The Futureheads and Maximo Park rocking the socks off the world's scenesters and Sting and Cheryl Cole entertaining the masses, the North East is a musical hotbed. For a legendary night out hit NewcastleGateshead – warm up at the Quayside bars before clubbing into the early hours. Middlesbrough has a vibrant club scene, it was here the Rolling Stones played their first gig outside London in 1963, and Middlesbrough Music Live is one of the biggest free music festivals in the UK.

Food and Drink

With the North Sea and endless countryside, it's no wonder the North East is bursting with gourmet chefs and artisan producers. Sample local delicacies like Lindisfarne Oysters and Craster smoked kippers before dining in style at Kenny Atkinson's – Finalist of the Great British Menu –The Orangery at Rockliffe Hall. Wash it all down with a bottle of Newky Brown at Ouseburn Valley or a cup of tea at Howick Hall Gardens, the home of Earl Grey.

Family Fun

If your kids want to build sandcastles on golden beaches and re-enact their own battles in dramatic castles perched high on the dunes, then the North East is for them. If you want them exhausted but deliriously happy, try seal-spotting around the Farne islands, surfing off Tynemouth and coasteering along the Northumberland coastline.

Handy Hints

Stars in your eyes - With the lowest levels of light pollution in England, Kielder Water is prefect for star gazing. Pick a spot for your blanket by the lake and count those shooting stars.

Bookworms - To warm your cockles around open fires in winter, and browse thousands of second-hand books, head to Barter Books in Alnwick.

Views - For arguably the best photo point along Hadrian's Wall climb to Steel Rigg. Steel Rigg is located adjacent to the monument and offers outstanding views of the Wall.

Marvel At - Head down to the Gateshead Millennium Bridge at tilt time to see the world's first and only tilting bridge in action. Middlesbrough has Transporter Bridge, a masterpiece of engineering.

OUT & ABOUT IN THE NORTH EAST

Day 5 - Islands in the Stream

- Visit the Holy Isle of Lindisfarne
- Sample the world-famous Lindisfarne Oysters
- Go seal-spotting around the Farne islands off the Northumberland coast

Day 1 - Sage Advice

- Engage with contemporary art at the Baltic Centre
- Take in a performance at the Sage Gateshead
- Hit the Quayside bars in NewcastleGateshead for a night to remember

Day 2 - Fly Away

- Check out Anthony Gormley's Angel of the North sculpture
- Go for a tour around St. James' Park – home to the Magpies
- For great views and fine dining head to SIX, the Baltic Centre's top floor restaurant

Day 6 - Surfin' Bird

- Learn how to catch a wave at the Rise Surf School in Tynemouth
- Experienced surfers should head to Saltburn by Sea for more powerful breaks
- Tuck into some award-winning fish and chips at Colmans in South Shields

Day 3 - Durham

- Explore Durham's cobbled streets and riverside cafés
- Admire the striking architecture at Durham Cathedral and Norman Castle
- Enjoy fine-dining at The White Room at Seaham Hall Hotel

Day 7 - Blown Away

- Learn how to blow glass at the National Glass Centre in Sunderland
- Relax in Sunderland's Winter Gardens
- Watch Shakespeare's word come to life at Newcastle's Theatre Royal

Day 4 - Another Brick in the Wall

- Follow in the footsteps of the Roman army as you walk along Hadrian's Wall
- Explore the Roman forts and archaeological finds at Vindolanda
- Explore an interactive Hadrian's Wall at the Great North Museum

Where to Go

 Attractions with this sign participate in the **Places of Interest Quality Assurance Scheme**.

 Attractions with this sign participate in the **Visitor Attraction Quality Assurance Scheme**.

Both schemes recognise high standards in all aspects of the visitor experience (see page 6)

ENTERTAINMENT & CULTURE

Bailiffgate Museum
Alnwick, Northumberland NE66 1LX
(01665) 605847
www.bailiffgatemuseum.co.uk
Bailiffgate Museum brings to life the people and places of North Northumberland in exciting interactive style.

BALTIC Centre for Contemporary Art
Gateshead, Tyne and Wear NE8 3BA
(01914) 781810
www.balticmill.com
BALTIC is the biggest gallery of its kind in the world - presenting a dynamic, diverse and international programme of contemporary visual art.

Beamish Museum
County Durham DH9 0RG
(01913) 704000
www.beamish.org.uk
Beamish - The Living Museum of the North, is an open air museum vividly recreating life in the North East in the early 1800s and 1900s.

Discovery Museum
Newcastle-upon-Tyne, Tyne and Wear NE1 4JA
(01912) 326789
www.twmuseums.org.uk/discovery
Discovery Museum offers a wide variety of experiences for all the family to enjoy.

DLI Museum and Durham Art Gallery
Durham, County Durham DH1 5TU
(01913) 842214
www.durham.gov.uk/dli
Museum tells the 200-year story of Durham's famous regiment. Art Gallery has changing exhibition programme.

Great North Museum: Hancock
Newcastle-upon-Tyne, Tyne and Wear NE2 4PT
(01912) 226765
www.greatnorthmuseum.org
See major new displays showing the wonder of the animal and plant kingdoms, spectacular objects from the Ancient Greeks and a planetarium and a life-size T-Rex.

Hartlepool Art Gallery
Hartlepool, Tees Valley TS24 7EQ
(01429) 869706
www.hartlepool.gov.uk/info/100009/ leisure_and_culture/1506/ hartlepool_art_gallery/1/3
Former church building also includes the TIC and a bell tower viewing platform looking over Hartlepool.

Hartlepool's Maritime Experience
Tees Valley TS24 0XZ
(01429) 860077
www.hartlepoolsmaritimeexperience. com
An authentic reconstruction of an 18th Century seaport.

Hatton Gallery
Newcastle-upon-Tyne Tyne and Wear NE1 7RU
(01912) 226059
www.twmuseums.org.uk/hatton
Temporary exhibitions of contemporary and historical art. Permanent display of Kurt Schwitters' Merzbarn.

Head of Steam Darlington Railway Museum
Tees Valley DL3 6ST
(01325) 460532
www.darlington.gov.uk/Culture/ headofsteam/welcome.htm
Restored 1842 station housing a collection of exhibits relating to railways in the North East of England, including Stephenson's Locomotion, call for details of events.

Hexham Old Gaol
Northumberland NE46 3NH
(01434) 652349
www.tynedaleheritage.org
Tour the Old Gaol, 1330AD, by glass lift. Meet the gaoler, see a Reiver raid and try on costumes.

Killhope, The North of England Lead Mining Museum
Bishop Auckland, County Durham DL13 1AR
(01388) 537505
www.killhope.org.uk
The North East's Small Visitor Attraction of the Year and the most complete lead mining site in Great Britain.

Laing Art Gallery
Newcastle-upon-Tyne
Tyne and Wear NE1 8AG
(01912) 327734
www.twmuseums.org.uk/laing
The Laing Art Gallery is home to an important collection of 18th and 19th century painting, which is shown alongside temporary exhibitions of historic and contemporary art.

Locomotion: The National Railway Museum at Shildon
Shildon, County Durham
DL4 1PQ
(01388) 777999
www.nrm.org.uk/locomotion
The first National Museum in the North East. Free admission. View over 60 vehicles, children's play area and interactive displays.

mima
Middlesbrough, Tees Valley
TS1 2AZ
(01642) 726720
www.visitmima.com
mima, Middlesbrough Institute of Modern Art, is a £14.2m landmark new gallery in the heart of Middlesbrough. mima showcases an international programme of fine art and applied art from the 1900s to the present day.

Museum of Hartlepool
Hartlepool, Tees Valley
TS24 0XZ
(01429) 860077
www.hartlepoolsmaritimeexperience.com
Hartlepool Museum, situated beside Hartlepool Historic Quay, includes local historical exhibits, PSS Wingfield Castle, exhibitions and the original lighthouse light.

Preston Hall Museum and Park
Stockton-on-Tees, Tees Valley
TS18 3RH
(01642) 527375
www.stockton.gov.uk/museums
A Georgian country house set in beautiful parkland overlooking the River Tees. A Museum of social history with a recreated Victorian street and working craftsmen.

RNLI Grace Darling Museum
Bamburgh, Northumberland
NE69 7AE
(01668) 214910
www.rnli.org.uk/gracedarling
A museum dedicated to Grace Darling and her family, as well as all those who Save Lives at Sea.

Segedunum Roman Fort, Baths and Museum
Wallsend, Tyne and Wear
NE28 6HR
(01912) 369347
www.twmuseums.org.uk/segedunum
Segedunum Roman Fort is the gateway to Hadrian's Wall. Explore the excavated fort site, visit reconstructions of a Roman bath house, learn about the history of the area in the museum and enjoy the view from the 35 metre viewing tower.

The Bowes Museum
Barnard Castle, County Durham
DL12 8NP
(01833) 690606
www.thebowesmuseum.org.uk
The Bowes Museum houses a collection of outstanding European fine and decorative arts and offers an acclaimed exhibition programme, alongside special events and children's activities.

Vindolanda (Chesterholm) Hadrian's Wall
Bardon Mill, Northumberland
NE47 7JN
(01434) 344277
www.vindolanda.com
Visitors may inspect the remains of the Roman fort and settlement, see its extraordinary finds in the superb museum. Full-scale replicas of Roman buildings. Please ring to check winter opening times.

FAMILY FUN

Centre for Life
Newcastle-upon-Tyne
Tyne and Wear NE1 4EP
(01912) 438210
www.life.org.uk
The Centre for Life is an award-winning science centre where imaginative exhibitions, interactive displays and special events promote greater understanding of science and provoke curiosity in the world around us.

Nature's World
Middlesbrough, Tees Valley
TS5 7YN
(01642) 594895
www.naturesworld.org.uk
Nature's World now has a new Adventure Arena with assault course, climbing walls, pedal go-karts and tractors.

HERITAGE

Arbeia Roman Fort and Museum
South Shields, Tyne and Wear
NE33 2BB
(01914) 561369
www.twmuseums.org.uk/arbeia
Arbeia is the best reconstruction of a Roman fort in Britain and offers visitors a unique insight into the every day life of the Roman army, from the soldier in his barrack room to the commander in his luxurious house.

Bamburgh Castle
Northumberland NE69 7DF
(01668) 214515
www.bamburghcastle.com
A spectacular castle with fantastic coastal views. The stunning Kings Hall and Keep house collections of armour, artwork, porcelain and furniture.

Belsay Hall, Castle and Gardens
Northumberland NE20 0DX
(01661) 881636
www.english-heritage.org.uk/belsay
With so much to see and do, a trip to Belsay is one of the best value family days out in North East England. Stunning gardens, beautiful acrchitecture and magnificent views all in one place.

Durham Castle
County Durham DH1 3RW
(01913) 343800
www.durhamcastle.com
Durham Castle is part of the Durham City World Heritage Site. Entrance by guided tour only. Opening can vary - please telephone 0191 334 3800 to check days open and guided tour times.

HMS Trincomalee
Hartlepool, Tees Valley
TS24 0XZ
(01429) 223193
www.hms-trincomalee.co.uk
HMS Trincomalee, built in 1817, is one of the oldest ship afloat in Europe. Come aboard for a unique experience of Navy life 2 centuries ago.

Housesteads Roman Fort
Haydon Bridge, Northumberland NE47 6NN
(01434) 344363
www.english-heritage.org.uk/daysout/properties/housesteads-roman-fort-hadrians-wall
The most complete example of a British Roman fort, Housesteads features magnificent ruins and stunning views of the countryside surrounding Hadrian's Wall.

Kielder Castle Forest Park Centre
Northumberland NE48 1ER
(01434) 250209
www.forestry.gov.uk/
northeastengland
Features include forest shop, information centre, tearoom and exhibitions. Bike hire available.

Lindisfarne Priory
Holy Island, Northumberland TD15 2RX
(01289) 389200
www.english-heritage.org.uk/
lindisfarnepriory
Take in panoramic views of the Northumbrian coast, unpack a picnic in the priory grounds, and take a break from the hustle and bustle of life.

National Glass Centre
Sunderland, Tyne and Wear SR6 0GL
(01915) 155555
www.nationalglasscentre.com
Enjoy an ever-changing programme of exhibitions, live glass blowing, and banqueting and a stunning restaurant overlooking the River Wear.

Raby Castle
Staindrop County Durham DL2 3AH
(01833) 660202
www.rabycastle.com
Home of Lord Barnard's family since 1626, includes a 200 acre deer park, gardens, carriage collection, adventure playground, shop and tearoom.

Saltburn Smugglers Heritage Centre
Saltburn-by-the-Sea, Tees Valley TS12 1HF
(01287) 625252
www.redcar-cleveland.gov.uk/
museums
Step back into Saltburn's past and experience the authentic sights, sounds and smells.

Warkworth Castle
Warkworth, Northumberland NE65 0UJ
(01665) 711423
www.english-heritage.org.uk/
warkworthcastle
Set in a quaint Northumberland town, this hill-top fortress and hermitage offers a fantastic family day out.

NATURE & WILDLIFE

Adventure Valley
Durham, County Durham DH1 5SG
(01913) 868291
www.adventurevalley.co.uk
Adventure Valley is Durham's newest day out! Split into 6 Play Zones (with 3 under cover), you'll find the very best in family fun come rain or shine.

Hall Hill Farm
Durham, County Durham DH7 0TA
(01388) 731333
www.hallhillfarm.co.uk
Award-winning farm attraction set in attractive countryside, see and touch the animals at close quarters.

High Force Waterfall
Middleton-in-Teesdale County Durham DL12 0XH
(01833) 640209
www.rabycastle.com/high_force.htm
The most majestic of the waterfalls on the River Tees.

Hamsterley Forest
Bishop Auckland County Durham DL13 3NL
(01388) 488312
www.forestry.gov.uk/
northeastengland
A 5,000 acre mixed woodland open to the public all year.

Saltholme Wildlife Reserve and Discovery Park
Middlesbrough, Tees Valley TS2 1TU
(01642) 546625
www.rspb.org.uk/reserves/guide/s/
saltholme
Saltholme is an amazing wildlife experience in the Tees Valley.

WWT Washington Wetland Centre
Washington, Tyne and Wear NE38 8LE
(01914) 165454
www.wwt.org.uk/visit/washington
45 hectares of wetland, woodland and wildlife reserve. Home to wildfowl, insects and flora with lake-side hides, wild bird feeding station, waterside cafe, picnic areas, sustainable garden, playground and events calendar.

Events 2012

Bishop Auckland Food Festival
Bishop Auckland
www.bishopaucklandfoodfestival.co.uk
April

Tees Valley Garden Show
Stockton on Tees
www.tgshow.co.uk
April - May

Evolution Festival
Newcastle
www.evolutionfestival.co.uk
May

Eat! NewcstleGateshead
NewcastleGateshead
www.newcastlegateshead.com/2138/Food_Festival.html
June - July

Durham Folk Party
Durham
www.communigate.co.uk/ne/durhamfolkparty
July

Gateshead Summer Flower Show
Gateshead
www.gateshead.gov.uk/summerflowershow
July

Haydon Bridge Beer Festival
Haydon Bridge
www.haydonbeerfestival.co.uk
July

Middlesbrough's Mega Mela! Weekend
Middlesbrough
visitmiddlesbrough.com/mela
July

Billingham International Folklore Festival
Billingham
www.billinghamfestival.co.uk
August

Alnwick Beer Festival
Alnwick
www.alnwickbeerfestival.co.uk
September

Hexham Abbey Festival
Hexham
www.hexhamabbey.org.uk/festival
September - October

Wunderbar Festival
Newcastle-upon-Tyne
www.newcastlegateshead.com/events/46010/Wunderbar_Festival.html
October - November

Tourist Information Centres

When you arrive at your destination, visit an Official Partner Tourist Information Centre for quality assured help with accommodation and information about local attractions and events, or email your request before you go. To find a Tourist Information Centre by region look at http://www.enjoyengland.com under Destination Finder.

ALNWICK	2 The Shambles	01665 510665	alnwick.tic@northumberland.gov.uk
AMBLE	Queen Street Car Park	01665 712313	amble.tic@northumberland.gov.uk
BARNARD CASTLE	Woodleigh	01833 690909	tourism@teesdale.gov.uk
BELLINGHAM	Station Yard	01434 220616	bellinghamtic@btconnect.com
BERWICK-UPON-TWEED	106 Marygate	01289 330733	berwick.tic@northumberland.gov.uk
BISHOP AUCKLAND	Town Hall Ground Floor	01388 604922	bishopauckland.touristinfo@durham.gov.uk
CORBRIDGE	Hill Street	01434 632815	corbridgetic@btconnect.com
CRASTER	Craster Car Park	01665 576007	craster.tic@northumberland.gov.uk
DARLINGTON	13 Horsemarket	01325 388666	tic@darlington.gov.uk
DURHAM	2 Millennium Place	0191 384 3720	touristinfo@durhamcity.gov.uk
GATESHEAD	Central Library	0191 433 8420	tic@gateshead.gov.uk

GATESHEAD	The Sage Gateshead	0191 478 4222	tourism@gateshead.gov.uk
GUISBOROUGH	Priory Grounds	01287 633801	guisborough_tic@redcar-cleveland.gov.uk
HALTWHISTLE	Railway Station	01434 322002	haltwhistletic@btconnect.com
HARTLEPOOL	Hartlepool Art Gallery	01429 869706	hpooltic@hartlepool.gov.uk
HEXHAM	Wentworth Car Park	01434 652220	hexham.tic@northumberland.gov.uk
MIDDLESBROUGH	(PO Box 69)	01642 729700	tic@middlesbrough.gov.uk
MORPETH	The Chantry	01670 500700	morpeth.tic@northumberland.gov.uk
NEWCASTLE -UPON-TYNE	Guildhall	0191 288 8000	tourist.info@newcastle.gov.uk
NEWCASTLE-UPON-TYNE	Newcastle Information Centre	0191 277 8000	tourist.info@newcastle.gov.uk
NORTH SHIELDS	Unit 18	0191 2005895	ticns@northtyneside.gov.uk
ONCE BREWED	Northumberland National Park Centre	01434 344396	tic.oncebrewed@nnpa.org.uk
PETERLEE	4 Upper Yoden Way	0191 586 4450	touristinfo@peterlee.gov.uk
REDCAR	West Terrace	01642 471921	redcar_tic@redcar-cleveland.gov.uk
ROTHBURY	Northumberland National Park Centre	01669 620887	tic.rothbury@nnpa.org.uk
SALTBURN by sea	3 Station Buildings	01287 622422	saltburn_tic@redcar-cleveland.gov.uk
SEAHOUSES	Seafield Car Park	01665 720884	seahouses.tic@northumberland.gov.uk
SOUTH SHIELDS	South Shields Museum & Gallery	0191 454 6612	museum.tic@southtyneside.gov.uk
SOUTH SHIELDS	(AMPHITHEATRE) Sea Road	0191 455 7411	foreshore.tic@southtyneside.gov.uk
STANHOPE	Durham Dales Centre	01388 527650	durham.dales.centre@durham.gov.uk
STOCKTON-ON-TEES	High Streey	01642 528130	touristinformation@stockton.gov.uk
SUNDERLAND	50 Fawcett Street	0191 553 2000	tourist.info@sunderland.gov.uk
WHITLEY BAY	Park Road	0191 2008532	Susan.clark@northtyneside.gov.uk
WOOLER	Wooler TIC, The Cheviot Centre	01668 282123	woolerTIC@berwick-upon-tweed.gov.uk

Regional Contacts and Information

Log on to the North East England website at **www.visitnortheastengland.com** for further information on accommodation, attractions, events and special offers throughout the region. A range of free information is available to download from the website.

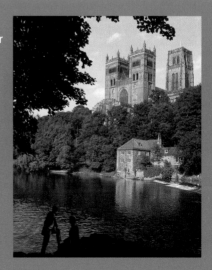

Where to Stay

Entries appear alphabetically by town name in each county. A key to symbols appears on page 6. Maps start on page 298. Further listings of VisitEngland assessed accommodation appear on the CD at the back of this guide.

DURHAM, Co Durham Map ref 5C2 — SAT NAV DH1 1TL

🚐 (76)   £15.30–£35.51
🚐 (76)   £15.30–£35.51
76 touring pitches

Grange Caravan Club Site

Meadow Lane, Durham, County Durham DH1 1TL
t (01913) 844778 **e** enquiries@caravanclub.co.uk
w **caravanclub.co.uk**

CARAVAN CLUB

Within easy reach of the City of Durham, a city steeped in history with panoramic views. A visit to Durham Catherdal and Castle is a must. **directions** A1(M) jct 62, A690 towards Durham. Turn right after 50 miles. Signposted Maureen Terrace and brown caravan sign. **open** All year **payment** credit/debit cards, cash, cheques

General 🗑 📶 🐕 📦 🌳 ☼ 🔌 🚰 🚻   Leisure ⛰

HAMSTERLEY COLLIERY, Co Durham Map ref 5C2 — SAT NAV NE17 7RT

🚐 (31)   £12.00–£1500.00
🚐 (6)   £12.00–£1500.00
⛺ (6)   £8.00–£15.00
31 touring pitches

Byreside Caravan Site

Hamsterley Colliery, Newcastle upon Tyne NE17 7RT
t (01207) 560280 **f** (01207) 560280 **e** byresidecaravansite@hotmail.co.uk
w **byresidecaravansite.co.uk** ONLINE MAP

A small, secluded family-run site on a working farm. Ideally situated for visiting Durham, Newcastle and Northumberland. Adjacent to Derwent Walk ideal for walkers and cyclists. **directions** From A1 at Swalwell follow A694 towards Consett. Turn left onto B6310 towards Medomsley. Turn right towards High Westwood. 1/2 mile on right hand side. **open** All year **payment** credit/debit cards, cash, cheques

General 🐕 📦 🌳 ☼ 🚲 🔌 🚰 🚻

Looking for something else?

You can also buy a copy of our popular guide 'Hotels' including country house and town house hotels, metro and budget hotels, serviced apartments and restaurants with rooms in England 2012. Now available in good bookshops and online at **visitbritainshop.com**   **£7.99**

STOCKTON-ON-TEES, Co Durham Map ref 5C3

SAT NAV TS18 2QW

White Water Caravan Club Park

Tees Barrage, Stockton-on-Tees TS18 2QW
t (01642) 634880 e enquiries@caravanclub.co.uk
w **caravanclub.co.uk**

THE
CARAVAN
CLUB

🚐 (115) £12.50–£30.80
🚃 (115) £12.50–£30.80
115 touring pitches

Pleasantly landscaped site. White-water canoeing and rafting course. Teesside Park for shopping, restaurants, cinema and bowling. Birdwatching and walking. **directions** Come off the A66 Teesside Park. Follow Teesdale sign, go over Tees Barrage Bridge, turn right. Site 200 yds on the left. **open** All year **payment** credit/debit cards, cash, cheques

General 🖥 🐕 🛁 🍴 ☼ ▦ 🔌 🕐 🚻 🆗 Leisure ► 🚣 🎣 ⛰

BAMBURGH, Northumberland Map ref 5C1

SAT NAV NE70 7JT

Kaims Country Park

Bradford House, Bamburgh NE70 7JT
t (01668) 213432 f (01668) 213838 e info@kaimscountrypark.com
w **kaimscountrypark.com**

🚐 (80) £22.00–£27.00
🚃 (80) £22.00–£27.00
80 touring pitches

Beautiful walking country, beaches, castles. Close to Bamburgh, Seahouses, Wooler and Cheviot Hills. Pre-booking advised during school holidays. Open March to January. Kaims Country Park is signposted from the B1341 (brown tourist signs), static holiday caravans for sale.

open Open 9th March/9th January
payment credit/debit cards, cash, cheques

directions Please contact us for directions

General 🖥 🐾 🐕 🛁 🛁 🍴 ☼ 🔌 🕐 🚻 ✕ Leisure ⛰

Looking for something else?

You can also buy a copy of our popular guide 'Self Catering' including self-catering holiday homes, approved caravan holiday homes, boat accommodation and holiday cottage agencies in England 2012.

Now available in good bookshops and online at
visitbritainshop.com   **£8.99**

BAMBURGH, Northumberland Map ref 5C1

SAT NAV NE70 7EE

Waren Caravan and Camping Park

Waren Mill, Bamburgh, Northumberland NE70 7EE
t (01668) 214366 f (01668) 214224 e waren@meadowhead.co.uk
w **meadowhead.co.uk** ONLINE MAP GUEST REVIEWS LAST MINUTE OFFERS

🚐 (144)	£14.00–£24.00
🚐 (144)	£14.00–£24.00
▲ (30)	£9.75–£20.50
🏕 (27)	£255.00–£595.00

144 touring pitches

SPECIAL PROMOTIONS
Please see website for
special offers and details of
our wigwams too!

Nestled in coastal countryside with spectacular views to Holy Island and Bamburgh Castle. Waren offers restaurant-bar, splash-pool and play facilities. Our happy environment is great if you wish to stay on-site but we also make a great base from which to explore Northumberland's coast and castles.

open 13 March to 30 October
payment credit/debit cards, cash, cheques, euros

directions Follow B1342 from A1 to Waren Mill towards Bamburgh. By Budle turn right, follow Meadowhead's Waren Caravan and Camping Park signs.

General 🔥🗄️♿🐕⛽🏪🚿☀️🎣🚲🚻📶✕ Leisure 🎣🎿🍽️🔦⛰️

BELLINGHAM, Northumberland Map ref 5B2

SAT NAV NE48 2JY

Bellingham Camping and Caravanning Club Site

Bellingham, Hexham, Northumberland NE48 2JY
t (01434) 220175 e Bellingham.Site@thefriendlyclub.co.uk
w **campingandcaravanningclub.co.uk/bellingham** ONLINE MAP GUEST REVIEWS

Camping and
Caravanning
Club
The Friendly Club

🚐	£23.00–£26.00
🚐	£23.00–£26.00
▲	£23.00–£26.00

64 touring pitches

Peace and tranquility in Northumberland National Park. Bring your bike, walking boots, canoe, a fishing rod or simply a good book to enjoy the site. Camping Pods also available. **directions** From A69 near Hexham take A68 north then left on B6318. Then B6320 to Bellingham. **open** 11 March - 30 October **payment** credit/debit cards, cash, cheques

General 🗄️♿🐕🚿🏪☀️🅿️🚐🚻 Leisure ⛵🚲🔦⛰️

BERWICK-UPON-TWEED, Northumberland Map ref 5B1

SAT NAV TD15 1QU

Seaview Caravan Club Site

Billendean Road, Spittal, Berwick-upon-Tweed, Northumberland TD15 1QU
t (01289) 305198 e enquiries@caravanclub.co.uk
w **caravanclub.co.uk**

THE
CARAVAN
CLUB

🚐 (98)	£13.50–£32.79
🚐 (98)	£13.50–£32.79

98 touring pitches

Spectacular scenery of Northumberland with visits across the border to Scotland. Overlooking the river estuary. 30-minute walk to Berwick's ramparts, shops and many places of interest. **directions** A1(M) stay on A1 Berwick bypass for 4.5 miles. Left onto the A1167 signposted Tweedmouth. 1.5 miles roundabout into Billendean Terrace, site on the right. **open** March to January **payment** credit/debit cards, cash, cheques

General 🗄️🐕🏪🚐🏪🚻📶 Leisure ▶🎿

HEXHAM, Northumberland Map ref 5B2

Fallowfield Dene Caravan and Camping Park

Fallowfield Dene Caravan and Camping Park, Acomb, Hexham NE46 4RP
t (01434) 603553 e info@fallowfielddene.co.uk
w **fallowfielddene.co.uk** ONLINE MAP

⌗ (26)	£17.50–£18.50
⌗ (6)	£17.50–£18.50
⌂ (5)	£11.00–£11.50
⌗ (1)	£225.00–£300.00
32 touring pitches	

Located in secluded, mature woodland, 3/4 miles from the village of Acomb, 2 miles from Hexham. The site is within easy reach of Hadrian's Wall and many places of interest. **directions** Only an hour's drive from the North Sea ferry terminal, and close to major roads **open** March to November **payment** credit/debit cards, cash, cheques

General 🚿🐕🛉🛗🌂☼🖵🕹🖱🏧 Leisure ⋃♪

HEXHAM, Northumberland Map ref 5B2

Hexham Racecourse Caravan Site

High Yarridge, Yarridge Road, Hexham NE46 2JP
t (01434) 606847 f (01434) 605814 e hexrace.caravan@btconnect.com
w **hexham-racecourse.co.uk**

⌗ (50)	£14.00–£17.00
⌗ (30)	£14.00–£17.00
⌂ (10)	£10.00
50 touring pitches	

Set in the heart of the stunning Northumberland country side, just 2 miles south of the town centre and within easy reach of the many places of interests for tourists. **directions** From Hexham take the B6305 Allendale Road for 3 miles turn left at T-Junction, site 1.5 miles on the right. **open** May to September **payment** credit/debit cards, cash, cheques

General 🚿🐕🛗🌂☼🚲🕹🖱 Leisure ⚑🚵🔍⛰

HEXHAM 6 MILES, Northumberland Map ref 5B2

Poplars Riverside Caravan Park

Eastland End, Haydon Bridge, Hexham, Northumberland NE47 6BY
t (01434) 684427

⌗ (8)	£15.00
⌗ (8)	£15.00
⌂ (3)	£9.00–£15.00

A secluded riverside site, situated on the banks of the river Tyne. With fishing, near to village and convenient for Hadrian's Wall. Railway station in village. **directions** A69. Newcastle–Carlisle Road. Come into Haydon Bridge village – look for caravan sign near bridge. **open** 1st March to end October **payment** cash, cheques

General 🚿🐕🛗🌂🕹🖱 Leisure ⋃♪⛰

MORPETH, Northumberland Map ref 5C2

Tomlinson's Cafe and Bunkhouse

Bridge Street, Rothbury, Morpeth NE65 7SF
t (01669) 621979 e info@tomlinsonsrothbury.co.uk
w **tomlinsonsrothbury.co.uk** ONLINE MAP GUEST REVIEWS ONLINE BOOKING LAST MINUTE OFFERS

Tomlinsons Cafe and Bunkhouse provides low cost accommodation overlooking the River Coquet in a newly renovated Grade 2 listed former schoolhouse. Family, Walker and Cyclist Friendly and Pet Friendly. **directions** Rothbury is 40 minutes by road from Newcastle upon Tyne and Newcastle International Airport. There are main line rail stations at Alnmouth and Morpeth. **open** All year **payment** credit/debit cards, cash, cheques, euros

General 📶🚿📺🐕🛉🛗☼✗ Leisure ⚑⋃🚵♪

POWBURN, Northumberland Map ref 5B1

SAT NAV NE66 4HY

TOURING & CAMPING PARK

🚐 (79) £13.50–£32.79
🏕 (79) £13.50–£32.79
79 touring pitches

River Breamish Caravan Club Site
Powburn, Alnwick, Northumberland NE66 4HY
t (01665) 578320 e enquiries@caravanclub.co.uk
w **caravanclub.co.uk**

THE CARAVAN CLUB

Excellent walking and cycling in the immediate area. A footbridge in Branton takes you over the river to the delightful Breamish Valley. National Park Centre nearby. **directions** Turn off A1 onto A697; in about 20 miles (0.25 miles past Powburn) turn left immediately past service station on right. Site on right. **open** March to November **payment** credit/debit cards, cash, cheques

General 🖥 🐕 🏍 📻 ☼ 🔌 ⊡ 🚻 🔒 🅦

ROTHBURY, Northumberland Map ref 5B1

SAT NAV NE61 4PZ

TOURING PARK

🚐 (84) £10.30–£25.20
🏕 (84) £10.30–£25.20
84 touring pitches

Nunnykirk Caravan Club Site
Nunnykirk, Rothbury, Northumberland NE61 4PZ
t (01669) 620762 e enquiries@caravanclub.co.uk
w **caravanclub.co.uk**

THE CARAVAN CLUB

The peace and tranquillity of this site makes it a haven for wildlife. Hill-walkers will enjoy the splendour of the nearby Simonside Hills. **directions** From B6342, cross bridge at foot of 1:8 hill and turn right into private road. Site on right in 0.25 miles. **open** April to October **payment** credit/debit cards, cash, cheques

General 🐕 🔌 🚻 Leisure 🎣

SEAHOUSES, Northumberland Map ref 5C1

SAT NAV NE68 7SP

ROSE AWARD

CARAVAN HOLIDAY PARK

HOLIDAY & TOURING PARK

🚐 (18) £25.00–£45.00
🏕 (18) £25.00–£45.00
🏠 (28) £345.00–£775.00
18 touring pitches

Seafield Caravan Park
Seafield Road, Seahouses NE68 7SP
t (01665) 720628 f (01665) 720088 e info@seafieldpark.co.uk
w **seafieldpark.co.uk** ONLINE MAP GUEST REVIEWS ONLINE BOOKING LAST MINUTE OFFERS

Luxurious holiday homes for hire on Northumberland's premier park. Superior, fully serviced touring pitches. Prices include full use of Ocean Club facilities. North East holiday park of the year 2009. **directions** Take the B1340 from Alnwick for 14 miles. East to coast. **open** 9th Feb to 9th Jan **payment** credit/debit cards, cash, cheques

General 🔌 🖥 📶 🐕 📻 ☼ 🔌 ⊡ 🔒 Leisure ▶ ∪ 🚴 🎣 ⚓ ⛺

BED & BREAKFAST 2012

Looking for something else?

You can also buy a copy of our popular 'B&B' guide including guest accommodation, B&B's, guest houses, farmhouses, inns, and campus and hostel accommodation in England 2012.

Now available in good bookshops and online at

visitbritainshop.com　　　　　£8.99

SEAHOUSES, Northumberland Map ref 5C1

SAT NAV NE68 7UR

Springhill Caravan & Camping Site, Wigwams & Bunkhouse

Springhill Farm, Seahouses, Northumberland NE68 7UR
t (01665) 721820 **e** enquiries@springhill-farm.co.uk
w springhill-farm.co.uk
ONLINE MAP GUEST REVIEWS ONLINE BOOKING LAST MINUTE OFFERS

⊕	£10.00–£28.00
⊞ (15)	£10.00–£28.00
▲ (20)	£12.00–£30.00
15 touring pitches	

Surrounded by open countryside with a sweep of incredible sea views towards the Farne Islands, Bamburgh Castle and with the Cheviot Hills, Springhill is home to the finest collection of holiday accommodation including our 50-pitch camping & caravan site, 5 wigwams and 32 bed bunkhouse.

The range of accommodation suits all, from independent travellers looking or one nights' accommodation to larger group get-togethers and family summer holidays whilst catering for all budgets. Only a short walk from Springhill you can find miles of empty beaches and country lanes to explore, perfect cycling and walking.

The fishing village of Seahouses (1 mile) boasts a wide range of shops, bars and restaurants, while only a short drive away you can discovers the spellbinding charm of Northumberland and it's renowned visitor attractions including Lindisfarne Island and Castle, the traditional market town of Alnwick noted for its garden, daily boat trips from Seahouses harbour to the famous Farne Islands and much more.

Further information on all accommodation can be found on our website.

open Caravan/camping site: Easter to October. Wigwams/bunkhouse: year round
payment credit/debit cards, cash, cheques

directions 1 mile from Seahouses, 3.25 miles from Bamburgh, 15 miles from Alnwick, 20 miles from Berwick.

General ⚡ 🖻 📺 🐾 ☼ 🛏 🔌 ☎ 🚐 **Leisure** ▶ ∪ 🚲 ➹ /Ⅲ\

Scotland

Scotland is a diverse and extraordinary country, with a rich and fascinating history. The country has nearly 800 islands, only 300 of which are inhabited, and these islands are home to some of the most beautiful landscapes in the world.

A land of contrasts, Scotland boasts vibrant and exciting cities to visit and breathtaking lochs, mountains and coastlines that shouldn't be missed. Scotland is bordered by England on the south, the Atlantic Ocean on the west and the North Sea on the east.

History and Heritage

Scotland's turbulent past is plain to see in its abundance of castles. Edinburgh Castle dominates the skyline and boasts a wealth of attractions including the nation's crown jewels. Visit Scone Palace, the ancient crowning site of Scottish kings. Stirling Castle, which sits on top of a volcanic crag, has a fascinating history due to its strategic defence location and great views over the battlefields below and you can follow in the childhood footsteps of the ill-fated Mary, Queen of Scots. Glamis Castle has been a royal residence since 1372 and Balmoral Castle is the Scottish home to the Royal Family.

Food & Drink

An unspoilt environment, natural ingredients and world-class producers all contribute to Scotland's vibrant, exciting and surprising food and drink scene. Delicious smoked salmon, buttery shortbread, tender Aberdeen Angus beef… you'll find all this and more in Scotland. And as for drink? You can't visit Scotland and not sample a dram or two at The Scotch Whisky Experience.

Arts and Culture

Scotland has produced some of the world's best writers, painters, sculptors, poets and musicians, and continues to do so. These great talents can often be seen at Scotland's many festivals, most notably the Edinburgh International Festival. Mention 'dance' and immediately swinging kilts and the 'Highland Fling' come to mind, and is still very much a tradition today, whether freeform, graceful Scottish country dancers or the precise solo Highland dancers. Scotland also boasts its own national ballet company; performances of all styles of dancing can be seen at the National Centre for Dance, Dance Base in Edinburgh's Grassmarket.

Sport

If there's one sport the Scottish landscape was made for, it's golf, which was invented by the Scots in the 15th century. Scotland boasts over 540 golf courses to choose from including world famous championship golf courses such as The Old Course St Andrews, Royal Troon, Carnoustie, Muirfield, Turnberry and Gleneagles.

Music & Nightlife

In Scotland, you'll never be far from a traditional pub playing great live music, gig venues and music attractions. And if you're around for events such as St Andrew's Day (30 November) and Burn's Night (25 January), you'll hear a lot more of it. If you want to party the night away at a nightclub, you won't be short of choices in Glasgow, which has over 150 pubs, clubs and bars.

Shopping

When it comes to shopping, Scotland's cities really shine. If you want to shop for bargains on the high street, head to Murraygate in Dundee. But if you've got a bit more cash to splash on designer labels, Harvey Nichols in Edinburgh's city centre is the place for you. Or if you're hunting for one-off vintage finds, Glasgow's West End is a haven for vintage shoppers.

Family Fun

Try wildlife watching on the rugged island of Mull for the chance to see eagles, otters and maybe porpoises. Or take your pick at one of the super Scottish science centres, for a hands-on, fun packed way to make sense of science; Sensation, Dundee; Glasgow Science Centre, Our Dynamic Earth, Edinburgh; and Satrosphere Science Centre in Aberdeen. And of course, you can't visit Scotland without trying to find Nessie at Loch Ness.

Handy Hints

Tee Off - Scotland is widely acknowledged as the 'Home of Golf' and boasts some of the best, most challenging and most beautiful courses in the world.

Get Active - Whether it's enjoying a gentle country stroll or scrambling amidst the majestic mountains, Scotland's breathtaking landscape and overwhelming spirit-of-place will refresh and enliven your senses.

Taste It - From restaurants and cafes to pubs and bistros, cheese makers to distillery tours, the Scottish food scene is vibrant, exciting and surprising.

Land a Catch - Whether it be in one of our iconic lochs or world famous rivers surrounded by stunning Scottish scenery, there is a wide variety of world-class fishing in Scotland, from salmon and trout to coarse and sea species.

OUT & ABOUT IN SCOTLAND - FOUR DAY TOUR OF WEST COAST

Day 1 - Barcaldine/Dunstaffnage/Craignure (Isle of Mull)

- Barcaldine - For Loch Creran, Barcaldine Castle and The Scottish Sea Life Sanctuary and local wildlife such as seals and otters
- Dunstaffnage - Dunstaffnage Castle near Dunbeg, built around 1275
- Now, take a scenic 45-minute ferry ride over to the Isle of Mull and head for Craignure
- Craignure (Isle of Mull) - See Duart Castle and Torosay Castle which has 12 acres of gardens

Day 2 - Isle of Mull

- Tobermory - Enjoy this quaint fishing village, built in 18th century, and its charming, brightly painted buildings
- Dervaig – Home to one of Scotland's most unusual churches, the Old Byre Heritage Centre and the Mull Theatre, apparently the smallest professional theatre in the UK
- Calgary Bay - for spectacular sea views along with the best swimming on Mull. Salen – Aros Castle dates back to the 13th century and features remarkable remains of its stone hall house

Day 3 - Strontian / Acharacle / Glenfinnan

- Strontian - Take the ferry from Fishnish back to Lochaline on the mainland. Head to Strontian, which means "Fairies' Point" in Gaelic, established in 1724 for local lead miners
- Acharacle - Built in the 13th century, Tioram Castle, sits on a small rocky island in Loch Moidart. The castle can only be accessed by boat, so use a local guide boat, or simply take in the breathtaking views from the shore
- Glenfinnan - Picturesque village overlooking the shores of Loch Shiel. The Glenfinnan monument, Church of St Mary & St Finnan and Glenfinnan House Hotel are great visitor favourites

Day 4 - Corpach/Fort William/Castle Rock of the Cormorants

- Corpach - Founded in early 1600s the village sits on the banks of the Loch Linnhe and is home to the Caledonian Canal Basin with impressive views of Ben Nevis, the highest mountain in Britain
- Fort William - Set between the commanding slopes of Ben Nevis and the shores of Loch Linnhe. Visit the West Highland Museum, which is one of the oldest museums in the Highlands and is famous for its extensive Jacobite collection
- Castle Rock of the Cormorants - The magnificent Stalker Castle sits on the Castle Rock of the Cormorants, within the Loch Laich. You can only reach it by boat, so take a local tour liner over to the island

Where to Go

Attractions with this sign participate in the **Visitor Attraction Quality Assurance Scheme** (see page 6) which recognises high standards in all aspects of the visitor experience.

ENTERTAINMENT & CULTURE

British Golf Museum
St. Andrews, Fife KY16 9AB
(01334) 460046
www.britishgolfmuseum.co.uk
The British Golf Museum traces the history of golf, in both Britain and abroad, from the middle ages through to the present day.

Clydebuilt (Scottish Maritime Museum Braehead)
Glasgow, Renfrewshire G51 4BN
(0141) 886 1013
www.scottishmaritimemuseum.org
The story of the River Clyde and the contribution it made to the development of West Central Scotland brought vividly to life at Clydebuilt, the Scottish Maritime Museum at Braehead.

Gordon Highlanders Museum
Aberdeen AB15 7XH
(01224) 311200
www.gordonhighlanders.com
Regimental collection of the Gordon Highlanders housed in St Lukes, former home of artist Sir George Reid.

National Museum of Scotland
Edinburgh EH1 1JF
(0131) 225 7534
www.nms.ac.uk
All our collections have tales to tell. See treasures from the edges of history and trace Scotland's story from fascinating fossils to popular culture. For generations we've collected key exhibits from all over Scotland and beyond.

Riverside Museum
Glasgow G3 8DP
(0141) 287 2720
www.glasgow.gov.uk
A unique collection of transport and technology which reflects Glasgow's history as the second city of the British Empire.

The Queen's Gallery
Edinburgh EH8 8DX
(0131) 556 5100
www.royalcollection.org.uk
Built in the shell of the former Holyrood Free Church and Duchess of Gordon's School, the Gallery provides purpose-built, state-of-the-art facilities to enable a programme of changing exhibitions of the most delicate works of art.

FAMILY FUN

Go Ape! High Wire Forest Adventure - Beecraigs
Linlithgow, West Lothian EH49 6PL
0845 643 9215
www.goape.co.uk
Take to the trees and experience an exhilarating course of rope bridges, tarzan swings and zip slides...all set high above the forest floor.

Our Dynamic Earth
Edinburgh EH8 8AS
(0131) 550 7800
www.dynamicearth.co.uk
Explore our planet's past present and future. You'll be shaken by volcanoes, fly over glaciers, feel the chill of polar ice, and even get caught in a tropical rainstorm.

New Lanark Visitor Centre
South Lanarkshire ML11 9DB
(01555) 661345
www.newlanark.org
Two hundred-year-old nominated World Heritage Site featuring a ride called the 'New Millennium Experience'.

FOOD & DRINK

Isle of Arran Distillery Visitor Centre
North Ayrshire KA27 8HJ
(01770) 830264
www.arranwhisky.com
Five years ago, Isle of Arran Distillers started production of a unique single malt whisky to rank with Scotland's greatest.

Talisker Distillery
Isle of Skye, Highland IV47 8SR
(01478) 614306
www.whisky.com/distilleries/talisker_distillery.html
The only distillery on the Isle of Skye, set in an Area of Outstanding Natural Beauty. Guided tours, exhibition, shop.

HERITAGE

Balmoral Castle
Aberdeenshire AB35 5TB
(01339) 742534
www.balmoralcastle.com
The Scottish holiday home of the Royal Family.

Caerlaverock Castle
Dumfries And Galloway DG1 4RU
(01387) 770244
www.historic-scotland.gov.uk
Caerlaverock is an awe inspiring ruin with a long history of lordly residence and wartime siege.

Culzean Castle & Country Park
Maybole, South Ayrshire KA19 8LE
0844 493 2149
www.nts.org.uk
An 18th century castle perched on a rocky promontory with superb panoramic views over the Firth of Clyde.

Edinburgh Castle
Edinburgh EH1 2NG
(0131) 225 9846
www.edinburghcastle.gov.uk
Perched on an extinct volcano, Edinburgh Castle is a powerful Scottish symbol.

Paxton House and Country Park
Berwick-upon-Tweed, Scottish Borders TD15 1SZ
(01289) 386291
www.paxtonhouse.com
An 18thC neo-palladian country house with Adam plasterwork, Chippendale and Trotter furniture.

Scone Palace
Perth And Kinross PH2 6BD
(01738) 552300
www.scone-palace.co.uk
Visit the Palace of Kings, the crowning place of Scottish Kings, where Macbeth, Robert the Bruce and Charles II were crowned.

The Official Loch Ness Monster Exhibition
Drumnadrochit, Highland IV63 6TU
(01456) 450573
www.loch-ness.scotland.com
An exhibition incorporating the latest in technology for visitor centres. Six room walkthrough is fully automated.

The Scotch Whisky Experience
Edinburgh EH1 2NE
(0131) 220 0441
www.scotchwhiskyexperience.co.uk
The mystery of whisky making revealed! Take a barrel ride through whisky history.

NATURE & WILDLIFE

Logan Botanic Garden
Tranrae, Dumfries And Galloway DG9 9ND
(01776) 860231
www.rbge.org.uk
One of the National Botanic Gardens of Scotland, where many rare and exotic plants from temperate regions flourish outdoors. A plantsman's paradise.

Events 2012

Yell Up-Helly-Aa
Cullivoe
www.up-helly-aa.org.uk
31st January

Perth Festival of the Arts
Perth
www.perthfestival.co.uk
May

British Superbike Challenge
Dunfermline
http://motorsport-events.knockhill.
com/british-superbikes-bsb.php
June

Hawick Common Riding
Scottish Boarders
www.hawickcommonriding.com
June

Langholm Common Riding
Langholm
www.langholm-online.co.uk
June

Lanimer Day
South Lanarkshire
www.lanarklanimers.co.uk
June

Glasgow River Festival
Glasgow
www.glasgowriverfestival.co.uk
July

Mega Scotland
Perth
www.megascotland.co.uk
July

Merchant City Festival
Glasgow
www.merchantcityfestival.com
July

T in the Park
Kinross
www.tinthepark.com
July

Crieff Highland Games
Crieff
www.crieffhighlandgathering.com
August

Edinburgh International Festival
Edinburgh
www.eif.co.uk
August - September

Piping Live!
Glasgow
www.pipingfestival.co.uk
August

Royal Edinburgh Military Tattoo
Edinburgh
www.edintattoo.co.uk
August

British Touring Cars
Dunfermline
www.knockhill.co.uk
September

Pitlochry Highland Games
Pitlochry
www.pitlochryhighlandgames.co.uk
September

Riding the Marches
Edinburgh
www.edinburghridingthemarches.
co.uk
September

Glasgow On Ice
Glasgow
www.glasgow-on-ice.co.uk
November - December

Tourist Information Centres

When you arrive at your destination, visit a Visitor Information Centre for help with accommodation and information about local attractions and events. Alternatively call **0845 22 55 121** to receive information and book accommodation before you go.

Aberdeen	01224 288828	23 Union Street, Aberdeen AB11 5BP
Aberfeldy	01887 820276	The Square, Aberfeldy PH15 2DD
Aberfoyle	01877 382352	Trossachs Discovery Centre FK8 3UQ
Abington	01864 502436	Welcome Break Services ML12 6RG
Alford	019755 62052	Old Station Yard AB33 8FD
Anstruther	01333 311073	Scottish Fisheries Museum KY10 3AB
Arbroath	01241 872609	Harbour Visitor Centre, Fishmarket Quay,DD11 1PS
Aviemore	01479 810930	7 The Parade PH22 1PP
Ayr	01292 290300	22 Sandgate KA7 2BW
Ballater	01339 755306	Old Royal Station AB35 5RB
Balloch	01389 753533	Old Station Building G83 8LQ
Banchory	01330 822000	Bridge Street AB31 5SX
Banff	01261 812419	Collie Lodge AB45 1AU
Blairgowrie	01250 872960	26 Wellmeadow PH10 6AS
Bo'ness	01506 826626	Bo'ness Station EH15 9AQ
Bowmore	01496 810254	The Square PA34 7JP
Braemar	01339 741600	The Mews AB35 5YP
Brechin	01356 623050	Pictavia Centre DD9 6RL
Brodick	01770 303774/776	The Pier KA27 8AU
Callander	01877 330342	Ancaster Square FK17 8ED
Campbeltown	01586 552056	MacKinnon House PA28 6EF
Castle Douglas	01556 502611	Market Hill Car Park DG7 1AE
Castlebay	01871 810336	Main Street HS9 5XD
Craignure	01680 812377	The Pierhead PA65 6AY
Crail	01333 450869	Museum & Heritage Centre KY10 3TL
Crieff	01764 652578	High Street PH7 3HU
Daviot Wood	01463 772971	The Picnic Area IV2 5ER
Discovery Cinema Rothesay	01700 502151	Isle of Bute Discovery Centre PA20 0AH
Dornoch	01862 810594	Council Service Point IV25 3SD
Drumnadrochit	01456 459086	The Car Park IV63 6TX

Dufftown	01340 820501	The Clock Tower AB55 4AD
Dumfries	01387 253862	64 Whitesands DG1 2RS
Dundee	01382 527527	Discovery Point DD1 4XA
Dunfermline	01383 720999	1 High Street KY12 7DL
Dunkeld	01350 727688	The Cross PH8 0AN
Dunoon	01369 703785	7 Alexandra Parade PA23 8AB
Dunvegan	01470 521581	2 Lochside IV55 8WB
Durness	01971 511368	Sango IV27 4PZ
Edinburgh	0845 255 121	3 Princes Street EH2 2QP
Edinburgh Airport	0131 344 3120	Edinburgh International Airport EH12 9DN
Elgin	01343 562608 /562614	Elgin Library IV30 1HS
Eyemouth	01890 750678	Auld Kirk TD14 5JE
Falkirk	01324 620244	Falkirk Wheel FK1 4RS
Fort Augustus	01320 366367	The Car Park PH32 4DD
Fort William	01397 701801	15 High Street PH33 6DH
Fraserburgh	01346 518315	3 Saltoun Square AB43 9DA
Glasgow	0141 204 4400	11 George Square G2 1DY
Glasgow Airport	0141 848 4440	International Arrivals Hall PA3 2ST
Grantown on Spey	01479 872242	54 High Street PH26 3EH
Gretna	01461 337834	Unit 38 DG16 5GG
Hawick	01450 373993	Heart of Hawick TD9 0AE
Helensburgh	01436 672642	Clock Tower G84 7PA
Huntly	01466 792255	9A The Square AB54 8BR
Inveraray	01499 302063	Front Street PA32 8UY
Inverness	01463 252401	Castle Wynd IV2 3BJ
Inverurie	01467 625800	18 High Street AB51 3XQ
Jedburgh	01835 863170	Murray's Green TD8 6BE
Kelso	01537 228055	Town House TD5 7HF
Kirkcaldy	01592 267775	The Merchant's House KY1 1JL
Kirkcudbright	01557 330494	Harbour Square DG6 4HY
Kirkwall	01856 872856	The Travel Centre KW15 1GU
Lanark	01555 661661	Horsemarket ML11 7LQ
Largs	01475 689962	Booking Office KA30 8AN
Lerwick	01595 693434	Market Cross ZE1 0LU
Lochboisdale	01878 700286	The Pier Road HS8 5TH
Lochgilphead	01546 602344	29 Lochnell Street PA31 8JL
Lochinver	01571 844194	Assynt Visitor Centre IV27 4LX
Lochmaddy	01876 500321	Pier Road HS6 5AA
Melrose	01896 822283	Abbey House TD6 9LG
Milton (Dumbarton)	01389 742306	A82 Northbound G82 2TZ
Moffat	01683 220620	Churchgate DG16 9EG
Newton Stewart	01671 402431	Dashwood Square DG8 6EQ
Newtongrange	0131 663 4262	Scottish Mining Museum EH22 4QN
North Berwick	01620 892197	1 Quality Street EH39 4HJ
North Kessock	01463 731836	Picnic Site IV1 1XB
Oban	01631 563122	Albany Street PA34 4AN
Peebles	01721 723159	The Chambers Institution EH45 8AG
Perth	01738 450600	Lower City Mills PH1 5QP
Pirnhall	01786 814111	M9/M80 Junction 9 Service Area FK7 8ET
Pitlochry	01796 472215	22 Atholl Road PH16 5BX
Portree	01478 614906	Bayfield House IV51 9EL
Rothesay	01700 502151	Isle of Bute Discovery Centre PA20 0AH
Selkirk	01750 20054	Halliwells House TD7 4BL
Southwaite	01697 473445	M6 Service Area CA4 0NS

t Andrews	01334 472021	70 Market Street KY16 9NU
tirling	01786 475019	41 Dumbarton Road FK8 2QQ
tonehaven	01569 762806	66 Allardice Street AB39 2AA
tornoway	01851 703088	26 Cromwell Street HS1 2DD
tranraer	01776 702595	28 Harbour Street DG9 7RA
trathcarron	01520 722882	Strathcarron Centre IV54 8YR
trathpeffer	01997 421985	Square Wheels IV14 9DW
tromness	01856 850716	Ferry Terminal Building KW16 1BH
trontian	01967 402382	Strontian PH36 4HZ
umburgh	01950 460905	Sumburgh Airport ZE3 9JP
arbert (Loch Fyne)	01880 820429	Harbour Street PA29 6UD
arbert Harris	01859 502011	The Pier HS3 3DG
arbet Loch Lomond	01301 702260	Tarbet G83 7DE
hurso	01847 893155	Riverside Road KW14 8BU
yndrum	01838 400246	6 Main Street FK20 8RY
Jllapool	01854 612486	Argyle Street IV26 2UB

Regional Contacts and Information

For more information on accommodation, attractions, activities, events and holidays in Scotland, contact the regional tourism organisation below. The website has a wealth of information and you can order or download publications.

The following is a selection of publications available online from VisitScotland.com or by calling the information and booking service on 0845 22 55 121:

Touring Map of Scotland £4.99
An up-to-date touring map of Scotland. Full colour with comprehensive motorway and road information, the map details over 20 categories of tourist information and names over 1,500 things to do and places to visit in Scotland.

Touring Scotland Guide to quality assured accommodation and dining £8.99

Indulge in Scotland your luxury accommodation and fine dining guide £8.99

Where to Stay

Entries appear alphabetically by town name in each region. A key to symbols appears on page 6. Maps start on page 298.

BRAEMAR, Aberdeenshire Map ref 7C3

SAT NAV AB35 5YQ

The Invercauld Caravan Club Site
Glenshee Road, Braemar, Ballater, Aberdeenshire AB35 5YQ
t (01339) 741373 **e** enquiries@caravanclub.co.uk
w **caravanclub.co.uk**

🚐 (97)   £13.50–£32.79
🚐 (97)   £13.50–£32.79
97 touring pitches

An ideal centre for walkers and mountain bikers. Herds of red deer roam freely and you may also glimpse capercaillie, red squirrels and badgers, golden eagles and herons. **directions** On A93 on southern outskirts of village. **open** December to October **payment** credit/debit cards, cash, cheques

General 🖸 ★ 🏕 📶 ☼ 🎱 🐕 🚻 🚐 Leisure ► ✈ ⚓

FORDOUN, Aberdeenshire Map ref 6D1

SAT NAV AB30 1SJ

Brownmuir Caravan Park
Fordoun, Laurencekirk AB30 1SJ
t (01561) 320786 **f** (01561) 320786 **e** brownmuircaravanpark@talk21.com
w **brownmuircaravanpark.co.uk** ONLINE MAP ONLINE BOOKING

🚐 (11)   £14.00–£15.50
🚐 (11)   £14.00–£15.50
🅰 (11)   £8.00–£13.00
🏠 (3)   £230.00–£250.00
11 touring pitches

A quiet park set in the Howe-of-the-Mearns, ideal for cycling and fishing, top golf courses are nearby. Children's play area on site. Toilet block with all amenities. **directions** 4 miles north of Laurencekirk turn left at junction signposted Fordoun/Auchenblae, then after 200 yards turn left over bridge, park is 1 mile on right. **open** April to October **payment** cash, cheques

General 🖸 ♨ ★ 🏕 📶 ☼ 🎱 🚲 🐕 🚻 Leisure ► ✈ ⚓

Looking for something else?

You can also buy a copy of our popular guide 'Hotels' including country house and town house hotels, metro and budget hotels, serviced apartments and restaurants with rooms in England 2012. Now available in good bookshops and online at **visitbritainshop.com** **£7.99**

FORFAR, Angus Map ref 6C1

SAT NAV DD8 1BT

Lochside Caravan Club Site
Forfar Country Park, Craig O'lock Road, Forfar, Angus DD8 1BT
t (01307) 468917 e enquiries@caravanclub.co.uk
w **caravanclub.co.uk**

CARAVAN
CLUB

(70)   £13.50–£32.79
(70)   £13.50–£32.79
70 touring pitches

Parkland site near town of Forfar. Flat, grassy park. Play area, crazy golf and leisure centre. Spectacular hallwalking and golf nearby.
directions A90 onto A94 (sp Forfar). Roundabout turn right sp Forfar; 1 mile at traffic lights left on A926, Kirriemuir. Site on Left.
open March to November

ARROCHAR, Argyll and Bute Map ref 6B1

SAT NAV G83 7AR

Ardgarten Caravan & Campsite
Ardgartan, Arrochar, Dunbartonshire G83 7AR
t (01301) 702293 e Ardgartan.Site@thefriendlyclub.co.uk
w **forestholidays.co.uk** ONLINE MAP GUEST REVIEWS

         £15.00–£29.00
         £15.00–£29.00
         £15.00–£29.00
100 touring pitches

Occupies an idyllic location on the edge of Scotland's Loch Long. Surrounded by magnificent mountains this is an ideal base to explore the beautiful scenery of the west of Scotland. **directions** Follow A82 to Tarbert, take the A83 (signposted Arrochar). Continue through the village and the site is on the left after approximately 1.5 miles **open** All year **payment** credit/debit cards, cash

General ⬛ ⵂ ⵗ ⓘ ⵚ ⵒ ⓓ ⓖ Leisure ⵘ

PORT LOGAN, Dumfries & Galloway Map ref 6B3

SAT NAV DG9 9NX

New England Bay Caravan Club Site
Port Logan, Drummore, Dumfries & Galloway DG9 9NX
t (01776) 860275 e enquiries@caravanclub.co.uk
w **caravanclub.co.uk**

CARAVAN
CLUB

(159)   £11.80–£30.80
(159)   £11.80–£30.80
159 touring pitches

This site has direct access to a safe, clean and sandy beach, ideal for sailing, watersports and sea angling. Great for exploring the Forests and Rhins of Galloway. **directions** From Newton Stewart take A75, then A715, then A716. Site on left 2.7 miles past Ardwell Filling Station. **open** March to November **payment** credit/debit cards, cash, cheques

General ⬛ ⵂ ⓘ ⵚ ⵗ ⵒ ⓖ ⓦ Leisure ⵘ ⵙ ⵐ

DIRLETON, East Lothian Map ref 6D2

SAT NAV EH39 5DS

Yellowcraig Caravan Club Site
North Berwick, East Lothian EH39 5DS
t (01620) 850217 e enquiries@caravanclub.co.uk
w **caravanclub.co.uk**

CARAVAN
CLUB

(116)   £15.30–£35.50
(116)   £15.30–£35.50
116 touring pitches

Acres of golden sands and rock pools close by and birds and wildlife around the dunes. Exceptional views of the Bass Rock and other islands. **directions** From North Berwick take A198, signposted Edinburgh. Turn right off bypass for Dirleton, then right again at International Camping sign. **open** March to November **payment** credit/debit cards, cash, cheques

General ⬛ ⵂ ⓘ ⵚ ⵗ ⵒ ⓖ ⓦ Leisure ⵙ ⵐ

DUNBAR, East Lothian Map ref 6D2

SAT NAV EH42 1TU

Belhaven Bay Caravan and Camping Park

Edinburgh Road, West Barns, Dunbar EH42 1TU
t (01368) 865956 **e** belhaven@meadowhead.co.uk
w meadowhead.co.uk ONLINE MAP GUEST REVIEWS LAST MINUTE OFFERS

(52)	£14.50–£26.50
(52)	£14.50–£26.50
(52)	£8.00–£24.50
(5)	£285.00–£595.00

52 touring pitches

SPECIAL PROMOTIONS
Please see our website for
special offers.

Located in the John Muir Country Park in the sunniest and driest part of Scotland, but only 30 minutes to Edinburgh's city centre! Perfect for a quiet and relaxing break and to explore Dunbar and East Lothian with its boutique shopping, castles, golf courses and spectacular countryside and sandy beaches.

open March to October and weekends up to and including Christmas
payment credit/debit cards, cash, euros

directions From A1 north Thistly Cross roundabout take A199 then A1087 at Beltonford roundabout (signposted Dunbar). Continue through West Barns. Belhaven Bay on left.

General ♿ 🖧 ⚐ 🐕 📶 🌂 ☼ ☎ 🛢 🖨 Leisure ► ∪ ⊿ ⋒

NORTH BERWICK, East Lothian Map ref 6D2

SAT NAV EH39 5NJ

Tantallon Caravan and Camping Park

Tantallon Road, North Berwick EH39 5NJ
t (01620) 893348 **e** tantallon@meadowhead.co.uk
w meadowhead.co.uk ONLINE MAP GUEST REVIEWS LAST MINUTE OFFERS

(132)	£14.75–£28.75
(132)	£14.75–£28.75
(40)	£8.50–£25.75
(10)	£295.00–£635.00

132 touring pitches

SPECIAL PROMOTIONS
Please go to our website for
all our special offers and for
details of our Wigwams!

Spectacular views to Bass Rock and Firth of Forth greet visitors to Tantallon. Situated on the East Lothian Coast, North Berwick is a bustling seaside town with a lively harbour, fine beaches, fabulous boutique shopping and many golf courses. Edinburgh is a short drive or 30 minutes by train.

open March to October and then weekends up to and including Christmas
payment credit/debit cards, cash, euros

directions From North Berwick, A198 towards Dunbar. From the south, turn off at A1 north of Dunbar and follow signs for North Berwick and Tantallon Park.

General ♿ 🖧 ⚐ 🐕 📶 🌂 ☼ ☎ 🛢 🖨 Leisure ► ⊿ ⋒

EDINBURGH, Edinburgh Map ref 6C2   SAT NAV EH21 8JS

Drummohr Caravan Park
Levenhall, Musselburgh EH21 8JS
t (0131) 6656867 **e** bookings@drummohr.org
w **drummohr.org** LAST MINUTE OFFERS

🚐	£18.00–£25.00
🚏	£18.00–£25.00
▲	£18.00–£25.00
🏠 (12)	£350.00–£995.00
108 touring pitches	

Premier park on the outskirts of Edinburgh, on the East Lothian coast. Excellent bus service and park and ride to city with many visitor attractions and retail outlets to visit. **directions** From south (A1), take A199 Musselburgh, then B1361. Follow park signs. From west (A1), come off at Wallyford and follow Park and Mining Museum signs. **open** open all year **payment** credit/debit cards, cash, cheques

General 🗑 📶 🐾 ⚡ 🖼 ☀ 🔌 🚻 ♿ Leisure ⚠

EDINBURGH, Edinburgh Map ref 6C2   SAT NAV EH4 5EN

Edinburgh Caravan Club Site
Marine Drive, Edinburgh EH4 5EN
t (01313) 126874 **e** enquiries@caravanclub.co.uk
w **caravanclub.co.uk**

THE CARAVAN CLUB

🚐 (146)	£15.30–£35.51
🚏 (146)	£15.30–£35.51
146 touring pitches	

The site provides easy access to Edinburgh. It's a historic setting - yet Edinburgh is a friendly, modern, cosmopolitan city with something for everyone. **directions** From A901 turn left at traffic lights; at roundabout turn right into Marine Drive. Site on left. **open** All year **payment** credit/debit cards, cash, cheques

General 🗑 📶 🐾 🖼 🔌 🚻 ♿ Leisure ▶ ⚠

EDINBURGH, Edinburgh Map ref 6C2   SAT NAV EH53 0HT

Linwater Caravan Park
West Clifton, East Calder, West Lothian EH53 0HT
t (0131) 3333326 **e** linwater@supanet.com
w **linwater.co.uk** ONLINE MAP GUEST REVIEWS

General 🗑 📶 🐾 🖼 ☀ 🚲 🔌 🚻 ♿ Leisure ♪

Looking for something else?

You can also buy a copy of our popular guide 'Self Catering' including self-catering holiday homes, approved caravan holiday homes, boat accommodation and holiday cottage agencies in England 2012.

Now available in good bookshops and online at **visitbritainshop.com**   **£8.99**

EDINBURGH, Edinburgh Map ref 6C2 — SAT NAV EH16 6TJ

Mortonhall Caravan and Camping Park
38 Mortonhall Gate, Frogston Road East, Edinburgh EH16 6TJ
t (0131) 664 1533 e mortonhall@meadowhead.co.uk
w **meadowhead.co.uk** ONLINE MAP GUEST REVIEWS LAST MINUTE OFFERS

🚐 (250)	£13.50–£31.00
🚍 (250)	£13.50–£31.00
⛺ (250)	£11.00–£26.75
🏕 (20)	£295.00–£795.00

250 touring pitches

SPECIAL PROMOTIONS
Please see our website for
all our current special offers
and details of our wigwams!

Situated in a 200 acre country estate and only 4 miles from Edinburgh's city centre. Mortonhall has beautifully maintained and landscaped parkland, with views to the Pentland Hills. Only a short bus trip or drive, the Capital's shopping, walking, arts, history and other leisure activities are all on our doorstep.

open All year
payment credit/debit cards, cash, euros

directions From the north or south, Exit the city bypass (A720) at Straiton or Lothianburn Junctions and follow the signs to Mortonhall.

General 🔊 ▣ ⓦ ⛺ ⚡ ▥ ⋒ ☼ ▦ ⚡ ☕ ☎ 📶 ✕   Leisure ▸ ∪ ⚲ ✦ ♈ ♦ ⋔

CRAIL, Fife Map ref 6D1 — SAT NAV KY10 3XJ

Sauchope Links Caravan Park
Warsea Road, Crail KY10 3XJ
t (01333) 450 460 e info@sauchope.co.uk
w **largoleisure.co.uk** ONLINE MAP

🚐 (33)	£16.00–£25.00
🚍 (33)	£16.00–£25.00
⛺ (2)	£14.00–£20.00
🏠 (6)	£35–£40
🏕 (6)	£210.00–£540.00

47 touring pitches

Beautifully located on the Fife coastal path between St Andrews and Anstruther. Spectacular views across the Firth of Forth to the Isle of May. **directions** From the A917 to Crail turn left onto Marketgate and follow the road for 1 mile. Right into Warsea Road and follow to the end. **open** 21st March to 31st October Touring, 1st March to January 4th holiday homes **payment** credit/debit cards, cash, cheques

General 🔊 ▣ ⓦ ⛺ ⚡ ▥ ⋒ ☼ ⚡ ☕ ☎ 📶   Leisure ▸ ∪ ⚲ ✦ ♈ ♦ ⋔

LEVEN, Fife Map ref 6C2 — SAT NAV KY8 5NT

Letham Feus Caravan Park
Cupar Road, Nr Lundin Links, Leven, Fife KY8 5NT
t (01333) 351900 e info@lethamfeus.co.uk
w **lethamfeus.co.uk** ONLINE MAP LAST MINUTE OFFERS

🏕 (3)	£180.00–£420.00

In an idyllic setting with stunning views of the Forth Estuary, Letham Feus Park is the perfect holiday location to relax and unwind. **directions** Please contact us for directions **payment** credit/debit cards, cash, cheques

General ▣ ⛺ ▥ ☼   Leisure ▸ ∪ ♈ ⋔

MARKINCH, Fife Map ref 6C2

SAT NAV KY7 6NR

🚐 (81) £13.50–£32.79
🚐 (81) £13.50–£32.79
81 touring pitches

Balbirnie Park Caravan Club Site
Balbirnie Road, Markinch, Fife KY7 6NR
t (01592) 759130
w **caravanclub.co.uk**

THE CARAVAN CLUB

Attractive site set in 400 acres of parkland. The Kingdom of Fife is on the doorstep and nearby are swimming pools, ten-pin bowling, an ice rink, go-karting and horse riding. **directions** From A92, follow signs to Markinch, then signs to Balbirnie Park Craft Centre. Site entrance inside park on right, 0.5 mile west of Markinch. **open** March to November **payment** credit/debit cards, cash, cheques

General 🔲🐕📵📷☀️🔌🛁🔌🚽🚿📞 Leisure ⚲

ROWARDENNAN, Glasgow Map ref 6B2

SAT NAV G63 0AW

🚐 £13.50–£28.50
🚐 £13.50–£28.50
🏕 £13.50–£28.50
168 touring pitches

Cashel Caravan & Campsite
Rowardennan G63 0AW
t (01360) 870234 e cashel.site@forestholidays.co.uk
w **forestholidays.co.uk** ONLINE MAP GUEST REVIEWS

Located on the shore of the famous Scottish Loch, Cashel offers breathtaking views of the loch and the surrounding Queen Elizabeth Forest Park. **directions** M8 to Glasgow - Greenock. Junction 30 - M898 Erskin bridge, follow - A82 Dunbarton, Loch Lomand, Trossachs. A811-Stirling. B837 - Balmaha Rowardennan. **open** 1st March - 31st October **payment** credit/debit cards, cash

General 🔲🐕🛶📵📷🔌🔌🚽📞 Leisure 🚣⚲

AVIEMORE, Highland Map ref 7C3

SAT NAV PH22 1QU

Glenmore Caravan & Campsite
Glenmore, Aviemore, Inverness-shire PH22 1QU
t (01479) 861271 e glenmore.site@forestholidays.co.uk
w **forestholidays.co.uk** ONLINE MAP GUEST REVIEWS

🚐 £13.50–£29.00
🚐 £13.50–£29.00
🏕 £13.50–£29.00
🛖 £180.00
206 touring pitches

Occupies an idyllic location beside the sandy beach at Loch Morlich, in the Cairngorms National Park. Enjoy walking, sailing, watersports, skiing and much more. **directions** From the A9 take the turn off for Aviemore. At B9152 and follow signs for Glenmore Village / Cairngorm Mountain National for 7 miles. **open** All year **payment** credit/debit cards, cash

General 🔲🐕📵📷🔌🚽📞 Leisure ⚲

BALMACARA, Highland Map ref 7B3

SAT NAV IV40 8DH

45 touring pitches

Reraig Caravan Site
Balmacara, Kyle of Lochalsh IV40 8DH
t (01599) 566215 e warden@reraig.com
w **reraig.com**

Small family-run site. Booking not necessary. No awnings during July and August. Tents: only small tents permitted. No youth groups. Prices, see our website. **directions** In the village of Reraig. On A87, 4 miles east of bridge to Isle of Skye. Two miles west of junction with A890. **open** May to September **payment** credit/debit cards, cash

General 💧🐕📷🛁🔌📞📵

BRORA, Highland Map ref 7C2   SAT NAV KW9 6LP

Dalchalm Caravan Club Site
Brora, Highland KW9 6LP
t (01408) 621479 e enquiries@caravanclub.co.uk
w **caravanclub.co.uk**

🚐 (52)   £13.50–£32.79
🚏 (52)   £13.50–£32.79
52 touring pitches

A sheltered site where you can play golf or relax on the nearby sandy beach. Marvellous walking, bird-watching, sea and loch fishing. **directions** 1.25 miles north of Brora on A9, turn right at Dalchalm. **open** April to October **payment** credit/debit cards, cash, cheques

General 🔲 🛒 📱 ☀ 🔲 🔲 🔲 ☎ 🔲   Leisure ▸ ⚓

CULLODEN, Highland Map ref 7C3   SAT NAV IV2 5EF

Culloden Moor Caravan Club Site
Newlands, Culloden Moor, Culloden, Highland IV2 5EF
t (01463) 790625 e enquiries@caravanclub.co.uk
w **caravanclub.co.uk**

🚐 (97)   £13.50–£32.79
🚏 (97)   £13.50–£32.79
97 touring pitches

A gently sloping site with glorious views over the Nairn Valley. Inverness, with impressive castle, great shops and fascinating museums, is 6 miles away. **directions** From A9 south of Inverness, take B9006 signposted Croy, site on left 1 mile past Culloden field memorial. **open** March to January **payment** credit/debit cards, cash

General 🔲 🛒 📱 ☀ 🔲 🔲 🔲 ☎ 🔲   Leisure ⚓

EVANTON, Highland Map ref 7C3   SAT NAV IV16 9UN

Black Rock Caravan Park
Balconie Street, Evanton IV16 9UN
t (01349) 830917 e enquiries@blackrockscotland.co.uk
w **blackrockscotland.co.uk**

🚐   £16.50–£18.50
🚏   £16.50–£18.50
⚐ (18)   £6.00–£18.00
🏠 (1)   £450.00
43 touring pitches

We are a small family run park located in the shelter of beautiful, wooded Glenglass with views of an impressive local landmark, the Fyrish Monument.

payment cash, cheques

directions One mile off the A9, 15 miles north east of Inverness.

General 🔲 🛒 📱 ☀ 🔲 🔲 🔲 ☎ 🔲   Leisure ∪ ⚓ 🎣 ⚠

FORT WILLIAM, Highland Map ref 6B1

SAT NAV PH33 6SX

Scottish TOURIST BOARD ★★★★★ HOLIDAY PARK

Glen Nevis Caravan and Camping Park

Glen Nevis, Fort William PH33 6SX
t (01397) 702191 **f** (01397) 702904 **e** holidays@glen-nevis.co.uk
w **glen-nevis.co.uk** ONLINE MAP ONLINE BOOKING LAST MINUTE OFFERS

(250)	£9.00–£21.00
(250)	£9.00–£21.00
(300)	£6.50–£18.00
(12)	£340.00–£625.00
(22)	£235.00–£525.00

250 touring pitches

SPECIAL PROMOTIONS
Short Breaks available.

Our award-winning touring caravan and camping park has a magnificent location in one of Scotland's most famous highland glens at the foot of mighty Ben Nevis, Britain's highest mountain.

open 15th March to end October
payment credit/debit cards, cash, cheques, euros

directions Follow A82 North to Mini-Roundabout at N outskirts of Fort William - Second Exit for Glen Nevis - Park 2.5 Miles on right

General 🔊 🖥 🐕 🧺 🏕 🌣 🍴 ❌ **Leisure** ▶ 🚴 ♪ 🎣 ⛰

FORT WILLIAM, Highland Map ref 6B1

SAT NAV PH33 7NL

Scottish TOURIST BOARD ★★★★★ HOLIDAY PARK

Linnhe Lochside Holidays

Corpach, Fort William PH33 7NL
t (01397) 772376 **f** (01397) 772376 **e** relax@linnhe-lochside-holidays.co.uk
w **linnhe-lochside-holidays.co.uk** ONLINE MAP GUEST REVIEWS LAST MINUTE OFFERS

(65)	£14.25–£16.50
(65)	£14.25–£16.50
(15)	£10.75–£15.50
	£375.00–£899.00
(14)	£375.00–£899.00
(57)	£310.00–£550.00

80 touring pitches

SPECIAL PROMOTIONS
Discounts for senior citizen groups and for 2nd week. Quotes arranged for block booking, rallies etc.

Luxury chalets and caravans set in well tended gardens, with a fantastic view down the loch. A rural haven of peace and quiet, the park is just five miles away from Ben Nevis. Our handy shop has its own bakery. Free fishing from our shore and our own slipway.

open 15 December to 31 October
payment credit/debit cards, cash, cheques

directions On A830 1.5 miles (3 km) west of Corpach village, 5 miles from Fort William. PH33 7NL.

General 🖥 🐕 🧺 🏕 🌣 **Leisure** 🚴 ♪ ⛰

GLENCOE, Highland Map ref 6B1 SAT NAV PH49 4HP

Invercoe Caravan & Camping Park
Invercoe, Glencoe PH49 4HP
t (01855) 811210 **e** holidays@invercoe.co.uk

🚐	£20.00–£24.00
🚐	£20.00–£24.00
⛺	£15.00–£20.00
🏠 (3)	£455.00–£800.00
🏠 (3)	£390.00–£705.00
🏠 (4)	£350.00–£470.00
55 touring pitches	

Situated on the shores of Loch Leven and surrounded by spectacular scenery, Invercoe is a small, award-winning, family-run park and is an excellent base for exploring the West Highlands. Booking advisable during high season (minimum three nights). Wi-Fi available throughout (chargeable). Small boat/dinghy slipway access to loch now complete.

open All year
payment credit/debit cards, cash, cheques, euros

directions Site is 0.25 miles from Glencoe crossroads (A82) on the Kinlochleven Road (B863).

General 🗑 📶 🐕 🚲 🅿️ ☼ 🔌 🚻 🚿 📶 Leisure ► ∪ ⚓ 🏔

INCHCREE, Highland Map ref 6B1 SAT NAV PH33 6SE

Bunree Caravan Club Site
Onich, Highland PH33 6SE
t (01855) 821283 **e** enquiries@caravanclub.co.uk
w caravanclub.co.uk

THE
CARAVAN
CLUB

🚐 (99)	£15.30–£35.51
🚐 (99)	£15.30–£35.51
99 touring pitches	

This site is quite literally breathtaking. Explore Ben Nevis, take a cable car to the upper terminal of the Aonach Mor Mountain for fabulous views of the whole mountain range. **directions** From A82 turn left 1 mile past Onich at Club Site sign into narrow track. Site in 0.25 mile. **open** March to January **payment** credit/debit cards, cash, cheques

General 🗑 📶 🐕 🏦 🅿️ 🔌 🚻 🚿 📶 Leisure ⚓ 🎣 🏔

JOHN O' GROATS, Highland Map ref 7D1 SAT NAV KW1 4YR

John O'Groats Caravan Park
John O'Groats KW1 4YR
t (01955) 611329 **e** info@johnogroatscampsite.co.uk
w johnogroatscampsite.co.uk

🚐	£16.00–£18.50
🚐	£16.00–£18.50
⛺	£13.00–£15.00
90 touring pitches	

On seashore overlooking Orkney Islands (day trips available). Hotel restaurant 400m, harbour 150m, sea birds 3km. Cliff scenery. **directions** At end of A99 on seafront beside last house in Scotland overlooking Orkney Islands. **open** April to September **payment** cash, cheques

General 🦽 🗑 🐕 🏦 🅿️ ☼ 🔌 🚻 🚿 📶 Leisure ⚓

KINLOCHEWE, Highland Map ref 7B3

Kinlochewe Caravan Club Site
Kinlochewe, Achnasheen, Highland IV22 2PA
t (01445) 760239 **e** enquiries@caravanclub.co.uk
w caravanclub.co.uk

CARAVAN CLUB

🚐 (56)   £11.80–£30.80
🚎 (56)   £11.80–£30.80
56 touring pitches

A small and intimate site at the foot of the rugged slopes of Ben Eighe. A paradise for both climbers and walkers alike. British national nature reserve 2.5 miles. **directions** Just north of Kinlochewe at junction of A832 and A896. Signposted. **open** March to October **payment** credit/debit cards, cash, cheques

General 🐕 ⛽ 🌣 🖥 🍴 🕐 ☎ 🖥

ROY BRIDGE, Highland Map ref 6B1

Bunroy Camping & Caravanning Site
Bunroy Park, Roy Bridge, Inverness-shire PH31 4AG
t (01397) 712332 **e** info@bunroycamping.co.uk
w bunroycamping.co.uk/index.html

🚐 (23)   £15.00–£17.00
🚎 (23)   £15.00–£17.00
⛺ (35)   £5.00–£6.00
🏠 (8)   £195.00–£490.00
23 touring pitches

3 star touring caravan & camping site in sheltered, peaceful, riverside location in Roy Bridge nr Fort William. Village shop, pubs and railway station all within 10 minute walk. **directions** A86 Newtonmore to Spean Bridge. Turn off opposite Stronlossit Inn in Roy Bridge, follow lane past school and over railway bridge 300yds to the end. **open** March - October (Lodges all year) **payment** credit/debit cards, cash, cheques

General 🖥 🐕 ⛽ 🌣 ♿ 🍴 🕐 ☎ 🖥   Leisure 🎣

SHIEL BRIDGE, Highland Map ref 7B3

Morvich Caravan Club Site
Inverinate, Shiel Bridge, Highland IV40 8HQ
t (01599) 511354 **e** enquiries@caravanclub.co.uk
w caravanclub.co.uk

CARAVAN CLUB

🚐 (106)   £13.50–£32.79
🚎 (106)   £13.50–£32.79
106 touring pitches

Morvich is perfect for those who enjoy the great outdoors. The site is on the level valley floor, surrounded by hills and mountains and dazzling scenery. Great for walkers. **directions** Right off A87 1.25 miles past Shiel Bridge. In 1 mile turn right. Site on left in 150 yds. **open** March to November **payment** credit/debit cards, cash, cheques

General 🖥 🐕 ⛽ 🌣 🍴 🕐 ☎ 🖥   Leisure 🎣 🔍

THURSO, Highland Map ref 7C1

Dunnet Bay Caravan Club Site
Dunnet, Thurso, Highland KW14 8XD
t (01847) 821319 **e** enquiries@caravanclub.co.uk
w caravanclub.co.uk

CARAVAN CLUB

🚐 (57)   £13.50–£32.79
🚎 (57)   £13.50–£32.79
57 touring pitches

Look out to Dunnet Head, the northernmost point of mainland Britain. Take a day trip over to Orkney from John O'Groats or Scrabster. Good for bird-watching and fishing. **directions** From east (John O'Groats) on A836. Site on right past Dunnet village. **open** April to October **payment** credit/debit cards, cash, cheques

General 🖥 🐕 🌣 🍴 🕐 🖥   Leisure 🎣

STEPPS, North Lanarkshire Map ref 6B2
SAT NAV G33 6AF

Craigendmuir Caravan & Camping Site
1 Village Drive, Red Deer Village, Main Office, Clayhouse Road, Stepps, Glasgow G33 6AF
t (01417) 794159 e info@craigendmuir.co.uk
w **craigendmuir.co.uk** ONLINE MAP LAST MINUTE OFFERS

⚌ (15)	£18.00–£22.00
🚐 (15)	£18.00–£22.00
Å (20)	£12.25–£14.25
⛺	£335.00–£500.00
🏠	£335.00–£500.00
🏚 (17)	£360.00–£660.00

30 touring pitches

Craigendmuir Park offers substantial touring caravan and camping areas, together with fully equipped chalets, static caravans and holiday homes. **directions** M8 junction 12 for approx 3 miles, through Stepps to Bannatyne Health Club right into Cardowan Road, 3rd right Clayhouse Road, park entrance at roundabout. **open** All year **payment** credit/debit cards, cash

General 🖥 🐕 📶 🔥 ☼ 🔌 ⏱ ⚐ Leisure ▶ ∪ ♪

CRIEFF, Perth and Kinross Map ref 6C1
SAT NAV PH7 4DH

Braidhaugh Park
South Bridgend, Crieff PH7 4DH
t (01764) 652951 f (01764) 652692 e info@braidhaugh.co.uk
w **braidhaugh.co.uk** ONLINE MAP GUEST REVIEWS LAST MINUTE OFFERS

⚌	£20.00–£23.00
🚐	£20.00–£23.00
⛺ (2)	£30.00–£38.00
🏚 (3)	£255.00–£450.00

40 touring pitches

Peaceful, riverside park, outskirts of Crieff, in the heart of Perthshire. Wigwams, hire caravans and hard-standing, level, fully serviced touring pitches. Information area, play park, games room and shop. **directions** On A822. From Stirling follow A9 to Greenloaning and take A822. From Perth follow A85 through Crieff, turn left onto A822, turn right after bridge. **open** All year **payment** credit/debit cards, cash, cheques

General 🖥 📶 🐕 🍴 📶 ☼ 🔌 ⏱ ⚐ 🏕 Leisure ▶ ∪ ♿ ♪ 🎣 ⚑

DUNKELD, Perth and Kinross Map ref 6C1
SAT NAV PH8 0JR

Invermill Farm Caravan Park
Inver, Dunkeld PH8 0JR
t (01350) 727477 e invermill@talk21.com
w **visitdunkeld.com/perthshire-caravan-park.htm** ONLINE MAP

⚌	£17.00–£18.00
🚐	£17.00–£18.00
Å (15)	£14.00–£18.00

50 touring pitches

We are situated in a very tranquil setting, scenic and beautiful part of Perthshire beside the river Braan, an ideal location to explore a large part of Scotland. **directions** Turn off A9 signposted A822 to Crieff turn right follow signs to Inver. **open** end of March to end of October **payment** cash, cheques, euros

General 🖥 🐕 📶 🔥 ☼ 🔌 ⏱ ⚐ Leisure ▶ ♿ ♪

COCKSBURNPATH, Scottish Borders Map ref 6D2
SAT NAV TD13 5YP

Pease Bay Leisure Park
Cockburnspath, Berwickshire TD13 5YP
t (01368) 830206 e holidays@peasebay.co.uk
w **peasebay.co.uk** ONLINE MAP ONLINE BOOKING LAST MINUTE OFFERS

⛺ (2)	£255.00–£745.00
🏚 (30)	£298.00–£425.00

Beachfront holiday park on the Berwickshire coast, popular with families, surfers and outdoor enthusiasts alike. Relax to the sounds of the sea. The park is mid-way between Edinburgh and Berwick-upon-Tweed. **directions** Just off the A1, between Dunbar and Berwick. At the Cockburnspath roundabout take the Pease Bay exit and follow the road down to the bay. **open** Open 1 March - 31 January **payment** credit/debit cards, cash, cheques

General 🖥 📶 🐕 🍴 📶 ☼ ✕ Leisure ▶ ∪ ♪ 🍷 🎵 🎣 ⚑

MELROSE, Scottish Borders Map ref 6C2

SAT NAV TD6 9RY

Gibson Park Caravan Club Site

High Street, Melrose, Scottish Borders TD6 9RY
t (01896) 822969 **e** enquiries@caravanclub.co.uk
w caravanclub.co.uk

🚐 (60)   £15.30–£35.51
🚎 (60)   £15.30–£35.51
60 touring pitches

Peaceful site overlooked by three hills which gave rise to its Roman name of Trimontium. Tennis courts and playing fields. Is within walking distance. **directions** Site adjacent to main road (A6091) close to centre of town. Approx 6 miles (10 km) from A68 Edinburgh/Newcastle road. **open** All year **payment** credit/debit cards, cash, cheques

General 🔲 ✝ 🌣 🔌 💬 ☐ 🔌 Leisure ► ⚲ ↗

AYR, South Ayrshire Map ref 6B2

SAT NAV KA8 0SS

Craigie Gardens Caravan Club Site

Craigie Road, Ayr, South Ayrshire KA8 0SS
t (01292) 264909 **e** enquiries@caravanclub.co.uk
w caravanclub.co.uk

🚐 (90)   £13.50–£32.79
🚎 (90)   £13.50–£32.79
90 touring pitches

Set in a beautiful park, a short walk from Ayr. Learn about 'Rabbie Burns' with the Burns Heritage Trail nearby. History fans will enjoy Vikingar at Largs. **directions** A77 to Whitletts roundabout, A719 via racecourse. Left into Craigie Road. 0.5 mile, after right-hand bend left into Craigie Gardens. Site 400 yds on right. **open** All year **payment** credit/debit cards, cash, cheques

General 🔲 ✝ 🏮 🌣 🔌 💬 ☐ 🔌 Leisure ► ↗ ⋀

AYR (5 MILES), South Ayrshire Map ref 6B2

SAT NAV KA7 4LD

Heads of Ayr Caravan Park

Dunure Road, Ayr KA7 4LD
t (01292) 442269 **e** stay@headsofayr.com
w headsofayr.com ONLINE MAP

🚐 (20)   £18.00–£23.00
🚎 (8)   £15.00–£21.00
🅰 (8)   £15.00–£23.00
🏠 (1)   £345.00–£615.00
🚏 (8)   £190.00–£540.00
36 touring pitches

Situated on the Ayrshire coast overlooking Arran, 10 minutes from the beach. Facilities include bar, shop, laundry and play area. Seasonal entertainment. Caravans to hire. Tourers and tents welcome. **directions** 5 miles south of Ayr on the A719 and 2 miles north of Dunure. **open** March to October **payment** credit/debit cards, cash, cheques

General 🔲 ✝ 🐾 🏮 🌣 🚿 💬 ☐ 🔌 Leisure ► ∪ ♿ ↗ ♟ ♫ ⚲ ⋀

ABERFOYLE, Stirling Map ref 6B1

SAT NAV FK8 3RR

Cobleland Caravan and Campsite

Station Road, Gartmore, Stirlingshire FK8 3RR
t (01877) 382392 **e** Cobleland.Site@forestholidays.co.uk
w forestholidays.co.uk ONLINE MAP GUEST REVIEWS

🚐   £13.50–£25.00
🚎   £13.50–£25.00
🅰   £13.50–£25.00
126 touring pitches

Situated the bank of the River Forth, shaded by majestic oak trees. A small, family-friendly site, a good base for exploring the Trossachs National Park and walking and cycling routes. **directions** Follow the A81, 1.5 miles before Aberfoyle village, turn left after Gartmore House (The Gartmore turn off). Continue until you reach the site. **open** 1st April- 31st October **payment** credit/debit cards, cash

General 🔲 ✝ 🏮 🏮 💬 ☐ 🔌 Leisure ♿ ⚲ ⋀

CALLANDER, Stirling Map ref 6B1 — SAT NAV FK17 8LE

Gart Caravan Park

Stirling Road, Callander FK17 8LE
t (01877) 330002 **e** enquiries@theholidaypark.co.uk

(128) £22.00–£24.00
(128) £22.00–£24.00
128 touring pitches

A peaceful and spacious park maintained to a very high standard with modern, heated shower block facilities. The ideal centre for cycling, walking and fishing. **directions** Leave jct 10 of the M9, west to Callander. **open** 1 April to 15 October **payment** credit/debit cards, cash, cheques

General ▯ ⊁ ▥ ⋒ ☼ ▣ ♨ ◨ ♗ ☕ Leisure ▸ U ♿ ✦ ⚲

CALLANDER, Stirling Map ref 6B1 — SAT NAV FK17 8LQ

Keltie Bridge Caravan Park

Keltie Bridge Caravan Park, Callander FK17 8LQ
t (01877) 330606 **e** stay@keltiebridge.co.uk

(50) £13.00–£15.00
(50) £13.00–£15.00
(50) £9.50–£18.00
50 touring pitches

Flat, grassy park in Scotland's Loch Lomond and The Trossachs National Park. High-quality shower block. Easily accessible from central Scotland's motorways. **directions** Well signposted off A84 outside Callander. **open** Easter to October **payment** cash, cheques

General ▯ ⊁ ▥ ⋒ ☼ ◨ ♗ Leisure ▸ ♿

KILLIN, Stirling Map ref 6B1 — SAT NAV FK21 8TN

Maragowan Caravan Club Site

Aberfeldy Road, Killin, Stirling FK21 8TN
t (01567) 820245 **e** enquiries@caravanclub.co.uk
w caravanclub.co.uk

CARAVAN CLUB

(100) £15.30–£35.51
(100) £15.30–£35.51
100 touring pitches

An ideal family holiday base, within walking distance of the shops and restaurants in Killin. There is a 9-hole golf course nearby and trout fishing in the river on site. **directions** Site on right of A827 (Killin-Kenmore) 0.5 mile past end of village. **open** March to November **payment** credit/debit cards, cash, cheques

General ▯ ⊁ ▥ ⋒ ◨ ♗ ☕ Leisure ▸ ♿ ✦

Looking for something else?

You can also buy a copy of our popular 'B&B' guide including guest accommodation, B&B's, guest houses, farmhouses, inns, and campus and hostel accommodation in England 2012.

Now available in good bookshops and online at

visitbritainshop.com   **£8.99**

LINLITHGOW, West Lothian Map ref 6C2   SAT NAV EH49 6PL

Beecraigs Caravan and Camping Site

Beecraigs Country Park, Nr Linlithgow, West Lothian EH49 6PL
t (01506) 844516 f (01506) 846256 e mail@beecraigs.com
w **beecraigs.com** LAST MINUTE OFFERS

⌸ (36)	£16.00–£18.00
⌷ (36)	£16.00–£18.00
Å (20)	£13.15–£21.00
56 touring pitches	

SPECIAL PROMOTIONS
Range of promotions –
please contact for further
details.

Open all year. Situated near historic Linlithgow town & within the Beecraigs Country Park. Onsite facilities include electric hook-ups, barbecues, modern toilet facilities with privacy cubicles, baby-change & laundrette facilities. Pets welcome. Leaflets available. Great for exploring central Scotland & the Lothians. Advised to book in advance.

open All year
payment credit/debit cards, cash, cheques

directions From Linlithgow, follow Beecraigs Country Park and International Caravan Park signposts. Park is 2mls south of Linlithgow. From M8, follow B792. From M9, follow A803.

General 🗑 🎣 📷 🔆 🔌 🛁 🍴 ✕   Leisure ▶ ∪ 🚣 ✂ 🏔

Looking for something else?

You can also buy a copy of our popular guide 'Hotels' including country house and town house hotels, metro and budget hotels, serviced apartments and restaurants with rooms in England 2012.

Now available in good bookshops and online at
visitbritainshop.com   **£7.99**

For **key to symbols** see page 6

Wales

So what do you need to know about Wales - the friendly green hilly country on the western side of Britain? Discover 3 National Parks; 1,200 km of coastline; 5 Areas of Outstanding Natural Beauty; 2 languages; 11 million sheep and more castles per square mile than anywhere else in the world – 641 at the last count.

If you want to experience the great outdoors, you're never more than half an hour away from the Welsh countryside. Why not learn a few words of Welsh, and get to know the locals... 'Shwmae' – that's Welsh for hello.

History and Heritage

Throughout Wales you will find prehistoric, Roman and Norman sites; the turbulent past is visible across Wales with hundreds of castles and fortresses still standing. Cardiff Castle is located in the city centre, originally a Roman fort. Visit Caerphilly Castle one of the largest medieval fortresses in Britain, Chepstow Castle Britain's first stone built castle, or perhaps one of the mighty UNESCO showpiece fortresses of Conwy, Caernarfon, Harlech or Beaumaris. St Davids on the West Coast is Britain's smallest city and its magnificent cathedral built in 1181 is the final resting place of St David, the patron saint of Wales.

Arts and Culture

The Dylan Thomas Centre has a permanent exhibition on his life and is home to many literary events through the year, including the annual Dylan Thomas Festival during October and November. Catch the annual Hay Festival of Literature (May), an event with a laid-back party atmosphere and a global reputation. Visit the National Eisteddfod (August) for a colourful celebration of Welsh Culture.

Food & Drink

Local foods include Laverbread made from seaweed; Bara Brith, a fruit bread, and Welsh Cakes for afternoon tea, Welsh lamb for dinner, or for a snack Welsh Rarebit. Cardiff offers great pubs, friendly wine bars, restaurants and attractive cafes to linger and relax in-between sightseeing. Visiting Aberaeron? The award winning honey ice cream from Hive on the Quay is a real treat. Try Pwll Mawr made by the family run Blaenafon Cheddar Company, which is actually matured at the bottom of Big Pit mineshaft.

Sport

Sports enthusiasts will delight in touring the magnificent Millennium Stadium in Cardiff. Run down the player's tunnel, and imagine being greeted by 74,500 cheering fans. Check out the fixtures rugby, football, motorsports and more. Wales has great golf courses, some 200, but none more so than the Celtic Manor Resort which was purpose-built for the 2010 Ryder cup. Enjoy the 'Sport of Kings' as Chepstow Racecourse which hosts a mixture of Jump and Flat race meetings.

Music & Nightlife

Live music is at the heart of Cardiff's entertainment scene, with live music somewhere in the city, every night of the week. Nightlife centres around local pubs with vibrant live music and entertainment. Grade II listed Hendre Hall just outside Bangor stages live musical events from classical music, rock to world music and DJ nights. Take in a live performance at The Wales Millennium Centre.

Shopping

Recently named the 6th best shopping destination in the UK, Cardiff has intriguing Victorian and Edwardian shopping arcades as well as modern shopping centres like St David's Dewi Sant. Known as the 'Bond Street' of South Wales, Cowbridge is a fantastic place to shop with a diversity and choice generally unexpected of a small town. Hay on Wye is not just about books, there are plenty of galleries, antique shops, and craft shops to tempt your wallet.

Family Fun

Visit the Museum of Welsh Life to see how people in the past worked and played. Take a trip on the narrow-gauge Ffestiniog Railways, one of the Great Little Trains of Wales. Go Dolphin spotting along The Cambrian Coast. Don a miner's lamp and go 92 metres underground with a real miner and learn what life was like working at the coal face.

Handy Hints

Adventure - Coasteering on the Pembrokeshire coast. Breathtaking exploits amidst breathtaking scenery.

Tee Time - A gateway to almost 200 more courses – including some of the world's top links courses – all packed into an area that's just 60 miles wide and 170 miles long.

Castles - Take your pick - there are over 600 of them in Wales, from Dolbadarn to Caldicot.

Walking - A memorable experience. Whether you're tramping the rugged coastal paths, discovering ancient woodlands or conquering mountains, walking in Wales is a unique experience.

OUT & ABOUT IN WALES

Day 1 - Newport/Cardiff

- Newport – Wales newest city. Visit Tredegar House, a fine example of restoration architecture. Don't miss the Celtic Manor Resort and the Caerleon amphitheatre.
- Cardiff – Cosmopolitan capital with plenty to see and do but don't miss: Shopping in St David's Dewi Sant; Millennium Stadium; The National Museum and Gallery of Wales; Cardiff Castle; St Fagans; National History Museum; Cardiff Bay and Wales Millennium Centre.

Day 2 - Swansea / Gower Peninsula

- Swansea – Birthplace of Dylan Thomas who described it as an "ugly, lovely town". Visit the Dylan Thomas Centre; the new Maritime Quarter; National Waterfront Museum and Swansea Market.
- Gower Peninsula - Britain's first 'Area of Outstanding Natural Beauty'. Take a stroll to 'Worms Head' on the western tip; the view from the Worm's Head Hotel is second to none.

Day 3 - Carmarthenshire

- Experience the intriguing mythology of Merlin and gritty wild-boy poetry of Dylan Thomas. Climb up to Carreg Cennen Castle and soak up the panoramic views. Visit The National Botanic Garden of Wales with its impressive glasshouse or nearby Aberglasney Gardens the 'garden lost in time'.

Day 4 - Pembrokeshire

- There are several small islands off the Pembrokeshire coast - Ramsey Island, Grassholm Island, Skomer Island and Caldey Island, which can be reached by boat. The UK's only coastal national park offers great coastal walking paths. Visit St David's Cathedral, St Govan's Chapel and Narbeth.

Day 5 - Ceredigion

- Northwards, just outside Newport are the Preseli Hills, where the giant Bluestones of Stonehenge are said to come from! Take in Aberaeron, a stylish fishing village. At Aberystwyth, take a ride to Devil's Bridge on The Vale of Rheidol Railway; then visit the Red Kite Centre.

Day 6 - Machynlleth/Portmeirion

- Machynlleth - Continue northwards to The Centre for Alternative Technology (CAT) one of the world's most renowned eco-centres. Take a water-balanced tram ride up the cliff, before exploring the energy-saving devices and hands-on activities. Head for Harlech Castle, spectacularly perched out on a rock, keeping a watchful eye over Snowdonia.
- Portmeirion - An Italianate village created by architect Sir Clough William-Ellis. This fantasy village was the setting for the 1960's cult TV series 'The Prisoner'.

Day 7 - Betws y Coed/Conwy

- Northward through spectacular Snowdonia. Just outside Betws y Coed, wander around the impressive Swallow Falls. Further north on the A470 is Bodnant Gardens famous for its 55 metre laburnum arch, most impressive in mid May-early June. Just north is Conwy Castle with its massive crenellated towers of dark stone and amazing views across the town and estuary.

Where to Go

 Attractions with this sign participate in the **Visitor Attraction Quality Assurance Scheme** (see page 6) which recognises high standards in all aspects of the vistor experience.

ENTERTAINMENT & CULTURE

Big Pit: National Coal Museum
Blaenavon, Torfaen
NP4 9XP
(01495) 790311
www.museumwales.ac.uk/en/bigpit
Don a miners lamp and go 92m underground with a real miner and learn what life was like for the thousands of men who worked at the coal face.

Great Orme Tramway
Llandudno, Conwy
LL30 2NB
(01492) 879306
www.greatormetramway.com
Take a ride on the 'San Francisco style' tramway - one of only 3 still in existence in the world today.

Millennium Stadium
Cardiff
CF10 1NS
(029) 2082 2228
www.millenniumstadium.com/tours/index.php
Take a tour. Run down the player's tunnel, and imagine yourself being greeted by 74,500 people eagerly awaiting the pain and the glory of rugby at its best.

Wales Millennium Centre
Cardiff
CF10 5AL
(029) 2063 6464
http://www.wmc.org.uk
Cardiff's multi purpose arts centre, and home to The Welsh National Opera. The building is all glass and slate and looks very much like a Welsh armadillo.

FAMILY FUN

Centre For Alternative Technology
Machynlleth, Powys
SY20 9AZ
(01654) 705950
www.cat.org.uk
Is one of the world's most renowned eco-centres, with interactive displays and practical examples of sustainable living, renewable energy and organic gardening.

The Dylan Thomas Centre
Swansea
SA1 1RR
(01792) 463980
www.dylanthomas.com
Dylan Thomas is perhaps one of greatest poets of the 20th century, and the most famous literary figure to come from Wales.

FOOD & DRINK

Penderyn Distillery
Aberdare Rhondda, Cynon, Taff
CF44 0SX
(01685) 810651
www.welsh-whisky.co.uk
It's the only distillery in Wales and one of the smallest in the world. Take a tour of the visitor centre and distillery.

HERITAGE

Cardiff Castle
Cardiff
CF10 3RB
(029) 2087 8100
www.cardiffcastle.com
Climb up to the top of the 12th century Norman keep for great views over the city.

Dolaucothi Gold Mines
Llanwrda, Carmarthenshire
SA19 8US
(01588) 650177
www.nationaltrust.org.uk/main/w-dolaucothigoldmines
Try your hand at panning for gold. Or take a guided underground tour through the Roman and underground workings and learn all about the history of the mine at the on-site exhibition and Interpretation Centre.

Harlech Castle
Harlech, Gwynedd
LL46 2YH
(01766) 780552
www.cadw.wales.gov.uk/default.asp?id=6&PlaceID=78
The castle's spectacular location atop a rocky crag assures you of a stunning photo opportunity.

Pontysycllte Aqueduct
Pontcysyllte, Wrexham
(01606) 723 800
www.waterscape.com
The highest cast-iron aqueduct in the world built to take a canal over the River Dee.

Powis Castle & Garden
Welshpool, Powys
SY21 8RF
(01938) 551929
www.nationaltrust.org.uk/main/w-powiscastle_garden
A mecca for garden lovers. The impressive red Medieval castle is framed by enormous clipped yew trees, and 18th century Italianate terraces with original lead statues, lush herbaceous borders and exotic plants cascading from the walls.

St Davids Cathedral
St. David's, Pembrokeshire
SA62 6QW
(01437) 720691
www.stdavidscathedral.org.uk
*Located in the smallest city in the UK,
St Davids Cathedral is the burial place
of Wales' patron saint St David (Dewi
Sant) has been a church since the 6th
century.*

Vale of Rheidol Railway
Aberystwyth, Ceredigion
SY23 1PG
(01970) 625819
www.rheidolrailway.co.uk
*A narrow-gauge heritage railway that
runs for just over 11 miles between
Aberystwyth and Devil's Bridge.*

NATURE & WILDLIFE

Bodnant Gardens
Colwyn Bay, Conwy
LL28 5RE
(01492) 650460
www.bodnantgarden.co.uk
*Situated above the River Conwy with
stunning views across Snowdonia,
Bodnant Gardens is most well known
for its laburnum arch, a 55m tunnel
of golden blooms, most impressive in
mid May-early June.*

Ceredigion Coast Path
Cardigan Bay, Ceredigion
(01545) 572105
www.ceredigioncoastpath.org.uk
*A 96km route between the Teifi and
Dyfi estuaries, offers walkers the
opportunity to discover towns and
villages, and take in the spectacular
coastal scenery. You might even spot
dolphins, seals and porpoises.*

Gigrin Farm
Powys
LD6 5BL
(01597) 810243
www.gigrin.co.uk
*Get up close and personal with the wild
Red Kites - you'll be just 30 metres from
the feeding ground. Feeding is every
day at 3pm and 2pm in winter.*

National Botanic Garden of Wales
Carmarthen, Carmarthenshire
SA32 8HG
(01558) 668768
www.gardenofwales.org.uk
*This was the first botanic garden in
the UK, dedicated to conserving plant
species. Set in 600 acres of 18th century
parkland the centrepiece is its great
glasshouse - the world's largest single
span glass structure.*

Events 2012

Gwyl Gregynog Festival
Newtown
www.gwylgregynogfestival.org/
Gwyl_Gregynog_Festival.html
June - July

Llangollen Comedy Festival
Llangollen
www.llancomedy.com
June

North Wales Bluegrass Music Festival
Conwy
www.northwalesbluegrass.co.uk
June - July

Ruthin Festival
Ruthin
www.ruthinfestival.co.uk
June - July

Cardiff Multicultural Mela
Cardiff
www.cardiffmela.com/contact
July

Gower Rock Festival
Swansea
www.gowerrockfestival.co.uk
July

Llangollen International Musical Eisteddfod
Llangollen
www.llangollen2010.co.uk
July

North Wales Boat Show
Bangor
www.northwalesboatshow.co.uk
July

Small Nations Festival
Llandovery
www.smallnations.co.uk
July

Brecon Jazz
Brecon
www.breconjazz.org
August

Ruthin Flower and Country Show
Ruthin
www.ruthingshow.org
August

Anglesey Beer Festival
Cemaes Bay
www.angleseybeerfestival.com
September

Cardiff Harbour Festival
Cardiff
www.cardiff-festival.com
September

The Great Llangollen Show
Llangollen
www.the-great-llangollen-show.
co.uk
September

Welsh Food Festival
Welshpool
www.welshfoodfestival.co.uk
September

Llangollen Food Festival
Llangollen
www.llangollenfoodfestival.co.uk
October

Tourist Information Centres

When you arrive at your destination, visit an Official Partner Tourist Information Centre for quality assured help with accommodation and information about local attractions and events, or email your request before you go. To find a Tourist Information Centre visit **www.visitwales.co.uk**

Aberaeron	The Quay	01545 570602	aberaerontic@ceredigion.gov.uk
Aberdulais Falls*	The National Trust	01639 636674	aberdulaistic@nationaltrust.org.uk
Aberdyfi *	The Wharf Gardens	01654 767321	tic.aberdyfi@eryri-npa.gov.uk
Abergavenny	Swan Meadow	01873 853254	abergavenny.ic@breconbeacons.org
Aberystwyth	Terrace Road	01970 612125	aberystwythtic@ceredigion.gov.uk
Anglesey	Station Site	01248 713177	anglesey@nwtic.com
Bala *	Pensarn Road	01678 521021	bala.tic@gwynedd.gov.uk
Barmouth	The Station	01341 280787	barmouth.tic@gwynedd.gov.uk
Barry Island *	The Promenade	01446 747171	barrytic@valeofglamorgan.gov.uk
Beddgelert *	Canolfan Hebog	01766 890615	tic.beddgelert@eryri-npa.gov.uk
Betws y Coed	Royal Oak Stables	01690 710426	tic.byc@eryri-npa.gov.uk
Blaenavon *	Blaenavon World Heritage Centre	01495 742333	Blaenavon.tic@torfaen.gov.uk
Borth *	Cambrian Terrace	01970 871174	borthtic@ceredigion.gov.uk
Brecon	Cattle Market Car park	01874 622485	brectic@powys.gov.uk
Bridgend	Bridgend Designer Outlet	01656 654906	bridgendtic@bridgend.gov.uk
Caerleon	5 High Street	01633 422656	caerleon.tic@newport.gov.uk
Caernarfon	Oriel Pendeitsh	01286 672232	caernarfon.tic@gwynedd.gov.uk
Caerphilly	The Twyn	029 2088 0011	tourism@caerphilly.gov.uk
Cardiff	The Old Library	029 20 873 573	visitor@cardiff.gov.uk
Cardiff Bay	Unit 1	029 2087 7927	visitorcentrecardiffbayf@cardiff.gov.uk
Cardigan	Theatr Mwldan	01239 613230	cardigantic@ceredigion.gov.uk
Carmarthen	113 Lammas Street	01267 231557	carmarthentic@carmarthenshire.gov.uk
Chepstow	Castle Car Park	01291 623772	chepstow.tic@monmouthshire.gov.uk
Conwy	Castle Buildings	01492 592248	conwytic@conwy.gov.uk
Dolgellau	Ty Meirion	01341 422888	tic.dolgellau@eryri-npa.gov.uk
Fishguard Harbour	Ocean Lab	01348 874737	fishguardharbour.tic@pembrokeshire.gov.uk

Fishguard Town	Town Hall	01437 776636	fishguard.tic@pembrokeshire.gov.uk
Harlech *	Llys y Graig	01766 780658	tic.harlech@eryri-npa.gov.uk
Haverfordwest	Old Bridge	01437 763110	haverfordwest.tic@pembrokeshire.gov.uk
Knighton	Offa's Dyke Centre	01547 528753	oda@offasdyke.demon.co.uk
Llanberis *	41b High Street	01286 870765	llanberis.tic@gwynedd.gov.uk
Llandovery	Heritage Centre	01550 720693	llandovery.ic@breconbeacons.org
Llandudno	Library Building	01492 577577	llandudnotic@conwy.gov.uk
Llanelli	Millennium Coastal Park Visitor Centre	01554 777744	DiscoveryCentre@carmarthenshire.gov.uk
Llangollen	Y Chapel	01978 860828	llangollen@nwtic.com
Merthyr Tydfil	14a Glebeland Street	01685 727474	tic@merthyr.gov.uk
Milford Haven *	Suite 19 Cedar Court	01437 771818	milford.tic@pembrokeshire.gov.uk
Mold	Library Museum & Art Gallery	01352 759331	mold@nwtic.com
Monmouth	Market Hall	01600 713899	monmouth.tic@monmouthshire.gov.uk
Mumbles	The Methodist Church	01792 361302	info@mumblestic.co.uk
New Quay *	Church Street	01545 560865	newquaytic@ceredigion.gov.uk
Newport	Museum & Art Gallery	01633 842962	newport.tic@newport.gov.uk
Newport (pembs) *	2 Bank Cottages	01239 820912	NewportTIC@Pembrokeshirecoast.org.uk
Oswestry Mile End	Mile End Services	01691 662488	oswestrytourism@shropshire.gov.uk
Oswestry Town	The Heritage Centre	01691 662753	ot@oswestry-welshborders.org.uk
Pembroke	Visitor Centre	01437 776499	pembroke.tic@pembrokeshire.gov.uk
Porthcawl *	Old Police Station	01656 786639	porthcawltic@bridgend.gov.uk
Porthmadog	High Street	01766 512981	porthmadog.tic@gwynedd.gov.uk
Presteigne *	The Judge's Lodging	01544 260650	presteignetic@powys.gov.uk
Pwllheli*	Min y Don	01758 613000	pwllheli.tic@gwynedd.gov.uk
Rhyl	Rhyl Childrens Village	01745 355068	rhyl.tic@denbighshire.gov.uk
Saundersfoot *	The Barbecue	01834 813672	saundersfoot.tic@pembrokeshire.gov.uk
St Davids	Visitor Centre	01437 720392	enquiries@stdavids.pembrokeshirecoast.org.uk
Swansea	Plymouth Street	01792 468321	tourism@swansea.gov.uk
Tenby	Unit 2	01834 842402	tenby.tic@pembrokeshire.gov.uk
Welshpool	The Vicarage Gardens Car Park	01938 552043	ticwelshpool@btconnect.com
Wrexham	Lambpit Street	01978 292015	tic@wrexham.gov.uk

* seasonal opening

Regional Contacts and Information

For more information on accommodation, attractions, activities, events and holidays in Wales, contact the national tourism organisation below. The website has a wealth of information and you can order or download publications.

t: 0845 010 3300

www.visitwales.com and www.visitwales.co.uk

There are hundreds of "Green" places to stay and visit in England from small bed and breakfasts to large visitor attractions and activity holiday providers. Businesses displaying this logo have undergone a rigorous verification process to ensure that they are sustainable (green) and that a qualified assessor has visited the premises.

We have indicated the accommodation which has achieved a Green award... look out for the 🌱 symbol in the entry.

Where to Stay

Entries appear alphabetically by town name in each region. A key to symbols appears on page 6. Maps start on page 298.

LLANELLI, Carmarthenshire Map ref 8A3 | SAT NAV SA16 0EJ

Cymru Wales
Parc Teithio Touring Park
★★★★

£16.00–£38.90
£16.00–£38.90
130 touring pitches

Pembrey Country Park Caravan Club Site

Pembrey, Llanelli, Carmarthenshire SA16 0EJ
t (01554) 834369 **e** enquiries@caravanclub.co.uk
w caravanclub.co.uk

THE CARAVAN CLUB

Site set in a country park vast range of outdoor sporting activities. Safe, sandy beach a mile away. Bird and butterfly watching and guided walks. **directions** From Pembrey follow signs to Country Park. **open** March to January **payment** credit/debit cards, cash, cheques

General 🚻 ♿ 🐕 ⌖ 🔌 💡 🕭 🗑 Leisure ▸ ⚓

WALES

BrynGloch
AA ▌▌
Cymru Wales
Parc Gwyliau Holiday Park
★★★★

Camping & Caravan Park

Award winning site in Snowdonia National Park with breathtaking views

Clean, peaceful site, electric hook-ups, luxury toilet/shower, shop & off-licence, games room, spacious play area, fishing, mini golf.

• **Static Caravans**
• **Bunkhouse**
• **Tent Pitchers**

• **Touring Pitches**
• **Seasonal Pitches**
• **OPEN ALL YEAR**

For a Brochure call **01286 650216**

Email: eurig@bryngloch.co.uk
Website: www.campwales.co.uk

Looking for something else?

You can also buy a copy of our popular guide 'Self Catering' including self-catering holiday homes, approved caravan holiday homes, boat accommodation and holiday cottage agencies in England 2012. Now available in good bookshops and online at **visitbritainshop.com £8.99**

LLANGADOG, Carmarthenshire Map ref 8B3

SAT NAV SA19 9NG

Cymru
Wales
Touring &
Camping Park
★★★★

Abermarlais Caravan Park

Abermarlais Caravan Park, Llangadog, Carmarthenshire, Wales SA19 9NG
t (01550) 777868 **e** aberma@tiscali.co.uk
w **abermarlaiscaravanpark.co.uk** ONLINE MAP

(60) £11.00–£13.00
(60) £11.00–£13.00
Å (28) £11.00–£13.00
88 touring pitches

A tranquil site in a beautiful woodland valley at the western end of the Brecon Beacons National Park, ideal for nature lovers and bird-watchers. The site's facilities are of the highest standard with excellent shower and toilet block. Camp shop and reception with comprehensive selection of groceries, gas, etc.

open 16 March to 16 November
payment credit/debit cards, cash, cheques

directions Situated on A40, 6 miles west of Llandovery or 6 miles east of Llandeilo. Signposted.

General 🐕 ⚡ 🏪 🚿 ☀ 🔧 🛁 💧 🛒 Leisure ∪ 🎣 ⛰

ABERAERON, Ceredigion Map ref 8A2

SAT NAV SA46 0JF

Cymru
Wales
Holiday, Touring
& Camping Park
★★★★★

Aeron Coast Caravan Park

North Road, Aberaeron SA46 0JF
t (01545) 570349 **e** enquiries@aeroncoast.co.uk
w **aeroncoast.co.uk** ONLINE MAP ONLINE BOOKING

£15.00–£25.00
£15.00–£25.00
Å £15.00–£25.00
100 touring pitches

SPECIAL PROMOTIONS
Rallies welcome outside
school holidays. £9 per
night per unit.

We are privileged to be part of Aberaeron with its picturesque harbour, shops and restaurants. River and coastal walks. Quiet out of high season but good leisure provision for families in school holidays including entertainment every evening. Apart from laundry, all facilities on-site including entertainment are free of charge.

open March to October
payment credit/debit cards, cash, cheques

directions On the main coastal road A487. Northern edge of Aberaeron. Brown signposting. Filling station at entrance.

General 📺 🐕 ⚡ 🏪 🚿 ☀ 🔧 🛒 💧 🛒 Leisure ► ∪ 🎣 🏊 🎾 🍸 ⛰

For **key to symbols** see page 6

OAKFORD, Ceredigion Map ref 8A2

SAT NAV SA47 0RN

Shawsmead Caravan Club Site

Oakford, Aberaeron, Ceredigion SA47 0RN
t (01545) 580423 e enquiries@caravanclub.co.uk
w **caravanclub.co.uk**

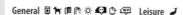

Situated about 4 miles from the coast which is dotted with bays and beaches ideal for the family. Llangranog is ideal for swimming and other water sports. **directions** From A487 into road signposted Ystrad Aeron, in 0.5 mile at cross roads continue onto road signposted Oakford. Site on right. **open** March to October

⊞ (50)   £13.50–£32.79
⊞ (50)   £13.50–£32.79
50 touring pitches

General ⊡ ⊁ ⏃ ⏃ ☼ ⊕ ⊕ ⏏   **Leisure** ⏌

LLANDDULAS, Conwy Map ref 8B1

SAT NAV LL22 8HG

Bron-Y-Wendon Touring Caravan Park

Wern Road, Llanddulas, Colwyn Bay, North Wales LL22 8HG
t (01492) 512903 f (01492) 512903 e stay@northwales-holidays.co.uk
w **northwales-holidays.co.uk**

Award winning, highest grade Park, with pitches overlooking the sea and beach short walk away. Snowdonia, Llandudno, Anglesey and Chester within easy reach, Wi-Fi and wide range of activities nearby. **directions** Leave the A55 at Llanddulas, junction 23, (A547) and follow the Tourist Information signs to the Park. **open** All year **payment** credit/debit cards, cash, cheques

⊞ (120)   £20.00–£23.00
⊞ (10)   £20.00–£23.00
130 touring pitches

General ⏃ ⊡ ⏃ ⊁ ⏃ ⏃ ☼ ⏃ ⏃ ⊕ ⊕ ⏏   **Leisure** ∪ ⏌ ⏃

Looking for something else?

You can also buy a copy of our popular 'B&B' guide including guest accommodation, B&B's, guest houses, farmhouses, inns, and campus and hostel accommodation in England 2012.

Now available in good bookshops and online at
visitbritainshop.com   **£8.99**

RHYL, Denbighshire Map ref 8B1

Cymru
Wales

Parc Gwyliau
Holiday Park
★★★★★

Golden Sands Holiday Park

Sandy Cove, Voryd, Rhyl, Denbighshire LL18 5NA
t (01745) 343606 **f** (01745) 343549 **e** bookings@goldensandsrhyl.co.uk
w **goldensandsrhyl.co.uk**

ONLINE BOOKING LAST MINUTE OFFERS

🚐 (361) £30.00–£99.00
🏠 (5) £164.00–£548.00
🚎 (55) £120.00–£845.00

SPECIAL PROMOTIONS
Midweek Savers - Save up
to 10% Bank Holiday
Bonanza - Save £20 Terms
and conditions apply.

A luxury 5 star Holiday Park, a stone's throw from the beach on the beautiful North Wales coast. Golden Sands is also open 365 days of the year, so you can enjoy all that the Holiday Park has to offer all year round.

Having been part of a thriving tourism area for over 78 years, recent investment of over 1.8million pounds has transformed the facilities into some of the best on the North Wales coast.

Golden Sands has been awarded many Awards over the years, more recently a 5 Star Wales Tourist Board Award and a David Bellamy Silver Award for conservation, Golden Sands was also a finalist for the Hoseason's Diamond Customer Services Award and a finalist for the Wales Business Achievement Tourism Award.

open All year
payment credit/debit cards, cash, cheques

directions For directions please contact the Park on 01745 343606 or visit our website www.goldensandsrhyl.co.uk and click on Contact Us.

General 🖥 📶 🔋 🏠 ☀ ✕ **Leisure** ♿ 🎣 ☂ 🍽 🎵 🔍 ⛩

ABERSOCH, Gwynedd Map ref 8A2

SAT NAV LL53 7AA

M40
The Warren, Abersoch, Gwynedd LL53 7AA
t (01234) 824467 f (01234) 824468 e DInskip@aol.com
w **rivieravistas.com**

£575.00–£1450.00

Beautiful, chalet with large sunny terrace seconds from the wonderful beach at The Warren. Fully equipped for all luxury comforts on holiday. Use of all leisure facilities of The Warren **directions** Between Llanbedrog and Abersoch when travelling on the coast road to Abersoch. **open** 1 March - 17 January **payment** cash, cheques, euros

General 📶 Leisure ▶ ∪ ॐ ఉ ৶ ৭ ৼ ৼ ⵟ ♫ ◈ ⋔

CAERNARFON, Gwynedd Map ref 8A1

SAT NAV LL54 5RS

Coed Helen Caravan Club Site
Coed Helen Road, Caernarfon, Gwynedd LL54 5RS
t (01286) 676770 e enquiries@caravanclub.co.uk
w **caravanclub.co.uk**

THE
CARAVAN
CLUB

🚐 (44)   £1180.00–£30.80
🚎 (44)   £11.80–£30.80
44 touring pitches

Near the historic town of Caernarfon, with views of the famous castle. Walk Snowdon or take the Mountain Railway to the top. Enjoy water based activities on Llyn Pedarn. **directions** A487 turn right into Fford Pant Road, in 20 yards right into Coed Helen Road, in 0.5 mile turn left. Site 200 yards on left. **open** March to November **payment** credit/debit cards, cash, cheques

General 🗊 🛒 🅿 📞 🚻 🆦 Leisure ৶

LLANABER, Gwynedd Map ref 8A2

SAT NAV LL42 1RR

Trawsdir Touring Caravans and Camping Park
Llanaber, Barmouth, Gwynedd LL42 1RR
t (01341) 280999 e enquiries@trawsdir.co.uk
w **barmouthholidays.co.uk** GUEST REVIEWS

🚐   £15.00–£30.00
🚎   £15.00–£30.00
▲ (30)   £10.00–£25.00
70 touring pitches

SPECIAL PROMOTIONS
September 6th to 6th
January: Basic Camping =
£10 per night, Tourers/
Camping with electric =
£15 per night.

Trawsdir is a luxury site situated on the mid-Wales coast with magnificent views over Cardigan Bay and the Lleyn Peninsula and top class facilities. Just a few minutes walk from miles of beautiful sandy beach. Ideal for families and couples. Booking required. RV Pitches available.

open 1st March to 6th January
payment credit/debit cards, cash, cheques

directions 2.5 miles north of Barmouth on the A496 on the mountain side of the main road. Access for all sizes of vehicle.

General 🔌 🗊 📶 🛒 🆚 🆦 ☼ 🖵 🚜 📞 🚻 🆦 Leisure ৶ ⋔

PORTHMADOG (3 MILES), Gwynedd Map ref 8A1 SAT NAV LL49 9YD

Garreg Goch Caravan Park
Black Roock Sands, Morfa Bychan, Porthmadog LL49 9YD
t (01766) 512210 **f** (01766) 515820 **e** info@garreggochcaravanpark.co.uk
w garreggochpark.co.uk

🚐 (7) £19.00–£49.00
🚏 (7) £19.00–£49.00
⛺ (8) £130.00–£520.00
7 touring pitches

Near to famous Black Rock Sands and ideal for touring Snowdonia.
directions In Porthmadog town centre take the turning between the Post Office and Factory Outlet. Then take the third left after the Spar shop. **open** 1st March - 10th January **payment** credit/debit cards, cash, cheques

General 🗐 📶 🐾 🛠 🔌 📷 ☼ 🔌 🖐 🚻 🖥 Leisure ▶ U ⚙ ✈ ⛰

BENLLECH, Isle of Anglesey Map ref 8A1 SAT NAV LL78 7JH

Penrhos Caravan Club Site
Brynteg, Benllech, Anglesey LL78 7JH
t (01248) 852617 **e** enquiries@caravanclub.co.uk
w caravanclub.co.uk

THE CARAVAN CLUB

🚐 (90) £13.50–£32.79
🚏 (90) £13.50–£32.79
90 touring pitches

Breathtaking views of Snowdonia, 5 minutes drive from a safe and sandy beach. Farm trail, bird sanctuary, Sea Zoo will suit families with young children. **directions** From B5110 (sp Llangefni) 1.75 miles continue straight on at cross roads with California Public House. Site on right in about 0.5 mile. **open** March to October

General 🗐 🐾 📷 🖥 🔌 🖐 🖥 Leisure ▶ ⛰

MARIANGLAS, Isle of Anglesey Map ref 8A1 SAT NAV LL73 8NY

Cae Mawr Caravan Club Site
Llangefni Road, Benllech, Anglesey LL73 8NY
t (01248) 853737
w caravanclub.co.uk

THE CARAVAN CLUB

🚐 (76) £10.70–£28.00
🚏 £10.70–£28.00
76 touring pitches

A sheltered site within a short drive of Anglesey's excellent beaches. Great for families. Nearby Traeth Bychan offers boat launching faclilties. **directions** From Marian - Glas (signposted B5110, Llangefni) site entrance on right in about 0.5 mile. **open** March to October **payment** credit/debit cards, cash, cheques

General 📶 🐾 🔌 🖐 Leisure ▶

RHOSNEIGR, Isle of Anglesey Map ref 8A1 SAT NAV LL64 5QZ

Ty Hen Holiday Park
Station Road, Rhosneigr, Anglesey, North Wales LL64 5QZ
t (01407) 810331 **e** info@tyhen.com
w tyhen.com ONLINE MAP GUEST REVIEWS

🚐 (5) £15.00–£25.00
🚏 (5) £15.00–£25.00
Å (10) £5.00–£25.00
🛏 (2) £360.00–£660.00
⛺ (1) £260.00–£400.00
5 touring pitches

"The Art of Relaxing"

'The Art Of Relaxation' isn't a gimmick. The Lake, Mountains, sky & sea views all add to a holiday that simply does your soul good!!" - The Roberts Family. **directions** Situated on the bank of Llyn Maelog, close to the picturesque village of Rhosneigr with beautiful panoramic views of the Snowdonia mountain range. **payment** credit/debit cards, cash, cheques

General 🗐 📶 🐾 🔌 📷 ☼ 🖥 🚲 🔌 🖐 🚻 🖥 Leisure ▶ ✈ ⚹ 🔍 ⛰

ABERGAVENNY, Monmouthshire Map ref 8B3 — SAT NAV NP7 8DR

Pandy Caravan Club Site
Pandy, Abergavenny NP7 8DR
t (01873) 890370 **e** enquiries@caravanclub.co.uk
w caravanclub.co.uk

THE CARAVAN CLUB

🚐 (53) £15.90–£35.51
🚐 (53) £15.90–£35.51
53 touring pitches

Visit the fine castle in Abergavenny or walk the Offa's Dyke Path. The area has many historical buildings. **directions** From south continue onto A465 (signposted Hereford). In 6.25 miles turn left by The Old Pandy Inn, onto minor road. Site on left. **open** March to October **payment** credit/debit cards, cash, cheques

General 🖥 ⌂ 🐕 ⊞ ℞ 🔌 🛒 ♿ 🚿 Leisure ▶ 🏊

NEWPORT, Newport Map ref 8B3 — SAT NAV NP10 8TW

Tredegar House Country Park Caravan Club Site
Tredegar House, Coedkernew, Newport NP10 8TW
t (01633) 815600 **e** enquiries@caravanclub.co.uk
w caravanclub.co.uk

THE CARAVAN CLUB

🚐 (79) £13.50–£32.79
🚐 (79) £13.50–£32.79
79 touring pitches

Site borders an ornamental lake. 7 miles from Cardiff. Park with orangery and garden and adventure playground opens throughout the year. **directions** M4 jct 28 via slip road. At roundabout turn onto A48 (Tredegar House). Left at roundabout. Next roundabout, turn left into Tredegar House. **open** All year **payment** credit/debit cards, cash, cheques

General 🖥 ⌂ 🐕 ℞ ☼ 🔌 🛒 ♿ 🚿 Leisure ▶ 🏊

FISHGUARD, Pembrokeshire Map ref 8A2 — SAT NAV SA65 9ET

Fishguard Bay Caravan & Camping Park
Garn Gelli, Fishguard, Pembrokeshire SA65 9ET
t (01348) 811415 **f** (01348) 811425 **e** inquiries@fishguardbay.com
w fishguardbay.com ONLINE MAP

🚐 (20) £17.00–£21.00
🚐 (20) £17.00–£21.00
⛺ (30) £16.00–£24.00
🏕 (12) £257.00–£570.00
20 touring pitches

Enjoy your stay on this beautiful stretch of Pembrokeshire National Park coastline. Ideal centre for walking and touring. Quiet, family-run park. Beautiful location, and superb views towards Fishguard harbour. **directions** Please contact us for directions **open** 1 March to 10 January **payment** credit/debit cards, cash, cheques

General ♿ 🖥 ⌂ 🐕 🛠 ℞ ☼ 🔌 🛒 ♿ 🚿 Leisure ∪ ⚓ ⛰

FISHGUARD, Pembrokeshire Map ref 8A2 — SAT NAV SA65 9TA

Gwaun Vale Touring Park
Llanychaer, Fishguard SA65 9TA
t (01348) 874698 **e** margaret.harries@talk21.com
w gwaunvale.co.uk ONLINE MAP

🚐 (19) £17.00–£20.00
🚐 (2) £17.00–£20.00
⛺ (8) £15.00–£23.00
🏕 (1) £200.00–£350.00
29 touring pitches

Situated in the beautiful Gwaun Valley, overlooking Pembrokeshire National Park. Ideal for walking, sightseeing or just relaxing. Close to Irish ferry. **directions** Follow signs for B4313 from Fishguard for just over a mile. We are on right hand side. **open** April 1st to October 31st **payment** cash, cheques, euros

General 🖥 🐕 🛠 ℞ ☼ 🚲 🔌 🛒 ♿ Leisure 🏊

MANORBIER, Pembrokeshire Map ref 8A3   SAT NAV SA70 7SN

Manorbier Country Park
Station Road, Manorbier, Tenby SA70 7SN
t (01834) 871952 f (01834) 871203 e enquiries@countrypark.co.uk
w **countrypark.co.uk** ONLINE MAP GUEST REVIEWS ONLINE BOOKING LAST MINUTE OFFERS

⊕ (45)	£15.00–£36.00
⊞ (5)	£15.00–£36.00
▲ (4)	£15.00–£31.00
⊞ (25)	£151.00–£854.00

50 touring pitches

SPECIAL PROMOTIONS
Short Break Booking from
£106.00 3/4nts for 4 people.

The small park with the big heart. Indoor heated pool, tennis court, fully licensed bar & club, restaurant, live family entertainment, children's play areas, family entertainment centre, gym & solarium, sauna & steam room, big screen SKY Sports, laundrette, shop. What more could you want from your holiday?

open March - November
payment credit/debit cards, cash, cheques

directions From Tenby follow A4139 to Pembroke, after Lydstep turn right for Manorbier Newton & Train Station, Park on left.

General ⚲ ▢ ♨ ✦ ☎ ❲❳ ☀ ▣ ⊞ ⊕ ☕ ☎ ⊞ ✕ Leisure ▶ ∪ ✆ ⚙ ✎ ⚘ ☍ ♫ ♥ ⟋△

NARBERTH, Pembrokeshire Map ref 8A3   SAT NAV SA67 8PR

Amroth Bay Holidays
Amroth Bay Holidays, Amroth, Narberth SA67 8PR
t (01834) 831259 f (01834) 831702 e amrothbayholidays@aol.com
w **amrothbay.co.uk** ONLINE BOOKING

⊞ (15)   £300.00–£780.00

Award winning Holiday Park set in peaceful picturesque setting. Luxury caravans (some with C/H D/G) and cosy cottages (4 star). Dogs welcome. Heated pool, playground. Couples discounts. **directions** A40 from Carmarthen, A477 from St. Clears to Llanteg, turn left at the Colby Woodland Gardens sign in Llanteg, park 0.5 mile on right. **open** March to end October **payment** credit/debit cards, cheques, euros

General ▢ ⚲ ⚘ ☀ Leisure ∪ ⟋ ✦

PEMBROKE, Pembrokeshire Map ref 8A3   SAT NAV SA71 5LJ

Freshwater East Caravan Club Site
Trewent Hill, Freshwater East, Pembroke, Pembrokeshire SA71 5LJ
t (01646) 672341 e enquiries@caravanclub.co.uk
w **caravanclub.co.uk**

THE
CARAVAN
CLUB

⊕ (130)	£13.50–£32.79
⊞ (130)	£13.50–£32.79

130 touring pitches

Site located in the Pembrokeshire Coast National Park. The coastal paths have magnificent cliff top views. Tenby nearby with its colourful harbour and sandy beaches. **directions** From A4139 signposted Tenby turn right onto B4584 and then right onto Trewent Hill. In 0.25 mile turn right into lane at Club sign. **open** March to October

General ▢ ⚲ ❲❳ ☕ ⊞ Leisure ⟋ △

ST DAVIDS, Pembrokeshire Map ref 8A3

SAT NAV SA62 6QT

Caerfai Bay Caravan & Tent Park
St Davids, Haverfordwest, Pembrokeshire SA62 6QT
t (01437) 720274 f (01437) 720577 e info@caerfaibay.co.uk
w **caerfaibay.co.uk**

(26)	£13.50–£18.00
(14)	£11.50–£18.00
A (72)	£11.50–£16.00
(9)	£250.00–£475.00
112 touring pitches	

SPECIAL PROMOTIONS
Senior Citizens discount
during low season (caravan
field only).

A quiet family-run park, situated within the Pembrokeshire Coast National Park. Caerfai Bay sandy bathing beach within 200 metres and St Davids within easy walking distance. Park situated at end of Caerfai Road on the right. No dogs in tent fields during school summer holidays.

open March to mid-November
payment credit/debit cards, cash, cheques

directions Haverfordwest to St Davids: A487. Turn left at Oriel Y Parc(OYP)/Visitor Centre, Caerfai signposted. From Fishguard: A487 to St Davids. Turn right at OYP.

General 🚶 Leisure 🚴

ST DAVIDS, Pembrokeshire Map ref 8A3

SAT NAV SA62 6PR

Lleithyr Meadow Caravan Club Site
Whitesands, St Davids, Pembrokeshire SA62 6PR
t (01437) 720401 e enquiries@caravanclub.co.uk
w **caravanclub.co.uk**

THE
CARAVAN
CLUB

(120)	£13.50–£32.79
(120)	£13.50–£32.79
120 touring pitches	

A marvellous holiday site on the Pembrokeshire Coast. Great for energetic families, swimming, surfing, windsurfing and sailing from Whitsands Bay. Anglers can fish in reservoir or sea. **directions** M4 to Carmarthen, A40 to Haverfordwest, A487 towards St Davids. Right onto B4583, crossroads. Sharp right opposite St Davids golf club. **open** April - October **payment** credit/debit cards, cash, cheques

General Leisure

BRECON, Powys Map ref 8B3

SAT NAV LD3 0LD

Anchorage Caravan Park
Bronllys, Brecon, Powys LD3 0LD
t (01874) 711246
w **anchoragecp.co.uk**

(60)	£12.00–£18.00
(10)	£12.00–£18.00
A (40)	£12.00–£15.00
110 touring pitches	

High standard family-run park. Panoramic views of the Brecon Beacons National Park. Ideal for touring and walking mid and south Wales. **directions** Midway between Brecon and Hay-On-Wye. In centre of Bronllys village. **open** All year **payment** cash, cheques

General Leisure

BRECON, Powys Map ref 8B3
SAT NAV LD3 7SH

Brynich Caravan Park
Brecon, Powys LD3 7SH
t (01874) 623325
w **caravanclub.co.uk**

🚐 (144)   £15.30–£35.51
🚐 (144)   £15.30–£35.51
144 touring pitches

Situated near the foothills of the Brecon Beacons, Brynich is well located with excellent facilities. It boasts some of the best views of the central Beacons. **directions** On A470 (Brecon - Builth Wells) 200 yards past roundabout junction A40 (eastern end Brecon Bypass). **open** March to November **payment** credit/debit cards, cash, cheques

General 🔲 ♿ 🐕 🎣 ☼ 🔌 🕐 🚻 ✗   Leisure ► ⛰

LLANBRYNMAIR, Powys Map ref 8B2
SAT NAV SY19 7EB

Gwern Y Bwlch Caravan Club Site
Llanbrynmair, Powys SY19 7EB
t (01650) 521351   e enquiries@caravanclub.co.uk
w **caravanclub.co.uk**

🚐 (37)   £10.00–£18.00
🚐 (37)   £10.00–£18.00
37 touring pitches

Lovely setting in Mid Wales between Snowdonia and Montgomeryshire. A great site for birdwatching or fishing. The RSPB has reserves at Lake Vyrnwy and Ynys-Hir. **directions** From A470 in 4 miles turn left at Club Site sign. **open** April to October **payment** credit/debit cards, cash, cheques

General 🐕 🎣 🔌 🕐 🚻 📶

SNEAD, Powys Map ref 8B2
SAT NAV SY15 6EB

Daisy Bank Touring Park
Churchstoke, Montgomery SY15 6EB
t (01588) 620471   e enquiries@daisy-bank.co.uk
w **daisy-bank.co.uk** ONLINE MAP ONLINE BOOKING LAST MINUTE OFFERS

🚐 (50)   £18.00–£26.00
🚐 (50)   £18.00–£25.00
🏕 (5)   £7.00–£9.00
50 touring pitches

An Adults Only Park situated on the Welsh / Shropshire Border. A Five Star site with outstanding views and luxurious facilities. The perfect place to get away from it all. **directions** We are situated on the A489 between Craven Arms and Churchstoke (2 miles East of Churchstoke). OS Sheet 137 Map Ref 303929 **open** All year **payment** credit/debit cards, cash, cheques

General ♿ 🔲 ♿ 🐕 🎣 🔌 ☼ 🔌 🕐 🚻   Leisure ∪ 🚲 ✈

SWANSEA, Swansea Map ref 8B3
SAT NAV SA4 3QP

Gowerton Caravan Club Site
Pont Y Cob Road, Gowerton, Swansea SA4 3QP
t (01792) 873050   e enquiries@caravanclub.co.uk
w **caravanclub.co.uk**

🚐 (135)   £13.50–£32.79
🚐 (135)   £13.50–£32.79
135 touring pitches

A level, well-designed site within an easy drive of the whole range of superb beaches on the Gower Peninsula, such as Oxwich and Caswell Bay. **directions** From B2496 turn right at traffic lights. In 0.5 miles turn right at traffic lights into Pont-y-Cob road. Site on right. **open** March to November **payment** credit/debit cards, cash, cheques

General 🔲 🐕 🎣 🔌 🔌 🕐 🚻 📶   Leisure ► ✈

FLEMINGSTON, Vale of Glamorgan Map ref 8B3

SAT NAV CF62 4QL

Cymru
Wales

Parc Gwyliau
Holiday Park
★★★

Happy Jakes
1 New Barn Holdings, Flemingston, Barry CF62 4QL
t (01446) 750174 f (01656) 659998 e info@happyjakes.com
w **happyjakes.com** ONLINE MAP GUEST REVIEWS ONLINE BOOKING

⊞ (25)	£12.00–£14.00
⊞ (5)	£12.00–£14.00
Å (15)	£10.00–£12.00
45 touring pitches	
★★	

Rural location within the Vale of Glamorgan. Close to the picturesque town of Cowbridge with vibrant shops and restaurants. Glamorgan Heritage Coastline with miles of footpaths and country lanes closeby. **directions** Follow A4232 to the village of St Athan. Turn into St Athan Village at the monument and continue for 2 miles, follow Brown Tourism Signs **open** All year **payment** cash, euros

General ⊟ ★ ⋔ ☼ ◘ ⬧ ⬢ ⬛ Leisure ► ∪ ⚲ ⤻

BANGOR-IS-Y-COED, Wrexham Map ref 8B1

SAT NAV LL13 0BG

Cymru
Wales

Parc Teithio
Touring Park
★★

Emral Gardens Caravan Park
Holly Bush, Bangor-on-Dee, Wrexham, N. Wales LL13 0BG
t (01948) 770401 e info@emralgardens.co.uk
w **emralgardens.co.uk** ONLINE MAP GUEST REVIEWS LAST MINUTE OFFERS

⊞ (20)	£15.00–£21.00
⊞ (20)	£15.00–£21.00
Å (10)	£13.00–£17.00
30 touring pitches	

Adults Only. Small friendly, rural touring park next to woodland and fields of horses. Luxury pitches. Gold David Bellamy Award. Convenient for Bangor-on-Dee Races, Wrexham and Chester. Seasonal & Storage. **directions** From Bangor-on-Dee take A525 1.5 miles south towards Whitchurch. Turn left at crossroads (signposted Worthenbury/Tallarn Green). Go 1/4 mile, site is 3rd entrance on right. **open** 1st March to 31st October **payment** cash, cheques

General ⚲ ⊕ ★ ⬧ ⋔ ☼ ⬛ ⬢ ◘ ⬧ Leisure ⤻

Looking for something else?

You can also buy a copy of our popular guide 'Hotels' including country house and town house hotels, metro and budget hotels, serviced apartments and restaurants with rooms in England 2012.

Now available in good bookshops and online at
visitbritainshop.com   **£7.99**

If you have
access needs...

Guests with hearing, visual or mobility needs can feel confident about booking accommodation that participates in the National Accessible Scheme (NAS).

Look out for the NAS symbols which are included throughout the accommodation directory. Using the NAS could help make the difference between a good holiday and a perfect one!

You can also search for NAS rated accommodation at **enjoyengland.com/access** or buy a copy of the new OpenBritain guide, available from Tourism for All - tel 0845 124 9971

Map 1

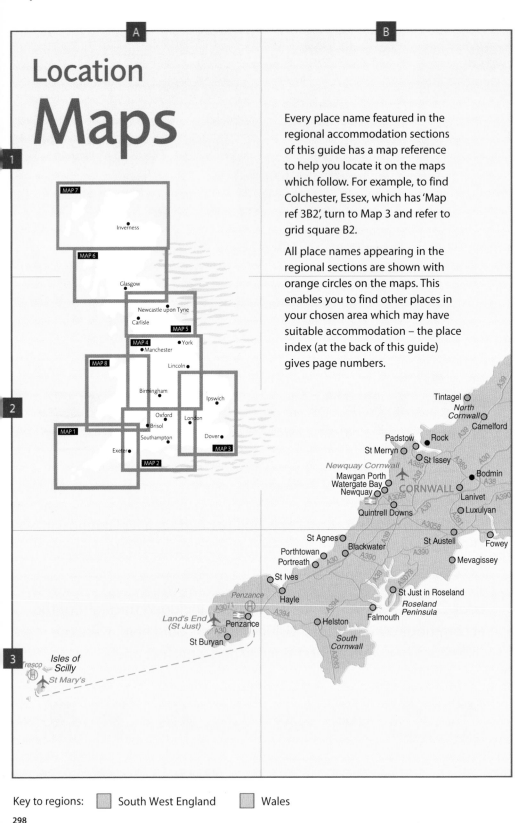

Location
Maps

Every place name featured in the regional accommodation sections of this guide has a map reference to help you locate it on the maps which follow. For example, to find Colchester, Essex, which has 'Map ref 3B2', turn to Map 3 and refer to grid square B2.

All place names appearing in the regional sections are shown with orange circles on the maps. This enables you to find other places in your chosen area which may have suitable accommodation – the place index (at the back of this guide) gives page numbers.

Key to regions: □ South West England □ Wales

Map 1

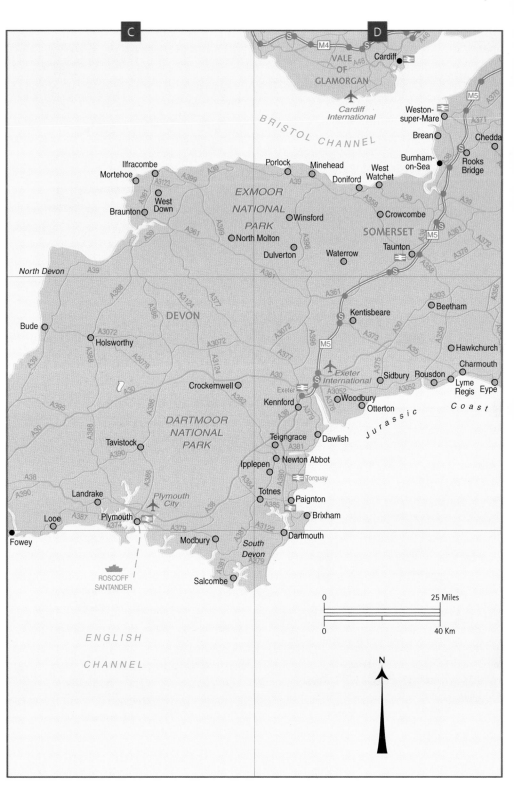

Map 2

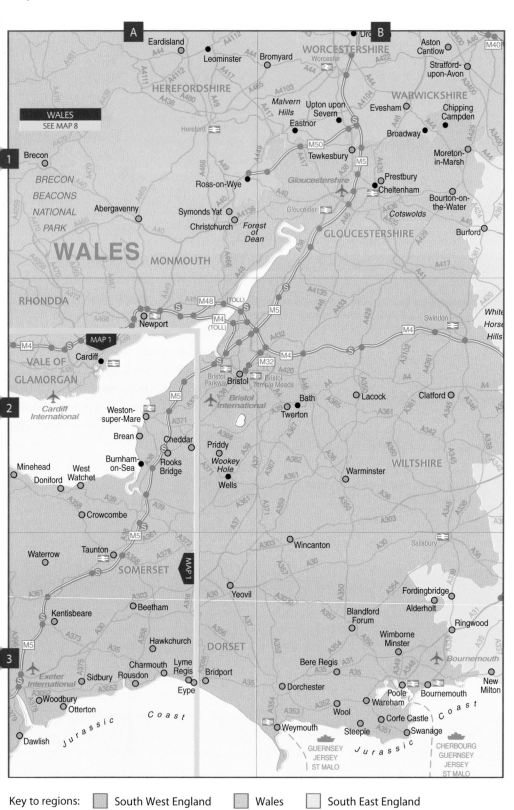

Key to regions: ☐ South West England ☐ Wales ☐ South East England

Map 2

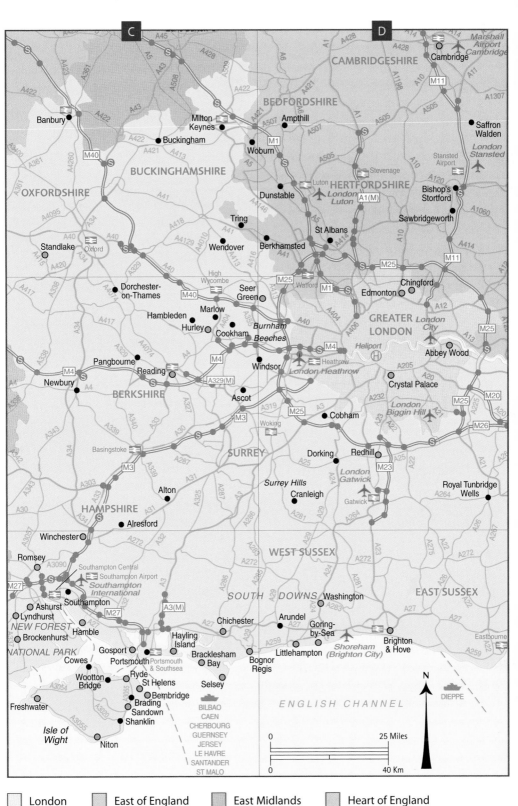

London   East of England   East Midlands   Heart of England

Orange circles indicate accommodation within the regional sections of this guide

Map 3

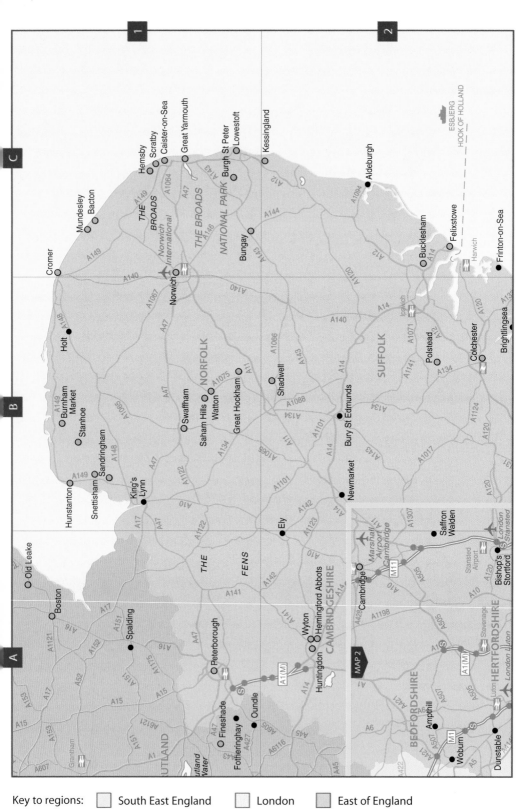

Key to regions: ☐ South East England ☐ London ☐ East of England

302

Map 3

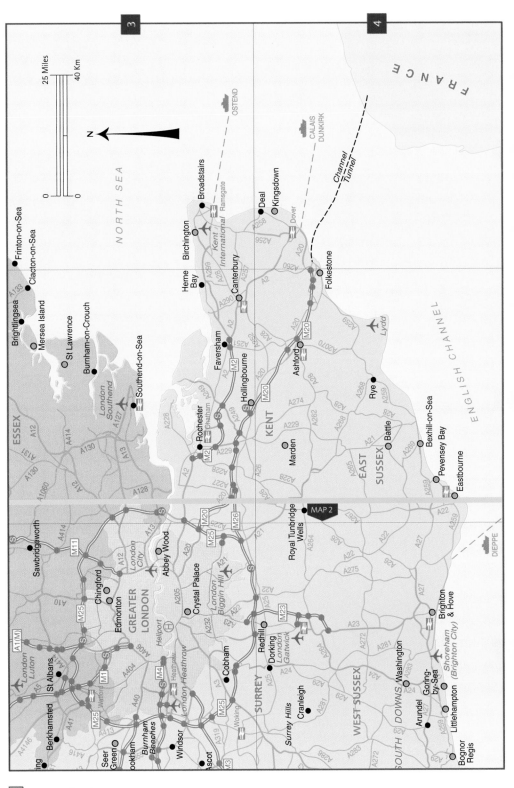

East Midlands

Orange circles indicate accommodation within the regional sections of this guide

Map 4

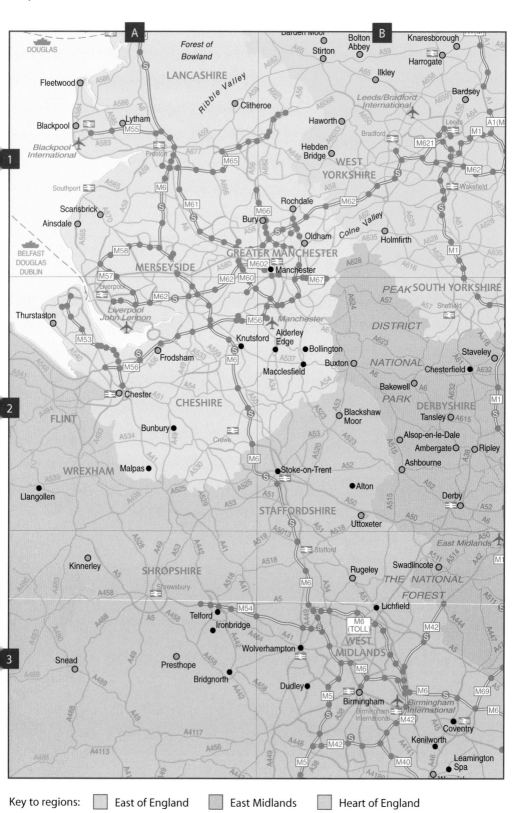

Key to regions: ☐ East of England ☐ East Midlands ☐ Heart of England

Map 4

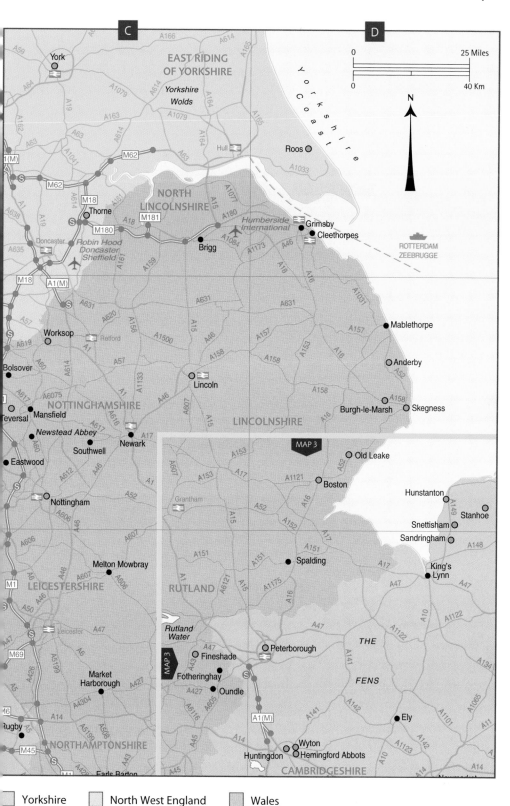

Yorkshire   North West England   Wales

Orange circles indicate accommodation within the regional sections of this guide

Map 5

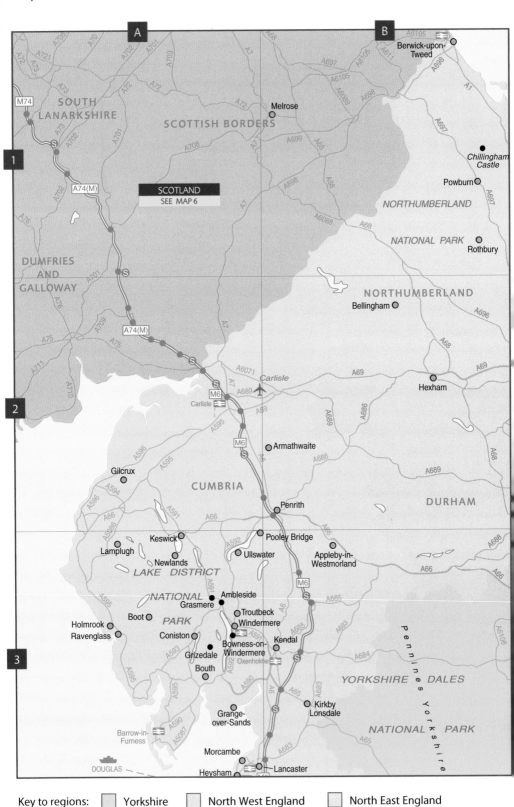

Key to regions: ☐ Yorkshire ☐ North West England ☐ North East England

Map 5

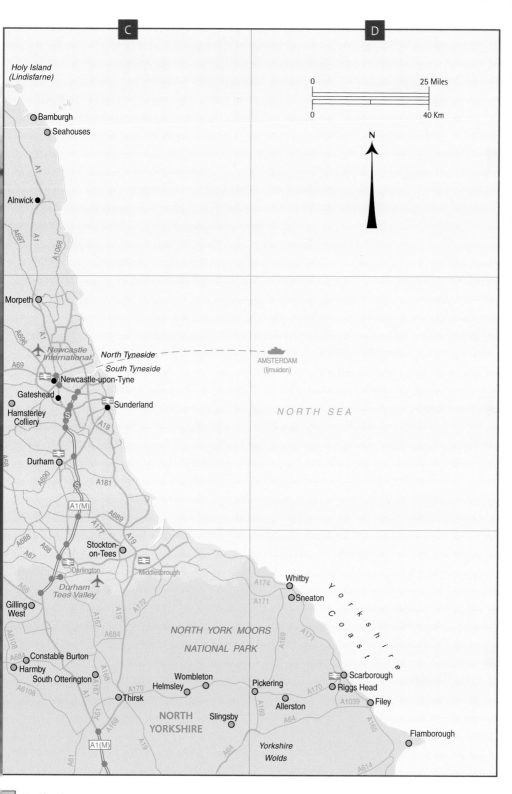

Holy Island
(Lindisfarne)

○ Bamburgh
○ Seahouses

Alnwick ●

Morpeth ○

Newcastle
International
Newcastle-upon-Tyne
North Tyneside
South Tyneside
Gateshead ●
Hamsterley
Colliery
Sunderland ●

Durham ○

A1(M)

Stockton-
on-Tees ○
Darlington
Durham
Tees Valley
Middlesbrough

Gilling ○
West

Constable Burton
Harmby ○
South Otterington ○
Thirsk ○

NORTH YORKSHIRE NATIONAL PARK
NORTH YORK MOORS

Wombleton ○
Helmsley ○
Slingsby ○

NORTH
YORKSHIRE

Pickering ○
Allerston ○

Yorkshire
Wolds

Whitby
Sneaton ○

Scarborough ○
Riggs Head ○
Filey ○

Flamborough ○

Yorkshire Coast

NORTH SEA

AMSTERDAM
(IJmuiden)

0   25 Miles
0   40 Km

N

Scotland

Orange circles indicate accommodation within the regional sections of this guide

Map 6

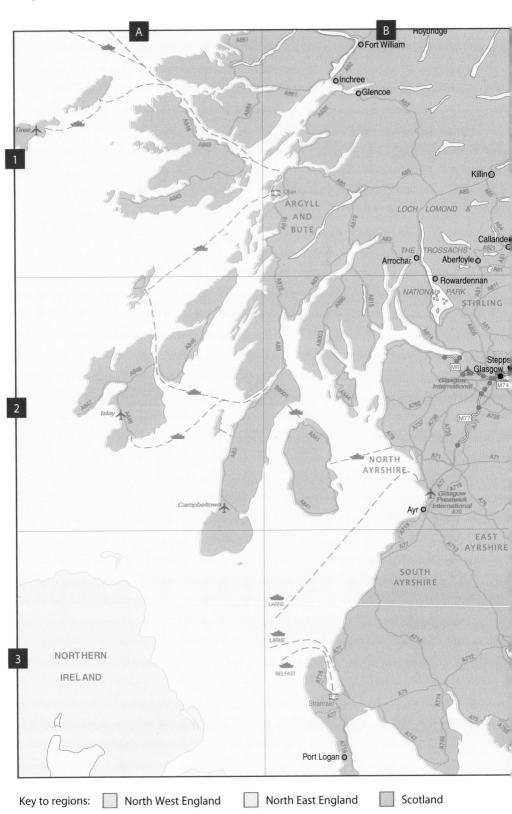

Key to regions: ☐ North West England ☐ North East England ☐ Scotland

Map 6

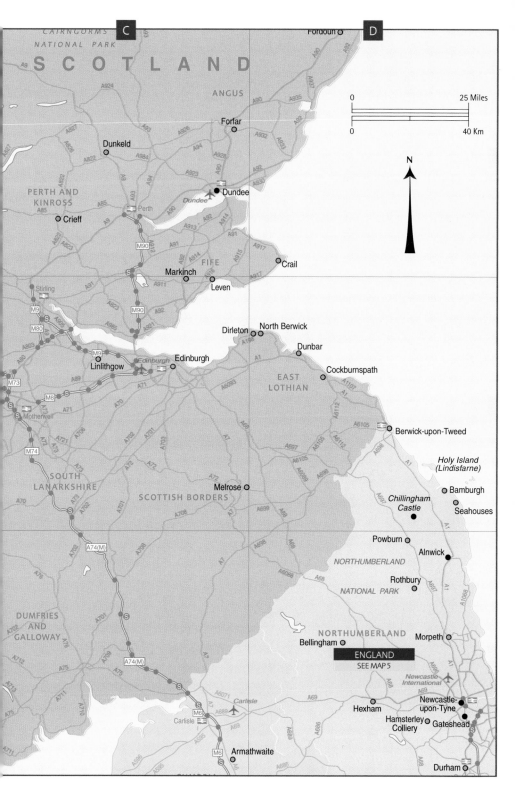

Map 7

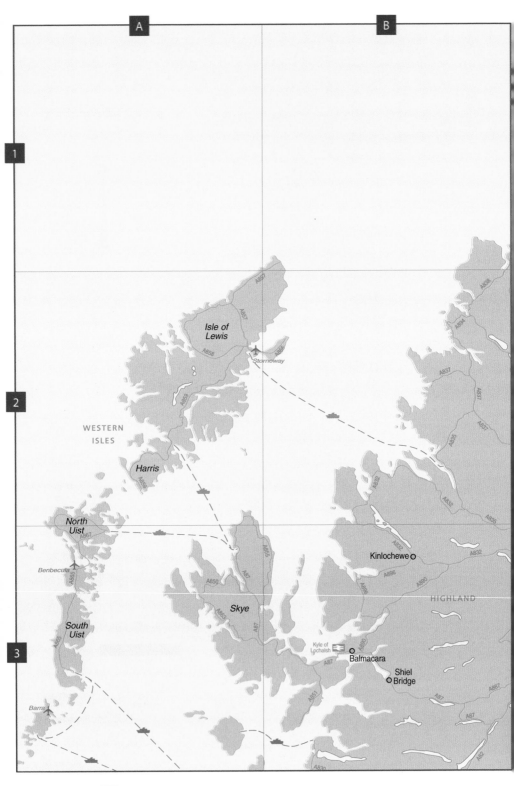

Key to regions: ▢ Scotland

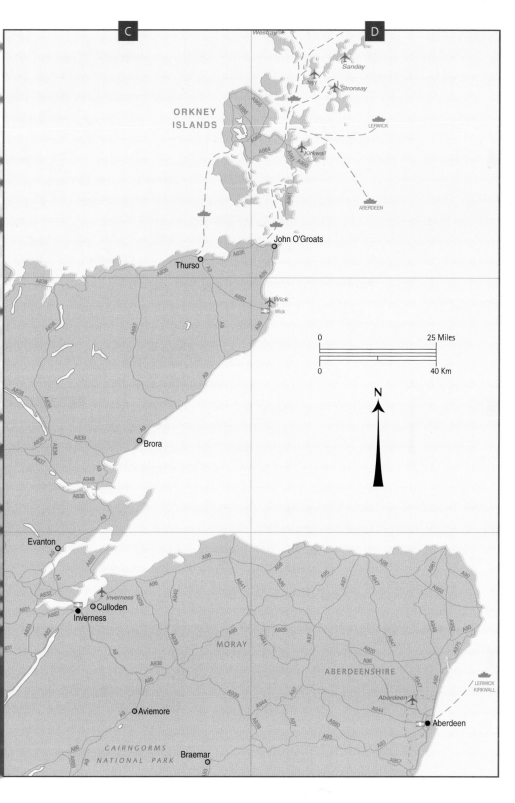

Map 7

Map 8

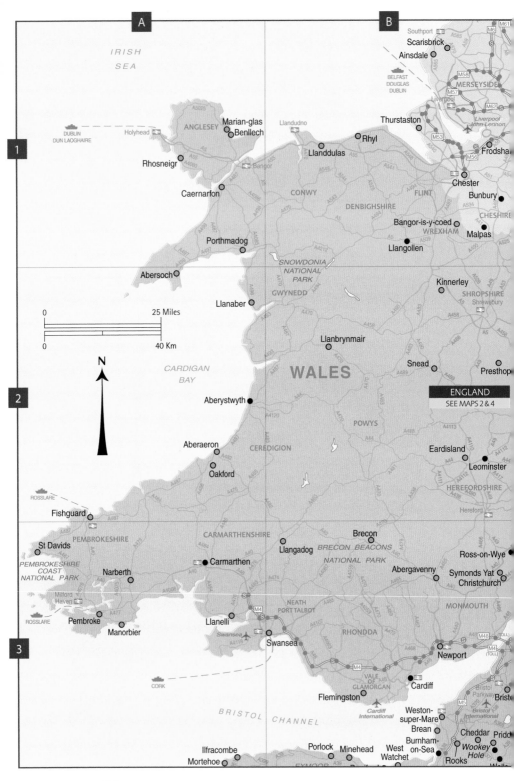

Key to regions: ▢ Wales

Orange circles indicate accommodation within the regional sections of this guide

Map 9

London

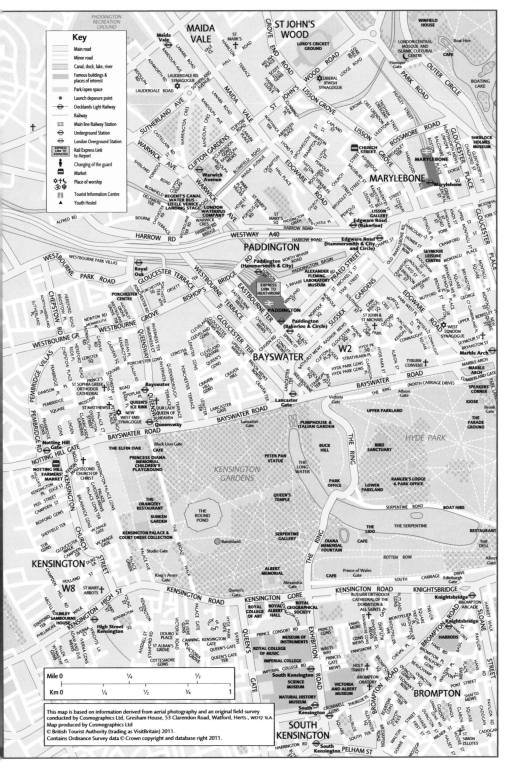

Map 10

London

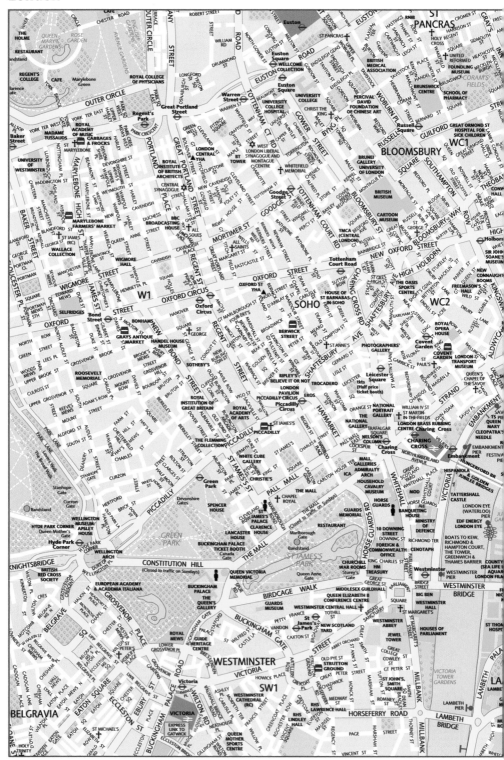

Map 10

London

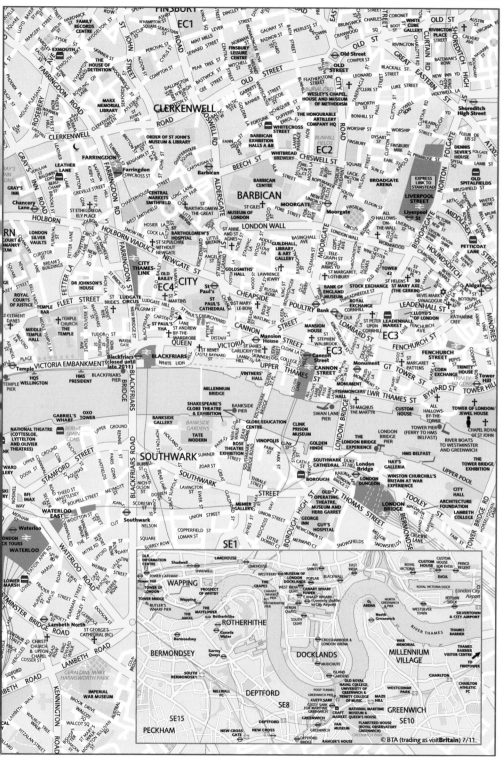

Motorway Service Area Assessment Scheme

Something we all use and take for granted but how good are they?

The star ratings cover over 250 different aspects of each operation including cleanliness, the quality and range of catering and also the quality of the physical aspects as well as the service. It does not however cover prices or value for money.

OPERATOR: EXTRA

Baldock	★★★
Beaconsfield	★★★★
Blackburn	★★★
Cullompton	★★
Peterborough	★★★★

OPERATOR: MOTO

Birch E	★★★
Birch W	★★★
Bridgwater	★★★
Burton in Kendall	★★★
Cherwell Valley	★★★
Chieveley	★★★
Doncaster N	★★★
Donington Park	★★★
Exeter	★★★★
Ferrybridge	★★★
Frankley N	★★★
Frankley S	★★★
Heston E	★★
Heston W	★★
Hilton Park N	★★★
Hilton Park S	★★★
Knutsford N	★★★
Knutsford S	★★★
Lancaster N	★★★
Lancaster S	★★★
Leigh Delamere E	★★★★
Leigh Delamere W	★★★
Medway	★★
Pease Pottage	★★★
Reading E	★★★★
Reading W	★★★★
Severn View	★★
Southwaite N	★★★
Southwaite S	★★★
Stafford N	★★★★

Tamworth	★★★
Thurrock	★★★
Toddington N	★★★
Toddington S	★★★
Trowell N	★★★
Trowell S	★★★
Washington N	★★
Washington S	★★★
Wetherby	★★★★
Winchester N	★★★★
Winchester S	★★★★
Woolley Edge N	★★★
Woolley Edge S	★★★★

OPERATOR: ROADCHEF

Chester	★★
Clacket Lane E	★★★
Clacket Lane W	★★★
Durham	★★★
Killington Lake	★★★
Maidstone	★★★
Northampton N	★★★
Northampton S	★★★
Norton Cranes	★★★★
Rownhams N	★★
Rownhams S	★★
Sandbach N	★★★
Sandbach S	★★★
Sedgemoor S	★★★
Stafford S	★★★
Strensham N	★★★
Strensham S	★★★★
Taunton Deane N	★★
Taunton Deane S	★★
Tibshelf N	★★★
Tibshelf S	★★★
Watford Gap N	★★★
Watford Gap S	★★★

OPERATOR: WELCOME BREAK

Birchanger Green	★★★
Burtonwood	★★
Charnock Richard N	★★★
Charnock Richard S	★★★
Corley E	★★★
Corley W	★★★
Fleet N	★★★
Fleet S	★★★★
Gordano	★★★★
Hartshead Moor E	★★★
Hartshead Moor W	★★★
Hopwood Park	★★★
Keele N	★★★
Keele S	★★★
Leicester Forest East N	★★★
Leicester Forest East S	★★★
London Gateway	★★★
Membury E	★★★
Membury W	★★★★
Michaelwood N	★★★
Michaelwood S	★★★
Newport Pagnell S	★★
Newport Pagnell N	★★★
Oxford	★★★★
Sedgemoor N	★★★
South Mimms	★★★★
Telford	★★★
Warwick N	★★★
Warwick S	★★★
Woodall N	★★★
Woodall S	★★★

WESTMORLAND

Tebay N	★★★
Tebay S	★★★★

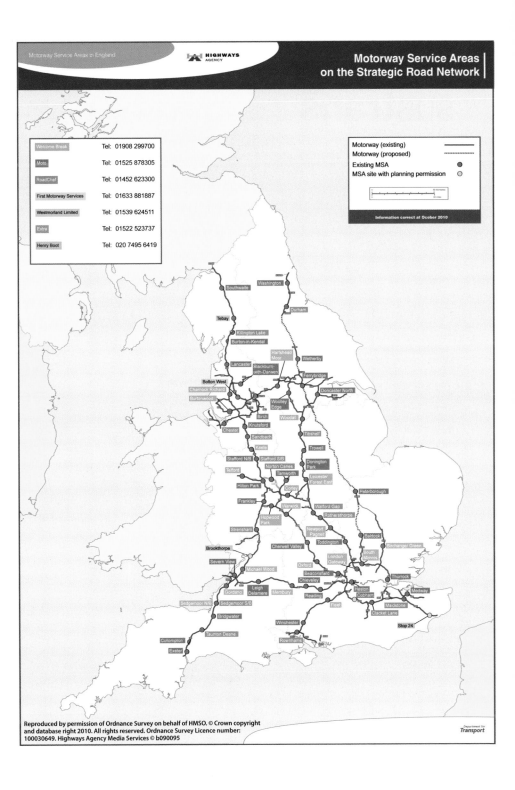

Motorway Service Areas in England

HIGHWAYS AGENCY

Motorway Service Areas on the Strategic Road Network

Welcome Break	Tel: 01908 299700
Moto	Tel: 01525 878305
RoadChef	Tel: 01452 623300
First Motorway Services	Tel: 01633 881887
Westmorland Limited	Tel: 01539 624511
Extra	Tel: 01522 523737
Henry Boot	Tel: 020 7495 6419

Motorway (existing)
Motorway (proposed)
Existing MSA
MSA site with planning permission

Information correct at October 2010

Reproduced by permission of Ordnance Survey on behalf of HMSO. © Crown copyright and database right 2010. All rights reserved. Ordnance Survey Licence number: 100030649. Highways Agency Media Services © b090095

Department for Transport

Here are just some of the most popular long distance routes on the 12,000 mile Sustrans National Cycle Network. To see the Network in it's entirety and to find routes near you, **visit www.sustrans.org.uk**

Sustrans is the UK's leading sustainable transport charity working on practical projects to enable people to choose to travel in ways which benefit their health and the environment.

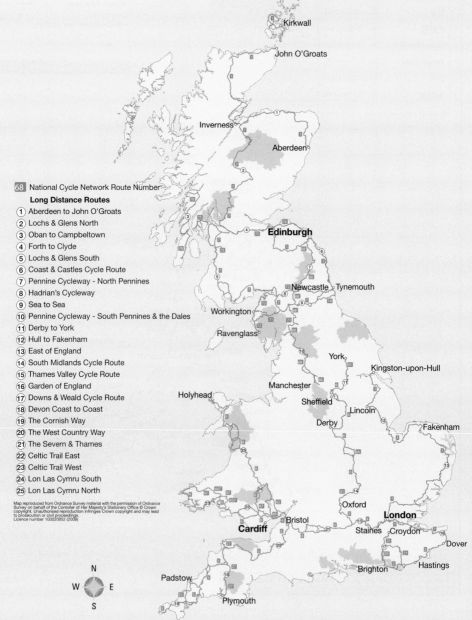

68 National Cycle Network Route Number

Long Distance Routes

1. Aberdeen to John O'Groats
2. Lochs & Glens North
3. Oban to Campbeltown
4. Forth to Clyde
5. Lochs & Glens South
6. Coast & Castles Cycle Route
7. Pennine Cycleway - North Pennines
8. Hadrian's Cycleway
9. Sea to Sea
10. Pennine Cycleway - South Pennines & the Dales
11. Derby to York
12. Hull to Fakenham
13. East of England
14. South Midlands Cycle Route
15. Thames Valley Cycle Route
16. Garden of England
17. Downs & Weald Cycle Route
18. Devon Coast to Coast
19. The Cornish Way
20. The West Country Way
21. The Severn & Thames
22. Celtic Trail East
23. Celtic Trail West
24. Lon Las Cymru South
25. Lon Las Cymru North

Map reproduced from Ordnance Survey material with the permission of Ordnance Survey on behalf of the Contoller of Her Majesty's Stationery Office © Crown copyright. Unauthorised reproduction infringes Crown copyright and may lead to prosecution or civil proceedings.
Licence number 100020852 (2009)

318

Further Information

Advice and information

Making a booking

When enquiring about a place to stay, make sure you check prices, the quality rating, and other important details. You will also need to state your requirements clearly and precisely.

Booking by letter or email

Misunderstandings can easily happen over the telephone, so do request a written confirmation together with details of any terms and conditions.

Deposits and advance payments

In the case of caravan, camping and touring parks, and holiday villages the full charge often has to be paid in advance. This may be in two instalments – a deposit at the time of booking and the balance by, say, two weeks before the start of the booked period.

Cancellations

Legal contract

When you accept a booking that is offered to you, by telephone or in writing, you enter a legally binding contract with the proprietor. This means that if you cancel or fail to take up your booking or leave early, the proprietor may be entitled to compensation if he or she cannot re-let for all or a good part of the booked period. You will probably forfeit any deposit you have paid and may well be asked for an additional payment.

At the time of booking you should be advised of what charges would be made in the event of cancelling the accommodation or leaving early. If this is not mentioned you should ask so that future disputes can be avoided. The proprietor cannot make a claim until after the booked period, and during that time he or she should make every effort to re-let the accommodation. If there is a dispute it is sensible for both sides to seek legal advice on the matter. If you do have to change your travel plans, it is in your own interests to let the proprietor know in writing as soon as possible, to give them a chance to re-let your accommodation.

And remember, if you book by telephone and are asked for your credit card number, you should check whether the proprietor intends charging your credit card account should you later cancel your booking. A proprietor should not be able to charge your credit card account with a cancellation fee unless he or she has made this clear at the time of your booking and you have agreed. However, to avoid later disputes, we suggest you check whether this is the intention.

Insurance

A travel or holiday insurance policy will safeguard you if you have to cancel or change your holiday plans both abroad and in the UK. You can arrange a policy quite cheaply through your insurance company or travel agent.

Finding a park

Tourist signs similar to the one shown here are designed to help visitors find their park. They clearly show whether the park is for tents or caravans or both.

Tourist information centres throughout Britain are able to give campers and caravanners information about parks in their areas. Some tourist information centres have camping and caravanning advisory services that provide details of park availability and often assist with park booking.

Electric hook-up points

Most parks now have electric hook-up points for caravans and tents. Voltage is generally 240v AC, 50 cycles. Parks may charge extra for this facility, and it is advisable to check rates when making a booking.

Avoiding peak season

In the summer months of June to September, parks in popular areas such as North Wales, Cumbria, the West Country or the New Forest in Hampshire may become full. Campers should aim to arrive at parks early in the day or, where possible, should book in advance. Some parks have overnight holding areas for visitors who arrive late. This helps to prevent disturbing other campers and caravanners late at night and means that fewer visitors are turned away. Caravans or tents are directed to a pitch the following morning.

Other caravan and camping places

If you enjoy making your own route through Britain's countryside, it may interest you to know that the Forestry Commission operates campsites in Britain's Forest Parks as well as in the New Forest. Some offer reduced charges for youth organisations on organised camping trips, and all enquiries about them should be made, well in advance of your intended stay, to the Forestry Commission.

Bringing pets to Britain

Dogs, cats, ferrets and some other pet mammals can be brought into the UK from certain countries without having to undertake six months' quarantine on arrival provided they meet all the rules of the Pet Travel Scheme (PETS).

For full details, visit the PETS website at
w defra.gov.uk/wildlife-pets/pets/travel
or contact the PETS Helpline
t +44 (0) 870 241 1710
e quarantine@animalhealth.gsi.giv.uk

Ask for fact sheets which cover dogs and cats, ferrets or domestic rabbits and rodents.

What to expect at holiday, touring and camping parks

In addition to fulfilling its statutory obligations, including complying with the Regulatory Reform (Fire Safety) Order 2005 and holding public liability insurance, and ensuring that all caravan holiday homes/chalets for hire and the park and all buildings and facilities thereon, the fixtures, furnishings, fittings and decor are maintained in sound and clean condition and are fit for the purposes intended, the management is required to undertake the following:

Prior to booking
- To describe accurately in any advertisement, brochure, or other printed or electronic media, the facilities and services provided;

- To make clear to guests in print, in electronic media and on the telephone exactly what is included in all prices quoted for accommodation, including taxes, and any other surcharges. Details of charges for additional services / facilities should also be made clear, for example showers, fuel etc;

- To provide information on the suitability of the premises for guests of various ages, particularly for the elderly and the very young;

- To allow guests to view the accommodation prior to booking if requested and possible.

At the time of booking
- To clearly describe the cancellation policy to guests i.e. by telephone, fax, internet/email as well as in any printed information given to guests;

- To adhere to and not to exceed prices quoted at the time of booking for accommodation and other services.

On arrival
- To welcome all guests courteously and without discrimination in relation to gender, sexual orientation, disability, race, religion or belief.

During the stay
- To maintain standards of guest care, cleanliness, and service appropriate to the style of operation.

- To deal promptly and courteously with all enquiries, requests, bookings and correspondence from guests;

- To ensure complaint handling procedures are in place and that complaints received are investigated promptly and courteously and that the outcome is communicated to the guest.

On departure
- To give each guests, on request, details or payments due and a receipt, if required/requested.

General
- To give due consideration to the requirements of guests with special needs, and to make suitable provision where applicable;

- To ensure the accommodation is prepared for the arrival of guests at all times when the operation is advertised as open;

- To advise guests, at any time prior to their stay, if there are any changes in what has been booked;

- To hold current public liability insurance and to comply with all relevant statutory obligations including legislation applicable to health and safety, planning and fire;

- To allow VisitEngland representatives reasonable access to the operation, on request, to confirm that the Code of Conduct is being observed or in order to investigate any complaint of a serious nature notified to them;

- When a business is sold or ceases to trade, every effort should be made to inform VisitEngland.

What to expect at holiday villages

The operator/manager is required to undertake the following:

Prior to booking
- To describe accurately in any advertisement, brochure, or other printed or electronic media, the facilities and services provided;

- To make clear to guests in print, on the internet and on the telephone exactly what is included in all prices quoted for accommodation, including taxes, and any other surcharges. Details of charges for additional services/facilities should also be made clear, for example breakfast, leisure etc;

Advice and information

- To provide information on the suitability of the premises for guests of various ages, particularly for the elderly and the very young;

- To allow guests to view the accommodation prior to booking if requested.

At the time of booking
- To clearly describe the cancellation policy to guests t. by telephone, fax, internet/email as well as in any printed information given to guests;

- To adhere to and not to exceed prices quoted at the time of booking for accommodation and other services;

- To advise guests at the time of booking, or subsequently in the event of any change in what has been booked;

- To make clear to guests, if the accommodation offered is in an unconnected annexe or similar, and to indicate the location or such accommodation and any difference in comfort and/or amenities from accommodation in the establishment.

On arrival
- To welcome all guests courteously and without discrimination in relation to gender, sexual orientation, disability, race, religion or belief.

During the stay
- To maintain standards of guest care, cleanliness, and service appropriate to the type of establishment;

- To deal promptly and courteously with all enquiries, requests, bookings and correspondence from guests;

- To ensure complaint handling procedures are in place and that complaints received are investigated promptly and courteously and that the outcome is communicated to the guest.

On departure
- To give each guests, on request, details or payments due and a receipt, if required/requested.

General
- To give due consideration to the requirements of guests with special needs, and to make suitable provision where applicable;

- To ensure the accommodation is prepared for the arrival of guests at all times when the operation is advertised as open to receive guests;

- To hold current public liability insurance and to comply with all relevant statutory obligations including legislation applicable to fire, health and safety, planning, food safety and all relevant statutory requirements;

- To allow VisitEngland representatives reasonable access to the establishment, on request, to confirm that the Code of Conduct is being observed or in order to investigate any complaint of a serious nature notified to them;

- When a business is sold or ceases to trade, every effort should be made to inform VisitEngland

Comments and complaints

Information
The proprietors themselves supply the descriptions of their establishments and other information for the entries (except ratings). They have all signed a declaration that their information conforms to The Consumer Protection from Unfair Trading Regulations 2008. VisitEngland cannot guarantee the accuracy of information in this guide, and accepts no responsibility for any error or misrepresentation.

All liability for loss, disappointment, negligence or other damage caused by reliance on the information contained in this guide, or in the event of bankruptcy or liquidation or cessation of trade of any company, individual or firm mentioned, is hereby excluded. We strongly recommend that you carefully check prices and other details when you book your accommodation.

Problems
Of course, we hope you will not have cause for complaint, but problems do occur from time to time.

If you are dissatisfied with anything, make your complaint to the management immediately. Then the management can take action at once to investigate the matter and put things right. The longer you leave a complaint, the harder it is to deal with it effectively.

In certain circumstances, VisitEngland may look into complaints. However, VisitEngland has no statutory control over establishments or their methods of operating. VisitEngland cannot become involved in legal or contractual matters or in seeking financial compensation.

If you do have problems that have not been resolved by the proprietor and which you would like to bring to our attention, please write to:

England
Quality in Tourism, Security House, Alexandra Way, Ashchurch, Tewkesbury, Gloucestershire GL20 8NB

Scotland
Customer Feedback Department, VisitScotland, Cowan House, Inverness Retail and Business Park, Inverness IV2 7GF

Wales
VisitWales, Ty Glyndwr, Treowain Enterprise Park, Machynlleth, Powys SY20 8WW

Useful contacts

British Holiday & Home Parks Association

Chichester House, 6 Pullman Court,
Great Western Road, Gloucester GL1 3ND
t (01452) 526911 (enquiries and brochure requests)
w parkholidayengland.org.uk

Professional UK park owners are represented by the British Holiday and Home Parks Association. Over 3,000 parks are in membership, and each year welcome millions of visitors seeking quality surroundings in which to enjoy a good value stay.

Parks provide caravan holiday homes and lodges for hire, and pitches for your own touring caravan, motor home or tent. On many, you can opt to buy your own holiday home.

A major strength of the UK's park industry is its diversity. Whatever your idea of holiday pleasure, there's sure to be a park which can provide it. If your preference is for a quiet, peaceful holiday in tranquil rural surroundings, you'll find many idyllic locations.

Alternatively, many parks are to be found at our most popular resorts – and reflect the holiday atmosphere with plenty of entertainment and leisure facilities. And for more adventurous families, parks often provide excellent bases from which to enjoy outdoor activities.

Literature available from BH&HPA includes a guide to over 600 parks which have this year achieved the David Bellamy Conservation Award for environmental excellence.

The Camping and Caravanning Club

Greenfields House, Westwood Way,
Coventry CV4 8JH
t 0845 130 7631
t 0845 130 7633 (advance bookings)
w campingandcaravanningclub.co.uk

Discover the peace and quiet of over 100 award-winning Club Sites. Experience a different backdrop to your holiday every time you go away, with sites in the lakes and mountains, coastal and woodland glades or cultural and heritage locations.

The Club is proud of its prestigious pedigree and regularly achieves awards for spotless campsites, friendly service and caring for the environment – a guarantee that you will enjoy your holiday.

Non-members are welcome at the majority of our sites and we offer special deals for families, backpackers, overseas visitors and members aged 55 and over. Recoup your membership fee in just six nights and gain access to over 1,300 Certificated Sites around the country.

For more details please refer to our entries listed at the back of this publication or if you require any more information on what The Friendly Club can offer you then telephone 0845 130 7632. Or call to request your free guide to The Club.

The Caravan Club

East Grinstead House,
East Grinstead,
West Sussex RH19 1UA
t (01342) 326944
w caravanclub.co.uk

The Caravan Club offers 200 sites in the UK and Ireland. These include city locations such as London, Edinburgh, York and Chester, plus sites near leading heritage attractions such as Longleat, Sandringham, Chatsworth and Blenheim Palace. A further 30 sites are in National Parks.

Virtually all pitches have an electric hook-up point. The toilet blocks and play areas are of the highest quality. Friendly, knowledgeable site wardens are on hand too.

Most Caravan Club Sites are graded four or five stars according to The British Graded Holiday Parks Scheme, run by the national tourist boards, so that you can be assured of quality at all times. Over 130 sites are open to non-members, but why not become a member and gain access to all sites, plus a further 2,500 Certificated Locations – rural sites for no more than five vans. Tent campers are welcome at over 60 sites.

Join The Club and you can save the cost of your subscription fee in just five nights with member discounts on site fees!

Useful contacts

Forest Holidays

Heart of the National Forest, Bath Yard, Moira, Derbyshire DE12 6BA
t 0845 130 8223 (cabins)
t 0845 130 8224 (campsites)
w forestholidays.co.uk

Forest Holidays, a new partnership between the Forestry Commission and the Camping and Caravanning Club, have over 20 camping and caravan sites in stunning forest locations throughout Great Britain in addition to three cabin sites. Choose from locations such as the Scottish Highlands, the New Forest, Snowdonia National Park, the Forest of Dean, or the banks of Loch Lomond. Some sites are open all year and dogs are welcome at most. Advance bookings are accepted for many sites.

For a unique forest experience, call Forest Holidays for a brochure on 0845 130 8224 or visit our website.

The Motor Caravanners' Club Ltd

1st Floor, Woodfarm Estate, Marlbank Road, Welland, Malvern WR13 6NA
t (0) 1684 311677
e info@motorcaravanners.eu
w motorcaravanners.eu

The Motor Caravanners' Club is authorised to issue the Camping Card International (CCI). It also produces a monthly magazine, Motor Caravanner, for all members. Member of The Federation Internationale de Camping et de Caravanning (FICC).

The National Caravan Council

The National Caravan Council, Catherine House, Victoria Road, Aldershot, Hampshire GU11 1SS
t (01252) 318251
w thecaravan.net

The National Caravan Council (NCC) is the trade body for the British caravan industry – not just touring caravans and motorhomes but also caravan holiday homes. It has in its membership parks, manufacturers, dealers and suppliers to the industry – all NCC member companies are committed continually to raise standards of technical and commercial excellence.

So, if you want to know where to buy a caravan, where to find a caravan holiday park or simply need advice on caravans and caravanning, see the website thecaravan.net where there is lots of helpful advice including:

- How to check whether the caravan, motorhome or caravan holiday home you are buying complies with European Standards and essential UK health and safety regulations (through the Certification scheme that the NCC operates).
- Where to find quality parks to visit on holiday.
- Where to find approved caravan and motorhome workshops for servicing and repair.

Caravan holidays are one of the most popular choices for holidaymakers in Britain – the NCC works closely with VisitBritain to promote caravan holidays in all their forms and parks that are part of the British Graded Quality Parks Scheme.

Enjoy England more.

If you're looking for ideas for a weekend break or just planning a day out you can be sure of reliable and inspirational ideas from England's tourist information services. And the best thing is that you can get information on the whole of England from any tourist information provider no matter where you are. Go online and find yours today.

enjoy**England**.com

About the accommodation entries

Entries

All the sites featured in this guide have been assessed or have applied for assessment under The British Graded Holiday Parks Scheme. Start your search for a place to stay by looking in the 'Where to Stay' sections of this guide where operators have paid to have their site featured in either a standard entry (includes photograph, description, facilities and prices) or an enhanced entry (photograph(s) and extended details). If you can't find what you're looking for, turn to the CD inside this guide for an even wider choice of accommodation.

Locations

Places to stay are generally listed under the town, city or village where they are located. If a place is in a small village, you may find it listed under a nearby town (providing it is within a seven-mile radius). Within each region, counties run in alphabetical order. Place names are listed alphabetically within each county, along with information on which county that is and their map reference.

Map references

These refer to the colour location maps at the back of the guide. The first figure shown is the map number, the following letter and figure indicate the grid reference on the map. Only place names under which standard or enhanced entries (see above) feature appear on the maps. Some entries were included just before the guide went to press, so they do not appear on the maps.

Telephone numbers

Booking telephone numbers are listed below the contact address for each entry. Area codes are shown in brackets.

Prices

The prices shown are only a general guide and include VAT where applicable; they were supplied to us by proprietors in summer 2011. Remember, changes may occur after the guide goes to press, so we strongly advise you to check prices when you book your accommodation.

Touring pitch prices are based on the minimum and maximum charges for one night for two persons, car and either caravan or tent. (Some parks may charge separately for car, caravan or tent, and for each person and there may be an extra charge for caravan awnings.) Minimum and maximum prices for caravan holiday homes are given per week.

Prices often vary through the year, and may be significantly lower outside peak holiday weeks. You can get details of other bargain packages that may be available from the sites themselves, regional tourism organisations or your local Tourist Information Centre (TIC). Your local travel agent may also have information, and can help you make bookings.

Opening period

If an entry does not indicate an opening period, please check directly with the site.

Symbols

The at-a-glance symbols included at the end of each entry show many of the services and facilities available at each site. You will find the key to these symbols on page 6.

Pets

Many places accept visitors with dogs, but we do advise that you check this when you book, and ask if there are any extra charges or rules about exactly where your pet is allowed. The acceptance of dogs is not always extended to cats, and it is strongly advised that cat owners contact the site well in advance. Some sites do not accept pets at all. Pets are welcome where you see this symbol 🐕.

The quarantine laws have changed in England, and dogs, cats and ferrets are able to come into Britain from over 50 countries. For details of the Pet Travel Scheme (PETS) please turn to page 321.

Payment accepted

The types of payment accepted by a site are listed in the payment accepted section. If you plan to pay by card, check that your particular card is acceptable before you book. Some proprietors will charge you a higher rate if you pay by credit card rather than cash or cheque. The difference is to cover the percentage paid by the proprietor to the credit card company. When you book by telephone, you may be asked for your credit card number as confirmation. But remember, the proprietor may then charge your credit card account if you cancel your booking. See under Cancellations on page 320.

Awaiting confirmation of rating

At the time of going to press some parks featured in this guide had not yet been assessed for their rating so their new rating could not be included. Rating Applied For indicates this.

Getting around

Travelling in London

London transport

London Underground has 12 lines, each with its own unique colour, so you can easily follow them on the Underground map. Most lines run through central London, and many serve parts of Greater London.

Buses are a quick, convenient way to travel around London, providing plenty of sightseeing opportunities on the way. There are over 6,500 buses in London operating 700 routes every day. You will need to buy a ticket before you board the bus – available from machines at the bus stop – or have a valid Oyster card (see below).

London's National Rail system stretches all over London. Many lines start at the main London railway stations (Paddington, Victoria, Waterloo, Kings Cross) with links to the tube. Trains mainly serve areas outside central London, and travel over ground.

Children usually travel free, or at reduced fare, on all public transport in London.

Oyster cards

Oyster cards can be used to pay fares on all London Underground, buses, Docklands Light Railway and trams; they are generally not valid for National Rail services in London.

Oyster cards are very easy to use – you just touch the card on sensors at stations or on buses and it always charges you the lowest fare available for your journey. You buy credit for your journey and when it runs out you simply top up with more.

Oyster is available to adults only. Children below the age of 11 can accompany adults free of charge. Children between the ages of 11 and 15 should use the standard child travel card. You can get an Oyster card at any underground station, at one of 3,000 Oyster points around London displaying the London Underground sign (usually shops), or from www.visitbritaindirect.com, or https://oyster.tfl.gov.uk/oyster

London congestion charge

The congestion charge is an £10 daily charge to drive in central London at certain times. Check whether the congestion charge is included in the cost of your car when you book. If your car's pick up point is in the congestion-charging zone, the company may pay the charge for the first day of your hire.

Low Emission Zone

The Low Emission Zone is an area covering most of Greater London, within which the most polluting diesel-engine vehicles are required to meet specific emissions standards. If your vehicle does not, you will need to pay a daily charge.

Vehicles affected by the Low Emission Zone are older diesel-engine lorries, buses, coaches, large vans, minibuses and other heavy vehicles such as motor caravans and motorised horse boxes. This includes vehicles registered outside of Great Britain. Cars and motorcycles are not affected by the scheme.

For more information visit www.tfl.gov.uk

Rail and train travel

Britain's rail network covers all main cities and smaller regional towns. Trains on the network are operated by a few large companies running routes from London to stations all over Britain, and smaller companies running routes in regional areas. You can find up-to-the-minute information about routes, fares and train times on National Rail Enquiries (nationalrail.co.uk). For detailed information about routes and services, refer to the train operators' websites (see page 331).

Railway passes

BritRail offers a wide selection of passes and tickets giving you freedom to travel on all National Rail services. Passes can also include sleeper services, city and attraction passes and boat tours. Passes can normally be bought from travel agents outside Britain or by visiting the Britrail website (britrail.com).

Bus and coach travel

Public buses

Every city and town in Britain has a local bus service. These services are privatised and run by separate companies. The largest bus companies in Britain are First (www.firstgroup.com/ukbus), Stagecoach (stagecoachbus.com), and Arriva (arrivabus.co.uk), which run buses in most UK towns. Outside London, buses usually travel to and from the town centre or busiest part of town. Most towns have a bus station, where you'll be able to find maps and information about routes. Bus route information may also be posted at bus stops.

Tickets and fares

The cost of a bus ticket normally depends on how far you're travelling. Return fares may be available on some buses, but you usually need to buy a 'single' ticket for each individual journey.

You can buy your ticket when you board a bus, by telling the driver where you are going. One-day and weekly travel cards are available in some towns, and these can be bought from the driver or from an information centre at the bus station. Tickets are valid for each separate journey rather than for a period of time, so if you get off the bus you'll need to buy a new ticket when getting on another bus.

Domestic flights

Flying is a time-saving alternative to road or rail when it comes to travelling around Britain. Domestic flights are fast and frequent and there are 33 airports across Britain operating domestic routes. You will find airports marked on the maps at the front of this guide.

Domestic flight advice

Photo ID is required to travel on domestic flights. It is advisable to bring your passport, as not all airlines will accept other forms of photo identification.

There are very high security measures at all airports in Britain. These include restrictions on items that may be carried in hand luggage. It is important that you check with your airline prior to travel, as these restrictions may vary over time. Make sure you allow adequate time for check-in and boarding.

Cycling

Cycling is a good way to see some of Britain's best scenery and there are many networks of cycling routes. The National Cycle Network offers over 10,000 miles of walking and cycling routes connecting towns and villages, countryside and coast across the UK. For more information and routes see page 318 or visit Sustrans at sustrans. co.uk.

Think green

If you'd rather leave your car behind and travel by 'green transport' when visiting some of the attractions highlighted in this guide you'll be helping to reduce congestion and pollution as well as supporting conservation charities in their commitment to green travel.

The National Trust encourages visits made by non-car travellers. It offers admission discounts or a voucher for the tea room at a selection of its properties if you arrive on foot, cycle or public transport. (You'll need to produce a valid bus or train ticket if travelling by public transport.)

More information about The National Trust's work to encourage car-free days out can be found at nationaltrust.org.uk. Refer to the section entitled Information for Visitors.

OPENBRITAIN.NET

ONE STOP SOLUTION
to accessible places to stay and visit in Britain.

To advertise your property or attraction, contact our friendly staff on 01603 216461 or sales@openbritain.net

By car and by train

Distance chart

The distances between towns on the chart below are given to the nearest mile, and are measured along routes based on the quickest travelling time, making maximum use of motorways or dual-carriageway roads. The chart is based upon information supplied by the Automobile Association.

To calculate the distance in kilometres multiply the mileage by 1.6

For example: Brighton to Dover
82 miles x 1.6 =131.2 kilometres

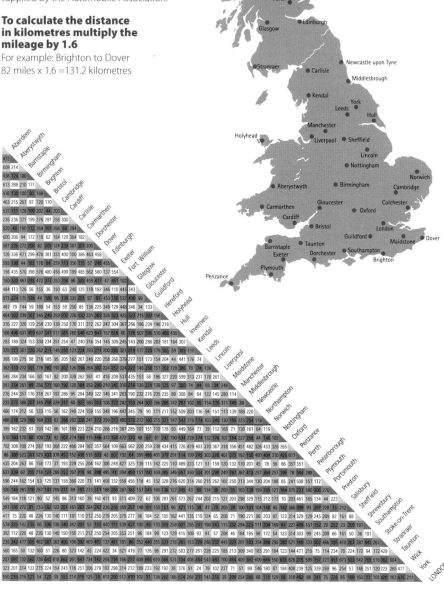

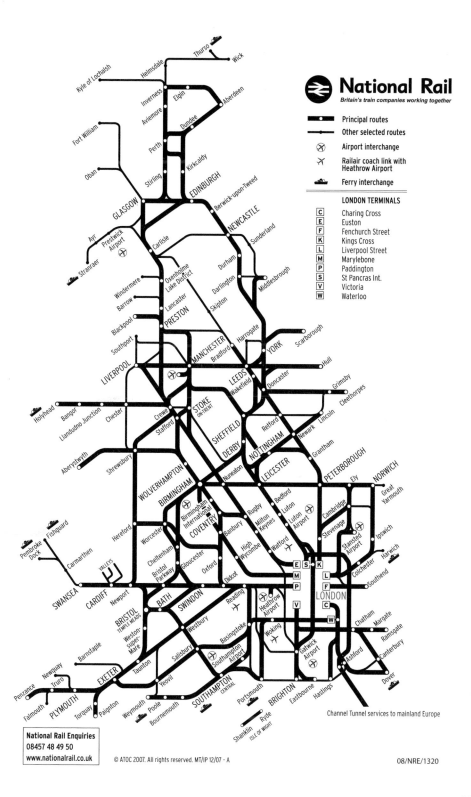

National Rail
Britain's train companies working together

▬▬	Principal routes
—•—	Other selected routes
⊗	Airport interchange
✈	Railair coach link with Heathrow Airport
⛴	Ferry interchange

LONDON TERMINALS

C	Charing Cross
E	Euston
F	Fenchurch Street
K	Kings Cross
L	Liverpool Street
M	Marylebone
P	Paddington
S	St Pancras Int.
V	Victoria
W	Waterloo

Channel Tunnel services to mainland Europe

National Rail Enquiries
08457 48 49 50
www.nationalrail.co.uk

© ATOC 2007. All rights reserved. MT/IP 12/07 - A

08/NRE/1320

Travel information

General travel information

Streetmap	www.streetmap.co.uk	
Transport Direct	www.transportdirect.info	
Transport for London	www.tfl.gov.uk	0843 222 1234
Travel Services	www.departures-arrivals.com	
Traveline	www.traveline.org.uk	0871 200 2233

Bus & coach

Megabus	www.megabus.com	0900 160 0900
National Express	www.nationalexpress.com	08717 818 181
WA Shearings	www.washearings.com	0844 824 6355

Car & car hire

AA	www.theaa.com	0870 600 0371
Green Flag	www.greenflag.co.uk	0845 246 1557
RAC	www.rac.co.uk	0870 572 2722
Alamo	www.alamo.co.uk	0871 384 1086*
Avis	www.avis.co.uk	0844 581 0147*
Budget	www.budget.co.uk	0844 544 3470*
Easycar	www.easycar.com	0871 050 0444
Enterprise	www.enterprise.com	0800 800 227*
Hertz	www.hertz.co.uk	0870 844 8844*
Holiday Autos	www.holidayautos.co.uk	0871 472 5229
National	www.nationalcar.co.uk	0870 400 4581
Thrifty	www.thrifty.co.uk	01494 751500

Air

Air Southwest	www.airsouthwest.com	0870 043 4553
Blue Islands (Channel Islands)	www.blueislands.com	08456 20 2122
BMI	www.flybmi.com	0844 848 4888
BMI Baby	www.bmibaby.com	0905 828 2828*
British Airways	www.ba.com	0844 493 0787
British International (Isles of Scilly to Penzance)	www.islesofscillyhelicopter.com	01736 363871*
CityJet	www.cityjet.com	0871 663 3777
Eastern Airways	www.easternairways.com	0870 366 9989
Easyjet	www.easyjet.com	0843 104 5000
Flybe	www.flybe.com	0871 700 2000*
Jet2.com	www.jet2.com	0871 226 1737*
Manx2	www.manx2.com	0871 200 0440*
Ryanair	www.ryanair.com	0871 246 0000
Skybus (Isles of Scilly)	www.islesofscilly-travel.co.uk	0845 710 5555
Thomsonfly	www.thomsonfly.com	0871 231 4787

Train

National Rail Enquiries	www.nationalrail.co.uk	0845 748 4950
The Trainline	www.trainline.co.uk	0871 244 1545
UK train operating companies	www.rail.co.uk	
Arriva Trains	www.arriva.co.uk	0845 748 4950
c2c	www.c2c-online.co.uk	0845 601 4873
Chiltern Railways	www.chilternrailways.co.uk	0845 600 5165
CrossCountry	www.crosscountrytrains.co.uk	08447 369 123
East Midlands Trains	www.eastmidlandstrains.co.uk	0845 712 5678
Eurostar	www.eurostar.com	08432 186 186*
First Capital Connect	www.firstcapitalconnect.co.uk	0845 026 4700
First Great Western	www.firstgreatwestern.co.uk	0845 700 0125
Gatwick Express	www.gatwickexpress.com	0845 850 1530
Heathrow Connect	www.heathrowconnect.com	0845 678 6975
Heathrow Express	www.heathrowexpress.com	0845 600 1515
Hull Trains	www.hulltrains.co.uk	0845 071 0222
Island Line	www.islandlinetrains.co.uk	0845 600 0650
London Midlands	www.londonmidland.com	0121 634 2040
Merseyrail	www.merseyrail.org	0151 702 2071
National Express East Anglia	www.nationalexpresseastanglia.com	0845 600 7245
National Express East Coast	www.nationalexpresseastcoast.com	0845 722 5333
Northern Rail	www.northernrail.org	0845 000 0125
ScotRail	www.scotrail.co.uk	0845 601 5929
South Eastern Trains	www.southeasternrailway.co.uk	0845 000 2222
South West Trains	www.southwesttrains.co.uk	0845 600 0650
Southern	www.southernrailway.com	0845 127 2920
Stansted Express	www.stanstedexpress.com	0845 850 0150
Translink	www.translink.co.uk	(028) 9066 6630
Transpennine Express	www.tpexpress.co.uk	0845 600 1671
Virgin Trains	www.virgintrains.co.uk	08450 008 000*

Ferry

Ferry Information	www.discoverferries.com	0207 436 2449
Condor Ferries	www.condorferries.co.uk	0845 609 1024*
Steam Packet Company	www.steam-packet.com	08722 992 992*
Isles of Scilly Travel	www.islesofscilly-travel.co.uk	0845 710 5555
Red Funnel	www.redfunnel.co.uk	0844 844 9988
Wight Link	www.wightlink.co.uk	0871 376 1000

Phone numbers listed are for general enquiries unless otherwise stated.
* Booking line only

OPEN BRITAIN

OpenBritain is a partnership between Tourism for All UK, with support from the National Federation of Shopmobility, and the backing of the national tourism agencies VisitEngland, VisitScotland and Visit Wales.

OpenBritain is the one-stop-shop to accessible Britain for those with access needs and their carers. You'll find just what you're looking for if you, or a member of your party, has an access need - whether impaired mobility, vision or hearing. If you need a ground floor room because you can't manage stairs, or you have a child in a buggy, or a wheelchair, or if you need staff trained to offer a welcome to all...

OpenBritain is the answer.

- Places to stay for holidays and short breaks
- Ideas for great days out
- Travel tips and resources
- Services and equipment

and much much more!

For further information on OpenBritain please visit www.openbritain.net or call 01603 216461

Magazine

The OpenBritain magazine is published each quarter, and distributed via Tourism for All, Shopmobility and Motability. It is filled with inspiring content: places to visit, human interest stories, and reviews, together with a wealth of practical information. The OpenBritain magazine is also available in digital format.

Website

www.openbritain.net is an unrivalled searchable website offering help, advice and inspiration, to make the most of all the UK has to offer. We are working with specialist partners to create a truly national and exciting website that meets the needs of all. Stay informed, inspired and active, and add your own feedback to help others with similar needs benefit from your experience.

App

The new OpenBritain GPS activated App will be available on both the Apple and Android platforms, allowing travellers to constantly search for access provision in real time.

VisitBritain is Britain's national tourism agency, responsible for marketing Britain worldwide and for developing Britain's visitor economy. VisitBritain work in partnership with thousands of organisations in the UK and overseas.

Tourism for All UK is a national charity dedicated to standards of world class tourism which are welcoming to all. **Tourism for All UK** contains the knowledge gained over the past 30 years in providing information to the public, especially to disabled or older people, on where their access needs can be met so that they can fully participate in travel and leisure.

David Bellamy
Conservation Award

Parks wishing to enter for a David Bellamy Conservation Award must complete a detailed questionnaire covering different aspects of their environmental policies, and describe what positive conservation steps they have taken. The park must also undergo an independent audit from a local wildlife or conservation body which is familiar with the area. Final assessments and the appropriate level of any award are then made personally by Professor Bellamy.

Parks with Bellamy Awards offer a variety of accommodation from pitches for touring caravans, motor homes and tents, to caravan holiday homes, holiday lodges and cottages for rent or to buy. Holiday parks with these awards are not just those in quiet corners of the countryside. Amongst the winners are much larger centres in popular holiday areas that offer a wide range of entertainments and attractions.

The parks listed on the following pages all have a detailed entry in this guide and have received a Gold, Silver or Bronze David Bellamy Conservation Award. Use the Index by Property Name starting on page 344 to find the page number.

For a free brochure featuring a full list of award-winning parks please contact:
BH&HPA, 6 Pullman Court, Great Western Road, Gloucester GL1 3ND
t (01452) 526911
e enquiries@bhhpa.org.uk
w davidbellamyconversation.org.uk

Rowlands Wait Touring Park	GOLD	Bere Regis	South West England
Golden Cap Holiday Park	GOLD	Bridport	South West England
Highlands End Holiday Park	GOLD	Bridport	South West England
Wooda Farm Holiday Park	GOLD	Bude	South West England
Cofton Country Holidays	GOLD	Dawlish	South West England
Sandyholme Holiday Park	GOLD	Dorchester	South West England
Silver Sands Holiday Park	GOLD	Helston	South West England
Ross Park	GOLD	Ipplepen	South West England
Forest Glade Holiday Park	GOLD	Kentisbeare	South West England
Croft Farm Holiday Park	GOLD	Luxulyan	South West England
Hendra Holiday Park	GOLD	Newquay	South West England
Dornafield Touring Park	GOLD	Newton Abbot	South West England
Mother Ivey's Bay Holiday Park (Camping)	GOLD	Padstow	South West England
Whitehill Country Park	GOLD	Paignton	South West England
Porlock Caravan Park	GOLD	Porlock	South West England
Tehidy Holiday Park	GOLD	Portreath	South West England
Trethiggey Touring Park	GOLD	Quintrell Downs	South West England
Ayr Holiday Park	GOLD	St Ives	South West England
Harford Bridge Holiday Park	GOLD	Tavistock	South West England
Waterrow Touring Park	GOLD	Waterrow	South West England
Wilksworth Farm Caravan Park	GOLD	Wimborne Minster	South West England
Halse Farm Caravan & Tent Park	GOLD	Winsford	South West England
Castle Brake Holiday Park	GOLD	Woodbury	South West England
Holiday Resort Unity	SILVER	Brean	South West England
Dolbeare Caravan & Camping Park	SILVER	Landrake	South West England
Treloy Touring Park	SILVER	Newquay	South West England

Ladram Bay Holiday Park	SILVER	Otterton	South West England
Padstow Touring Park	SILVER	Padstow	South West England
Porthtowan Tourist Park	SILVER	Porthtowan	South West England
Trevalgan Touring Park	SILVER	St Ives	South West England
Watergate Bay Touring Park	BRONZE	Watergate Bay Newquay	South West England
Crowhurst Park	GOLD	Battle	South East England
Heathfield Farm Camping	GOLD	Freshwater	South East England
Hurley Riverside Park	GOLD	Hurley	South East England
Tanner Farm Park	GOLD	Marden	South East England
Bay View Park Ltd	GOLD	Pevensey Bay	South East England
Whitefield Forest Touring Park	GOLD	Ryde	South East England
Cheverton Copse Holiday Park Ltd	GOLD	Sandown	South East England
Shamba Holidays	SILVER	Ringwood	South East England
Riverside Holidays	BRONZE	Hamble	South East England
Deer's Glade Caravan and Camping Park	GOLD	Cromer	East of England
Searles Leisure Resort	GOLD	Hunstanton	East of England
Heathland Beach Caravan Park	GOLD	Kessingland	East of England
Pakefield Caravan Park	GOLD	Lowestoft (3 miles)	East of England
Waldegraves Holiday Park	GOLD	Mersea Island	East of England
Sandy Gulls Caravan Park	GOLD	Mundesley	East of England
Wyton Lakes Holiday Park	SILVER	Huntingdon	East of England
Cable Gap Holiday Park	SILVER	Norwich	East of England
Rivendale Caravan & Leisure Park	GOLD	Alsop-En-le-Dale	East Midlands England
Orchard Park	GOLD	Boston	East Midlands England
Skegness Water Leisure Park	GOLD	Skegness	East Midlands England
Island Meadow Caravan Park	GOLD	Aston Cantlow	Heart of England
Ranch Caravan Park	GOLD	Evesham	Heart of England
Silver Trees Holiday Park - Static Vans	GOLD	Rugeley	Heart of England
Arrow Bank Holiday Park	SILVER	Eardisland	Heart of England
Vale of Pickering Caravan Park	GOLD	Allerston	Yorkshire England
Rudding Holiday Park	GOLD	Harrogate	Yorkshire England
Upwood Holiday Park	GOLD	Haworth	Yorkshire England
Holme Valley Camping and Caravan Park	GOLD	Holmfirth	Yorkshire England
Cayton Village Caravan Park Ltd	GOLD	Scarborough	Yorkshire England
Lebberston Touring Park	GOLD	Scarborough	Yorkshire England
Middlewood Farm Holiday Park	GOLD	Whitby	Yorkshire England
Goosewood Holiday Park	GOLD	York	Yorkshire England
Thornwick and Sea Farm Holiday Centre	SILVER	Flamborough	Yorkshire England
Wild Rose Park	GOLD	Appleby-in-Westmorland	North West England
Crake Valley Holiday Park	GOLD	Coniston	North West England
Castlerigg Hall Caravan & Camping Park	GOLD	Keswick	North West England
Woodclose Park	GOLD	Kirkby Lonsdale	North West England
Flusco Wood	GOLD	Penrith	North West England
Waterfoot Caravan Park	GOLD	Ullswater	North West England
Fallbarrow Park	GOLD	Windermere	North West England
Hill of Oaks Park	GOLD	Windermere	North West England
Limefitt Park	GOLD	Windermere	North West England
Park Cliffe Camping & Caravan Estate	GOLD	Windermere	North West England
Todber Holiday Park	SILVER	Clitheroe	North West England
Ocean Edge Leisure Park, Heysham	BRONZE	Heysham	North West England
Regent Leisure Park	BRONZE	Morecambe	North West England
Waren Caravan and Camping Park	GOLD	Bamburgh	North East England
Seafield Caravan Park	GOLD	Seahouses	North East England
Sauchope Links Caravan Park	GOLD	Crail	Scotland
Belhaven Bay Caravan and Camping Park	GOLD	Dunbar	Scotland
Linwater Caravan Park	GOLD	Edinburgh	Scotland
Mortonhall Caravan and Camping Park	GOLD	Edinburgh	Scotland
Linnhe Lochside Holidays	GOLD	Fort William	Scotland
Letham Feus Caravan Park	GOLD	Leven	Scotland

National Accessible Scheme index

Establishments with a detailed entry in this guide who participate in the National Accessible Scheme are listed below. At the front of the guide you can find information about the scheme. Establishments are listed alphabetically by place name. Further basic listings appear on the CD at the back of this guide.

Mobility level 1

Bacton East of England	**Castaways Holiday Park ★★★★**	139
Burgh St. Peter East of England	**Waveney River Centre ★★★★**	139
Lowestoft (3 miles) East of England	**Pakefield Caravan Park ★★★★**	148
Poole South West	**South Lytchett Manor Caravan & Camping Park ★★★★★**	66
Whitby (3 miles) Yorkshire	**Whitby Holiday Park ★★★★**	207

Mobility level 2

Ainsdale North West	**Willowbank Holiday Home and Touring Park ★★★★★**	233
Burgh St. Peter East of England	**Waveney River Centre ★★★★**	139

Hearing impairment level 1

Bacton East of England	**Castaways Holiday Park ★★★★**	139
Lowestoft (3 miles) East of England	**Pakefield Caravan Park ★★★★**	148
Poole South West	**South Lytchett Manor Caravan & Camping Park ★★★★★**	66
Whitby (3 miles) Yorkshire	**Whitby Holiday Park ★★★★**	207

Visual impairment level 1

Ainsdale North West	**Willowbank Holiday Home and Touring Park ★★★★★**	233
Lowestoft (3 miles) East of England	**Pakefield Caravan Park ★★★★**	148

Official tourist board guide **Camping, Touring & Holiday Parks**

Walkers & cyclists welcome

Establishments particpating in the Walkers Welcome and Cyclists Welcome schemes provide special facilities and actively encourage these recreations. Accommodation with a detailed entry in this guide is listed below. Place names are listed alphabetically.

Walkers Welcome and Cyclists Welcome

Acton East of England	Castaways Holiday Park ★★★★	139
Boot North West	Eskdale Camping and Caravanning Club Site ★★★★★	222
Brecon Wales	Brynich Caravan Park ★★★★★	295
Burgh St. Peter East of England	Waveney River Centre ★★★★	139
Burnham Market East of England	Deepdale Backpackers and Camping ★★★★	139
Fishguard Wales	Fishguard Bay Caravan & Camping Park ★★★★	292
Ilkley Yorkshire	Faweather Grange ★★★★★	199
Landrake South West	Dolbeare Caravan & Camping Park ★★★★★	36
Lincoln East Midlands	Tattershall Lakes Country Park ★★★★	165
Morpeth North East	Tomlinson's Cafe and Bunkhouse	249
St Davids Wales	Caerfai Bay Caravan & Tent Park ★★★★	294
St Issey South West	Trewince Farm Holiday Park ★★★★	44
Tavistock South West	Harford Bridge Holiday Park ★★★★	56
Tavistock South West	Langstone Manor Holiday Park ★★★★	57
Woodbury South West	Castle Brake Holiday Park ★★★★ rose	58
Yeovil South West	Long Hazel Park ★★★★	77

Walkers Welcome

St Agnes South West	Beacon Cottage Farm Touring Park ★★★★	43

So much to see, so little time - how do you choose?

Make the most of your leisure time; look for attractions with the Quality Marque.

VisitEngland operates the Enjoy England Visitor Attraction Quality Assurance Scheme.

Annual assessments by trained impartial assessors test all aspects of the customer experience so you can visit with confidence.

For ideas and inspiration visit www.enjoyengland.com/attractions

Families and Pets Welcome

Establishments participating in the Families Welcome or Welcome Pets! schemes provide special facilities and actively encourage families or guests with pets. Accommodation with a detailed entry in this guide is listed below. Place names are listed alphabetically.

Families and Pets Welcome

Bacton East of England	**Castaways Holiday Park ★★★★**	139
Holmfirth Yorkshire	**Holme Valley Camping and Caravan Park ★★★★**	198
Lincoln East Midlands	**Tattershall Lakes Country Park ★★★★**	165
St Issey South West	**Trewince Farm Holiday Park ★★★★**	44

Families Welcome

Blackpool North West	**Newton Hall Holiday Park ★★★★**	229
Bognor Regis South East	**Butlins Bognor Regis ★★★★**	106
Bouth North West	**Black Beck Caravan Park ★★★★★** rose	222
Minehead South West	**Butlins Minehead ★★★★**	73
Morpeth North East	**Tomlinson's Cafe and Bunkhouse**	249
Otterton South West	**Ladram Bay Holiday Park ★★★★** rose	53
Skegness East Midlands	**Butlins Skegness ★★★★**	166
Slingsby Yorkshire	**Robin Hood Caravan Park ★★★★★**	204

Pets Welcome

Bamburgh North East	**Waren Caravan and Camping Park ★★★★** rose	248
Cromer East of England	**Deer's Glade Caravan and Camping Park ★★★★★**	140
Felixstowe East of England	**Peewit Caravan Park ★★★★**	148
Frodsham North West	**Ridgeway Country Holiday Park ★★★★**	221
Holsworthy South West	**Noteworthy Caravan and Campsite ★★**	49
Ilkley Yorkshire	**Faweather Grange ★★★★★**	199
Ipplepen South West	**Ross Park ★★★★★**	50
Scarborough Yorkshire	**Cayton Village Caravan Park Ltd ★★★★★**	201
Seahouses North East	**Seafield Caravan Park ★★★★★** rose	250
Skegness East Midlands	**Skegness Water Leisure Park ★★★**	167

Quick reference index

If you're looking for a specific facility use this index to see at a glance detailed accommodation entries that match your requirement. Establishments are listed alphabetically by place name.

🔍 Indoor pool

Place	Establishment	Page
Abersoch Wales	M40 ★★★★★	290
Battle South East	Crowhurst Park ★★★★★ rose	104
Bembridge South East	Whitecliff Bay Holiday Park ★★★	100
Birchington South East	Two Chimneys Caravan Park ★★★★★ rose	102
Blackpool North West	Newton Hall Holiday Park ★★★★	229
Blackpool North West	Windy Harbour Holiday Park ★★★★	229
Bognor Regis South East	Butlins Bognor Regis ★★★★	106
Brean South West	Holiday Resort Unity ★★★★	71
Bridport South West	Highlands End Holiday Park ★★★★★ rose	62
Bude South West	Sandymouth Holiday Park ★★★★★ rose	31
Burgh St. Peter East of England	Waveney River Centre ★★★★	139
Dawlish Warren South West	Welcome Family Holiday Park ★★★★ rose	48
Filey Yorkshire	Orchard Farm Holiday Village ★★★★★	195
Flamborough Yorkshire	Thornwick and Sea Farm Holiday Centre ★★★★ rose	196
Fleetwood North West	Broadwater Caravan Park ★★★	230
Fordingbridge South East	Sandy Balls Holiday Centre ★★★★★ rose	95
Great Yarmouth East of England	Summerfields Holiday Park ★★★★	142
Harrogate Yorkshire	High Moor Farm Park ★★★★★	197
Hayle South West	St Ives Bay Holiday Park ★★★★	35
Hayling Island South East	Mill Rythe Holiday Village	97
Hemsby East of England	Hemsby Beach Holiday Park ★★★	142
Heysham North West	Ocean Edge Leisure Park, Heysham ★★★	230
Hunstanton East of England	Searles Leisure Resort ★★★★★	143
Kentisbeare South West	Forest Glade Holiday Park ★★★★ rose	50
Kingsdown South East	Kingsdown Park Holiday Village ★★★★★	103
Lincoln East Midlands	Tattershall Lakes Country Park ★★★★	165
Looe South West	Tencreek Holiday Park ★★★★	36
Looe South West	Tregoad Park Quality Family Touring Site ★★★★	37
Manorbier Wales	Manorbier Country Park ★★★★★	293
Minehead South West	Butlins Minehead ★★★★	73
Morecambe North West	Regent Leisure Park ★★★★	231
Morecambe North West	Venture Caravan Park ★★★★	231
Mundesley East of England	Mundesley Holiday Village ★★	144
Newquay South West	Hendra Holiday Park ★★★★★ rose	39
Newquay South West	Riverside Holiday Park ★★★★	39
Otterton South West	Ladram Bay Holiday Park ★★★★ rose	53
Paignton South West	Beverley Holidays ★★★★★	54
Rhyl Wales	Golden Sands Holiday Park ★★★★★	289
Ringwood South East	Shamba Holidays ★★★★	98
Rousdon South West	Pinewood Holiday Homes ★★★★★ rose	55
Rugeley Heart of England	Silver Trees Holiday Park - Static Vans ★★★★ rose	182
Scarborough Yorkshire	Crows Nest Caravan Park ★★★★ rose	202
Scarborough Yorkshire	Flower of May Holiday Parks Ltd ★★★★★	202
Scarisbrick North West	Hurlston Hall Country Caravan Park ★★★★	232
Seahouses North East	Seafield Caravan Park ★★★★★ rose	250
Selsey South East	Green Lawns Holiday Park ★★★★★ rose	109
Selsey South East	Warner Farm Camping & Touring Park ★★★★★	109

⤳ Indoor pool continued

elsey South East	West Sands Holiday Park ★★★★ rose	110
elsey South East	White Horse Holiday Park ★★★★ rose	110
kegness East Midlands	Butlins Skegness ★★★★	166
t Austell South West	River Valley Holiday Park ★★★★★	43
wanage South West	Swanage Bay View Holiday Park ★★★	66
horne Yorkshire	Elder House Touring Park ★★★★	205
Vatchet (4 miles) South West	Saint Audries Bay Holiday Club ★★★★	76
Vatergate Bay Newquay South West	Watergate Bay Touring Park ★★★★	46
Vindermere North West	White Cross Bay Holiday Park and Marina ★★★★	228

⤳ Outdoor pool

beraeron Wales	Aeron Coast Caravan Park ★★★★★	287
bersoch Wales	M40 ★★★★★	290
ppleby-in-Westmorland North West	Wild Rose Park ★★★★★	221
amburgh North East	Waren Caravan and Camping Park ★★★★ rose	248
embridge South East	Whitecliff Bay Holiday Park ★★★	100
irchington South East	Two Chimneys Caravan Park ★★★★★ rose	102
rean South West	Holiday Resort Unity ★★★★	71
rixham South West	Hillhead Caravan Club Site ★★★★★	47
ude South West	Budemeadows Touring Park ★★★★★	31
amelford South West	Juliots Well Holiday Park ★★★★	33
anterbury South East	Yew Tree Park ★★★★	102
harmouth South West	Manor Farm Holiday Centre ★★★	63
heddar South West	Broadway House Holiday Park ★★★★ rose	71
olchester East of England	Cosways Holiday Park ★★★★★	136
rail Scotland	Sauchope Links Caravan Park ★★★★★ thistle	266
romer East of England	Seacroft Caravan Club Site ★★★★★	141
rowcombe South West	Quantock Orchard Caravan Park ★★★★★	72
awlish South West	Cofton Country Holidays ★★★★ rose	48
oniford South West	Sunnybank Holiday Park ★★★★★	72
vesham Heart of England	Ranch Caravan Park ★★★★★ rose	183
ordingbridge South East	Sandy Balls Holiday Centre ★★★★★ rose	95
arrogate Yorkshire	Rudding Holiday Park ★★★★★ rose	197
ayle South West	Beachside Holiday Park ★★★★	34
ayling Island South East	Mill Rythe Holiday Village	97
unstanton East of England	Searles Leisure Resort ★★★★★	143
untingdon East of England	Grafham Water Caravan Club Site ★★★★★	135
essingland East of England	Heathland Beach Caravan Park ★★★★★ rose	148
ooe South West	Tencreek Holiday Park ★★★★	36
owestoft (3 miles) East of England	Pakefield Caravan Park ★★★★	148
owestoft East of England	Beach Farm Residential and Holiday Park Limited ★★★★	148
Mersea Island East of England	Waldegraves Holiday Park ★★★★	137
Mevagissey South West	Seaview International Holiday Park ★★★★★ rose	38
Minehead South West	Butlins Minehead ★★★★	73
Narberth Wales	Amroth Bay Holidays ★★★★★	293
Newquay South West	Hendra Holiday Park ★★★★★ rose	39
Newquay South West	Treloy Touring Park ★★★★	40
Paignton South West	Beverley Holidays ★★★★★	54
Paignton South West	Whitehill Country Park ★★★★	55
Portreath South West	Cambrose Touring Park ★★★	42
Rhosneigr Wales	Ty Hen Holiday Park	291
Ringwood South East	Shamba Holidays ★★★★	98
Roos Yorkshire	Sand-le-Mere Caravan & Leisure Park ★★★★ rose	201
Rousdon South West	Pinewood Holiday Homes ★★★★★ rose	55
Selsey South East	Green Lawns Holiday Park ★★★★★ rose	109
Selsey South East	Warner Farm Camping & Touring Park ★★★★★	109
Selsey South East	West Sands Holiday Park ★★★★ rose	110

🏊 Outdoor pool continued

Index to display advertisers

BRITAIN'S HERITAGE - OPEN TO VISITORS

HUDSON's

HISTORIC HOUSES & GARDENS

2012

HUDSON's

HUDSON's

2012

HUDSON's

celebrate

25

years with us

The 2012 – 25th anniversary edition of Hudson's presents the most comprehensive directory of Heritage properties open to visitors including a 150 page vibrant, informative and entertaining magazine style section of fabulously photographed and superbly written features on Britain's Heritage and those intimately involved within it.

Special Offer:

Order your copy today for only £12.00 (normally £15.99) + free p&p

To order call 01603 216460

Or order online at:
www.hudsonsheritage.com

The Guide

In addition to a bumper directory section Hudson's 2012 will include an array of wonderfully informative and entertaining articles that bring Britain's Heritage to life, including:

- Foreword by *HRH The Prince of Wales*
- *Brian Sewell* on Central London's great houses and paintings
- *Loyd Grossman* (Chair of The Churches Conservation Trust) on seeking out undiscovered treasures
- *Michael Portillo* on his visit by train to Wotton House in Bucks
- *Lord Lieutenant of Banffshire, Clare Russell* on food and lifestyle in romantic Speyside
- *Jonathan Wild*, on developments in garden design through the ages at historic properties
- *Dan Cruickshank*, profile of this charasmatic TV presenter and writer
- *Robert Seatter*, Head of BBC History, celebrates the BBC's historic buildings and new developments

Plus many more articles including a celebration of the Queen's Diamond Jubilee.

'Hudson's is uniquely positioned to bring properties and visitors together – providing amazing value for all.'

Index by property name

Accommodation with a detailed entry in this guide is listed below.

C continued *page*

D *page*

E *page*

F *page*

G *page*

H *page*

I *page*

Index by property name

Index by place name

The following places all have detailed accommodation entries in this guide. If the place where you wish to stay is not shown, the location maps (starting on page 328) will help you to find somewhere to stay in the area.